Love, Sanity, or Medical School: A Memoir

Stephanie Benjamin, MD

3/28/19

Enjoy!

— Stephanie
Benjamin

Love, Sanity, or Medical School: A Memoir

Visit my website ThirdYear.org to view the paintings mentioned throughout the book and read other related content.

Cover Design by James, GoOnWrite.com
Author photo by Kati, katibeshore.photography

Disclaimer
This book is a memoir, written solely from my point of view. The book reflects my personal interpretation of the events around me. Some dialogue has been reconstructed from memory. All names and all identifying information of my patients, classmates, and co-workers have been changed. Additionally, the order of events and dates on which patient encounters occurred has been scrambled to further ensure patient privacy.

First Edition.

My book is dedicated to my parents, Sandra and Howard, and to my mentor, Dr. B. I would not have made it to medical school without you. I would not have survived the events within these pages without you. I would not be where I am now without you. Thank you.

Table of Contents

Music & Beverage Pairing Menu

I have carefully curated the following song and drink menu to accompany each chapter and enhance your reading experience. The playlist is available on my website, Thirdyear.org, as well as on Spotify, under the title 'Love, Sanity, or Medical School.'
Please read responsibly.

Intersession I
Song: The xx. "Intro." *xx*. XL Studios. 2009.
Drink: Large dark roast, 2% milk, no sugar

Inpatient Internal Medicine
Song: Arcade Fire. "We Used to Wait." *The Suburbs*. Rouge Trade Records, Merge Records. 2010.
Drink: Sauvignon Blanc, or other crisp white wine

Outpatient Internal Medicine
Song: Passion Pit. "Swimming in the Flood." *Manners*. Columbia Records. 2009.
Drink: Bottomless mimosas

Thoracic Surgery
Song: Cold War Kids. "Hang Me Up to Dry." *Robbers & Cowards*. Downtown Records, V2 Records. 2007.
Drink: Rhinegeist Zen, Session IPA

General Surgery
Song: Miike Snow. "Cult Logic." *Miike Snow*. Columbia Records. 2010.
Drink: Moerlein Emancipator Doppelbock

Intersession II
Song: Metric. "Help I'm Alive." *Fantasies*. Last Gang Records. 2008.

Drink: Grande Pumpkin Spice Latte

Family Medicine
Song: Coconut Records. "Nighttiming." *Nighttiming*. Young Baby Records. 2007.
Drink: Chili Mango Margarita, or any other drink featuring Tequila

Neurology
Song: The Shins. "New Slang." *Oh, Inverted World*. Sub Pop Records. 2001.
Drink: MadTree Thunder Snow Scottish Ale

December Break
Song: Ratatat. "Loud Pipes." *Classics*. XL Recordings. 2006.
Drink: Veuve Clicquot Demi-Sec Champagne

Inpatient Psychiatry
Song: Miike Snow. "Silvia." *Miike Snow*. Columbia Records. 2010.
Drink: Bombay Sapphire martini, slightly dirty, with three olives

Psychiatry Consults
Song: Broken Bells. "The High Road." *Broken Bells*. Columbia Records. 2009.
Drink: Mulled wine

Radiology
Song: Two Door Cinema Club. "What You Know." *Tourist History*. Kitsuné Records. 2011.
Drink: Bulleit Rye Old Fashioned

Intersession III
Song: alt-J. "Something Good." *An Awesome Wave*. Infectious Records. 2012.
Drink: Red eye coffee

Outpatient Pediatrics
Song: MGMT. "Kids." *Oracular Spectacular*. Columbia Records. 2008.
Drink: Hot chocolate with whipped cream

Inpatient Pediatrics
Song: Modest Mouse. "Float On." *Good News for People Who Love Bad News*. Epic Records. 2004.
Drink: Rhinegeist Bubbles Rosé Ale

Emergency Medicine
Song: MGMT. "Electric Feel." *Oracular Spectacular*. Columbia Records. 2008.
Drink: Tempranillo, or other full-bodied, peppery red wine

Obstetrics
Song: Passion Pit. "Little Secrets." *Manners*. Columbia Records. 2009.
Drink: MadTree Happy Amber Red Ale

Gynecology
Song: The Naked and Famous. "Young Blood." *Passive Me, Aggressive You*. Somewhat Damaged Records. 2010.
Drink: Woodford Reserve Double Oaked Bourbon

Epilogue
Song: Sea Wolf. "Visions." *Song Spells, No.1: Cedarsmoke*. Self released. 2014.
Drink: Mezcal Paloma

Intersession I

Song: The xx. "Intro." *xx*. XL Studios. 2009.
Drink: Large dark roast, 2% milk, no sugar

June 24: Monday

8:24 am: "Welcome to third year!" a smiling Dean of Something Educational boomed across the medical school's packed auditorium. I didn't hear many remarks past those beginning words of the requisite welcome speech because I became distracted in catching up with my friends. I'd recently returned from vacation with my longtime boyfriend, R. Casey Jones, and had not yet seen anyone. Aside from all my friends looking expectantly at me to share news that I do not have to share, while not so subtly glancing at my left ring finger, it is wonderful to see everyone.

9:17 am: All medical students are warned that the third year of medical school is the most stressful, exhausting, and confusing year in the whole process of becoming a doctor. I first learned this a few months ago when reading a 2009 study published in *Academic Medicine* entitled "The devil is in the third year: a longitudinal study of erosion of empathy in medical school."[1] Some disturbing phenomenon happens during this year where medical students morph from cheerful, motivated, optimistic future doctors into bitter, cynical individuals. Since reading that article, I've come across multiple other studies and reports highlighting the horror that is the third year of medical school. Even just last week I came across an article in *Slate* magazine ominously titled "The Darkest Year of Medical School," which discusses how third-year medical students experience a dangerous rise in depression, suicide, and substance abuse.[2]

I'm curious about how this happens and to what extent it will happen to my classmates and me. I intend to record this entire year on my iPad mini, which happens to fit comfortably in the pocket of my short white doctor's coat. My goal is to subtly jot down notes throughout the day using

5

the app "Notability." I'll be recording events not only as they unfold in real time, but also capturing how I interpret these events and how I react to them. Medical student secretly turned gonzo journalist!

At most schools, mine included, medical students spend the first two years hunkered down in hiding, memorizing textbooks. We learn basics such as chemistry, immunology, pathology, physiology, anatomy, etc. In stark contrast, years three and four of medical school are spent rotating through the different medical specialties, letting us try out each one for a month or two. Every medical student in the country completes the same core rotations: surgery, internal medicine, family medicine, neurology, psychiatry, pediatrics, and obstetrics and gynecology. The goal is to expose us to each of the major specialties, helping us determine which medical field we will enter.

10:30 am: Oh, I should probably listen now, the speaker is explaining how third year will work for us. There are three blocks of rotations this year; each block is 16 weeks long. At my school, the students are split into three large groups, and each group rotates through each of the blocks. Kicking off each block is an intersession week, where I am right now, designed to prep the students for their upcoming rotations. As my first block consists of internal medicine and surgery, my lectures this intersession will review common medical conditions (heart disease, diabetes, etc.), basic surgery skills (such as suturing and tying knots), and anatomy. There will be two other intersession weeks this year. Intersession two will precede my block of family medicine, neurology, and psychiatry. The third intersession week will be before my final block of pediatrics, and obstetrics and gynecology.

11:45 am: Immediately following the welcome lecture, we were treated to a talk about not letting residents and attending physicians physically, emotionally, mentally, and/or sexually torture you. Apparently, many med schools have poor track records when it comes to abuse of third year med students. At least my school is aware of this issue and is preparing us for potential exploitations? The speaker also casually mentioned that we're not supposed to work more than 80 hours in a week or more than 28 continuous hours.

June 25: Tuesday

12:35 pm: In general, doctors all wear white coats. However, there is a well-established hierarchy in medicine and not all white coats are the same. Atop the totem pole is the attending physician. The attending has completed their entire medical training and is in charge. Next down are the fellows. Fellows have finished residency and are completing optional specialized training (one to three years) before becoming an attending. Fellowship is not required, and most residents go straight into being an attending.

The residents are next down on the ladder; residents are licensed physicians. The first year of residency is called intern year. Interns and residents see and examine patients, write orders for lab tests and prescriptions, and make decisions regarding patient care. The resident has more power than the intern, though the attending has the final say on all matters. Interns are more heavily supervised than other residents and tend to do the most scut work. Throughout residency (which is three to seven years, depending on the specialty), a newbie intern develops into a senior resident. Supervision gradually becomes less and less, with the senior residents having the most freedom.

Medical students are doctors-in-training. We have not yet graduated medical school, and we do not yet have our medical licenses. We can see patients and perform procedures under the supervision or direction of an intern, resident, fellow, or attending. First and second year medical students aren't even on the totem pole since they're locked away studying.

Visually, the totem pole looks like this:

Attending physician
Fellow
Senior resident
Junior resident
Intern

7

Fourth year medical student
Third year medical student (my current location)

Teams are led by a single attending, but may include any combination of residents and students. Hospitals with residents and medical students are referred to as teaching hospitals.

2:15 pm: FYI, all medical students and residents move up the medical totem pole by one rung on July 1. Always. If you're a patient, you may want to avoid teaching hospitals in July. We're all new to our respective roles.

3:23 pm: Learning how to gown and glove for surgery is surprisingly more complicated than it appears.

7:22 pm: Ouch. Rough afternoon. I spent the afternoon hours in anatomy lab being pimped by surgery residents and attending surgeons. "PIMP" stands for "Put In My Place;" it is a technique used throughout medical training whereby it is established that the superior has more knowledge and expertise than anyone below them on the totem pole. Pimping stems from the Socratic method of questioning a student, with the goal of leading them towards a correct answer. If the teacher poses questions in a logical and progressive manner then the student should ideally be able to work through the problem and come to a conclusion on their own, even if they did not initially think they knew the answer. The College of Medicine endorses the use of the Socratic method. Pimping differs from the Socratic method in that the goal of pimping is to point out that the student does not know as much as anyone senior to them. A student is asked questions repeatedly until they answer one incorrectly, at which point the teacher (be it a resident, or attending, or even a fourth-year medical student, if they're being a total dick) can point out how little they know, deride them for not studying enough, or otherwise embarrass them. Ultimately, the student is reminded of their lowly stature on the totem pole. So yes, today I was pimped during anatomy lab.

June 26: Wednesday

11:15 am: Cancer, obesity, and genetics. A thoroughly depressing day of lectures.

2:10 pm: During lunch I received my schedule for the next eight weeks. I start with four weeks of inpatient internal medicine, followed by four weeks of outpatient medicine. Inpatient means the patient is admitted to the hospital and stays there overnight. Within the hospital, the sickest patients go to the Intensive Care Unit (ICU). Slightly less sick patients are in the Step-down unit; which is one tier less intense than ICU-level care. The most stable inpatients are on the floor, and are called floor patients. On the other hand, outpatient typically means a clinic, where a patient goes for doctors' appointments or checkups. This may seem obvious to some people, but my mother, who has no medical background, has informed me that I need to explain these distinctions.

5:25 pm: Afternoon lectures on wound care provided us with some nasty images of pus-ridden infections and made me excited for my surgery rotation. I've never fainted at the sight of blood and guts, but we were just warned that third years happen to faint with alarming regularity. The professor informed us that it usually happens on days when we're feeling really sleep deprived and haven't eaten, drank, or sat down all day. Which apparently are most days of third year.

June 27: Thursday

11:53 am: Morning lectures were chock full of review about viruses, bacteria, and other infectious diseases.

5:43 pm: I decided to go to medical school at age 24. After studying art history and studio art in undergrad, I earned a master's degree in counseling psychology and art therapy. I then worked at a top-notch hospital in Chicago. My mornings were spent on the inpatient psychiatry ward and in the afternoons I did bedside counseling and art therapy with children and young adults. Most of my patients on the various medicine wards were severely ill, often staying in the hospital for weeks at a time. I developed wonderful relationships with my patients and would inevitably bond with them. I mourned them when they died,

9

attended their memorials, and cried with their family members; it felt as if my friends were routinely dying. I hated my job but loved being at the hospital, so, the abridged story is that I decided to go to medical school.

I left my job and forged ahead into the world of medicine, completing my pre-medical school requirements at Northwestern University. Casey matched to a teaching hospital called The General Hospital for his surgery residency. We packed up our lives in Chicago and relocated to this random Midwest City. I applied to medical school and was accepted to The College of Medicine, which is the medical school affiliated with The General Hospital. So now here I am. I'm a 29-year-old artist-former-counselor-turned-medical student from Long Island, NY, living in a random little Midwest City, about to start my third year of medical school.

June 28: Friday

7:30 am: I've kept journals since I was five years old. I have over 20 journals lined up on my bookcase, all penned in my terrible handwriting. I've never shared them with anyone. The idea of writing for a potential audience to read is terrifying.

However, writing a book has also been a lifelong dream of mine. Capturing the events of third year by journaling electronically seemed like the perfect set-up. To provide some distance, I've decided to refer to myself by a pseudonym, almost as if I am recording someone else's story and not my own. After spending much of the week deliberating, I chose the name Silvia for myself in homage to my favorite song by the band Miike Snow.

12:15 pm: An all-morning review of the pharmacology of immunology is precisely as boring as it sounds. But no matter how boring, I have to know this stuff. At each rotation's end is a multi-hour, nationwide, standardized flogging, politely known as a final exam. Our grades are used to compare us not only to each other, but also to all the other third-year medical students across the nation.

We also get graded on our clinical skills. This includes how well we interact with our patients, our competency doing procedures, and if we go above and beyond the requirements of the rotation. Our overall grade combines our exam score and our clinical grade for a final mark of fail, pass, high pass, or honors. Our grades influence our class rank, and where we will be able to match for residency. In order to get a residency spot, or 'to match' into a specialty, one must be a competitive candidate. As there are now more medical students graduating each year than there are residency positions, medical students tend to get über-competitive when it comes to grades and class rank.

2:15 pm: We're back in the auditorium, sitting through a ceremony officially welcoming all the third-year students to our clinical years. Everyone looks prim, proper, and eager in freshly laundered white coats. We're reciting the oath we took at our induction into the field of medicine at the start of medical school. Instead of reciting the Hippocratic Oath, a few students wrote an oath to represent our class and what entering medicine means to us at this time and place in our lives. The Dean of Something Important is back at the podium, spewing more warnings about third year. Right now she is reminding us to rely on each other and help each other through the year. She is telling us to reach out if we are drowning and need help. "Suicide is not the answer," she informs us. I look at my closest friends, Piper, Sophia, Jane, and Maggie, and get the feeling I have no idea what I'm in for but I'm glad these women are sitting on either side of me. The Dean of Whatever concludes her speech with, "Congratulations on making it to third year. Thank you for listening, and good luck."

Ipad in hand, down I go into the rabbit hole of third year.

Inpatient Internal Medicine

Song: Arcade Fire. "We Used to Wait." *The Suburbs.*
Rouge Trade Records, Merge Records. 2010.
Drink: Sauvignon Blanc, or other crisp white wine

July 1: Monday

1:00 pm: They just handed me a pager. Now what?

I'm sitting in a barren, windowless classroom tucked away on a top floor within The General Hospital, surrounded by a small group of newly-minted third-year medical students. It's our first day on the wards. We are waiting for the senior residents to collect us and distribute us to the various medicine teams.

2:15 pm: Still waiting…

3:30 pm: Turns out that the senior residents didn't know that we, every medical student in the entire College of Medicine, were starting today so we sat there until three pm. We tried calling them. We tried paging them. Finally, an attending physician randomly passing by came to our rescue and located the seniors. They seemed pleasantly surprised to see that we'd been patiently sitting there for hours.

3:55 pm: I met my team, comprised of a fourth-year medical student, an intern, and a senior resident, and then was dismissed. Everyone seemed welcoming.

July 2: Tuesday

7:01 am: I have no idea what I'm supposed to be doing.

8:15 am: My attending, the young Dr. Osler, immediately comes across as friendly and enthusiastic. We discussed my goals for the rotation. His focus is on improving my patient presentation skills and teaching me to come up with broad differential diagnoses (aka medical explanations) for my patients' problems. Sounds good. My 'personal' goals: 1. Avoid personal embarrassment. 2. No

12

crying if I get yelled at. My first impression is that Osler doesn't seem like the type of attending who torments third years, though I guess I'll find out soon enough.

The crux of "having a patient" is rounding. Each medical student and resident takes turns presenting their patients to the rest of the team during rounds. We hop around the hospital, traveling room-to-room, until we have checked in on every patient on our list. Rounds are nerve wracking because it is imperative to know every single detail about your patient's work up. The 'work up' is a generic term referring to all the data collected on a patient, including physical exam findings, daily blood tests (aka lab values, or, labs), and imaging results (such as x-rays and MRI scans). Knowing how a patient is responding to their treatments is essential, too. All of your decisions regarding their care are debated and nitpicked. If the attending finds your management of a patient to be unsatisfactory, the consequences may range from an eye roll, to an audible sigh, to a verbal berating, to being locked in a dungeon without food or water until such a time when your attending believes you can once again be let loose on the wards.

I officially have my own patient! He is in the hospital for a ginormous (proper medical terminology right there) foot ulcer. I could call him Mr. FU for foot ulcer, but let's go with Mr. UFO instead. Having my own patient means I now have someone to present on rounds. Each morning, before the team arrives, I'll get to The General Hospital super early to read up on any new lab studies or overnight developments in his care. This is called pre-rounding. After presenting him on rounds, I'll write a note on his progress and goals for the day, while helping plan for his discharge. Waaaay better than being in the classroom.

12:59 pm: Every Tuesday afternoon all students on the internal medicine rotation have class together from 1-5 pm. In an effort to make these four hours of lecture more exciting the internal medicine people have coined these afternoons "Super Tuesdays." Sure. Whatever. There are a lot of stereotypes in medicine. Internal medicine folks are known to be super nerdy. So far, so true. And unfortunately, I can't go home afterwards because I'm on call tonight. Being "on call" on the medicine service basically means an extra-long day, so instead of leaving at 5:00 pm I'll be here until about 10:00 pm.

July 3: Wednesday

8:43 am: People take bad news quite differently. A patient on our service was told his fiancé gave him Hepatitis C and he nonchalantly commented, "Oh well, I'm marrying her anyway so I guess that's that." When the fiancé found out that she may have contracted Hepatitis B from him in return, she was NOT happy. I thought she was going to punch him or break the engagement right then and there.

10:15 am: While on morning rounds we met an elderly new patient named Mr. BH, who was admitted by the overnight team. He is suffering and in excruciating pain from multiple medical problems and a broken hip. As the overnight intern started presenting Mr. BH to our team, Mr. BH began reaching out past the intern and signaling for me to come closer. I was at the end of the bed and Mr. BH persistently motioned for me to move nearer to him. The whole time he was moaning in agonizing pain and it was confusing because we couldn't figure out what he wanted. When I finally got close enough, he grabbed my hand and held it tightly. Turns out he needed some comfort and just wanted to hold my hand. He gripped my hand tightly the entire time we were in his room. It was very sweet and very sad. Pulling my hand away so I could grab my stethoscope and perform a physical exam felt more than a little heartless.

Happy Fourth of July: Thursday

8:20 am: It's hard to watch people in pain. A professor taught us last year that patients should never be in pain, should never be short of breath, and should not die alone. These are deceptively difficult goals. Give too many meds and they stop breathing, give too few and their pain is intolerable. My team is trying to balance controlling Mr. BH's pain without causing a deadly respiratory depression.

Noon: My day was brightened when I ran into my Sig O, Casey. We met nearly seven years ago on a random Tuesday at a dive bar in Chicago. It wasn't exactly love at first sight but there was definitely some spark, some attraction, so we began dating. Dating casually grew into a relationship, falling in love, and moving in together.

1:12 pm: My team is constantly busy, and I feel like I'm in the way or at least just not on their radar this afternoon. Patients are sick as shit, and I don't know my role yet. I'm keeping myself busy by reading and studying.

2:29 pm: I tried to learn to draw blood but was informed by the intern, "Don't waste your time, you'll never do that, nurses will do that for you." Only thing is, I want to learn and I'm bored because I don't know what else I could be doing right now aside from studying.

July 5: Friday

3:32 pm: I updated Mr. UFO and his family. I answered his questions and then discussed his progress and discharge plans. It feels better than simply being out of the classroom, it feels like I am finally learning to be a doctor. Wonderful!

10:18 pm: I managed to sneak in a dinner with Casey tonight. It's been forever since I've seen his red hair and blue eyes, which is impressive considering we live together and work at the same hospital. As he is a general surgery resident, his schedule is even worse than mine. His muscular former-football-player frame is still tan from our recent trip to Central America. Even with the unseasonable amount of rain we still managed to sneak in some scuba diving and visit the breathtaking Tikal Mayan ruins. Most importantly, I was able to check another box off my bucket list - I swam with sharks. It was a phenomenal experience. My love of the ocean and my most recent bucket list is not relevant at the moment though; I need to get some sleep because I'm on call again tomorrow.

July 6: Saturday

11:00 am: Four and a half hours down, ten hours to go. The problem with Saturday call is that you have to come in post-call on Sunday. This means that my first day off since starting third year will be *next* Saturday.

Turns out, drawing blood is a clinical skill requirement for this rotation.

Mr. UFO is doing well and is going home tonight so hopefully I'll get another patient, maybe even two. It's hard knowing that I am the weakest link and that I slow the team down, but there's really nothing I can do other than keep learning and try to improve as quickly as possible. In these couple of days my presentation skills, with the help of my attending Dr. Osler, have improved a lot. However, I still suck at describing wounds using proper medical terminology.

Dr. Osler: "Silvia, how would you describe this man's ulcer?"

Me: "Um..." And I'm thinking to myself, well it smells really foul and looks super gnarly, as if someone took an ice cream scoop and scooped out a portion of the man's heel, leaving behind a bloody, smelly, pus-filled hole. Hmm... need to learn how to translate that into words a grown-up doctor would utilize.

I was right about Dr. Osler though; he is not one to torture medical students. He gives detailed feedback and frequently checks in with me. Even better, he has not once threatened to throw me in the brig! So far, so good.

Noon: The family of Mr. BH, the one who held my hand, updated his advanced directives to solely comfort care. Everything will be done to manage his pain but nothing else - no other medical interventions, no CPR, no life support, nothing. His family believes that his quality of life will never again be at a point that he will find acceptable or enjoyable. In order to effectively manage his pain, we need to increase his meds. Any time we did that in the past few days he would get drowsy and hard to awaken so we'd back off on the dosage. However, alleviating pain is the only goal now. We increased his pain meds once again, which means he'll likely go into respiratory depression again, which means he will die.

3:30 pm: I was assigned my second patient. She's admitted for an intentional drug overdose that caused her liver to fail. I know quite little about liver physiology, but I'll be able to put my master's degree in psychology to use so she'll be a good patient for me.

July 7: Sunday

8:58 am: Nope, no I take that back, she is no longer my patient. Turns out her psychoses and medical management are too far beyond my meager third year skills. It sucks to realize that my master's degree in psych is not useful at all; I had envisioned being successful with psych patients but no, just like everything else, I have to learn from scratch. Instead, now under my care is a sweet young girl named Barbie with a nasty eye problem.

It's weird waiting for someone to die. A resident from another team casually inquired, "So, has your guy Mr. BH died yet?" It wasn't asked in a disrespectful way either, merely run-of-the-mill resident lounge conversation.

For the first time, and this may not happen again for a while, the senior resident on my team conceded, "You were right about your patient." I'd asked if Barbie could have some anti-anxiety medication. He'd firmly replied "no", that she doesn't need any. She is young and healthy and shouldn't be given anxiety medications because they're addictive and potentially dangerous and blah, blah, blah. He then went and saw her in person and decided yep, Barbie is indeed super anxious and would benefit from a little Ativan. A small victory for the med student!

Barbie has a horrific eye infection and must have eye drops placed every 30 minutes for 48 hours. A nurse will go in her room and literally pry open her sleeping eyes every 30 minutes for two full days. Wow. The alternative is she risks vision loss from not treating her infection properly. OMG she is going to be a zombie from lack of sleep!

Speaking of zombies, there is another patient on my team with a leg infection that reminds me of a zombie wound every time I see it. You know those decaying zombies where it looks like strips of skin got peeled off and it's all beefy red underneath? That is exactly what this woman's leg looks like. Creepy.

July 8: Monday

11:48 am: There are three, nationwide standardized exams that have to be passed throughout medical school in order to get one's medical license. They are referred to as the boards, and are composed of Step 1, Step 2, and Step 3. Step 1 is taken just prior to starting the third year of medical school. It's a beast of a test and our scores are coming out soon. If you fail Step 1, you are immediately pulled off rotations and are not allowed to continue with third year until you have a passing score. Yikes! While I don't think I failed, I know I will be incredibly relieved to see a passing score...

I picked up another patient today, a young woman named Ms. AI, with a difficult to control autoimmune disease. I didn't actually offer to pick her up; she was assigned to me. No one on the team wanted her because she is known to be super bitchy and argumentative. Amazing how quickly patients develop reputations. Ms. AI is emaciated from a string of recent illnesses. My goals are to help her gain weight, get her strength back, and get her labs under control. I wonder if she sensed my distraction while we spoke. No offense to her but my brain is entirely consumed with thoughts of my Step 1 score posting soon.

3:12 pm: I keep offering to my team to let me do things but they keep saying, "It's ok, we've got this," or, "Thanks but no thanks."

July 9: Tuesday

6:30 am: Uh-oh. Apparently, Ms. AI has been moved to Step-down, a more acute care wing of the hospital. That's bad. She became unresponsive overnight and a "rapid response" was called (not quite a code blue like when your heart stops and you're actively dying but still really bad, and people are concerned that you might die). Scary. She seemed fine when I left last night...

11:00 am: Surprisingly, Mr. BH is doing well. Sure, we amped up his pain meds and risked killing him (at his family's request, of course) but he pulled through. He has even been moved from Step-down to the floor. I'm too new to know whether or not this is an unusual occurrence. All I know is my team felt fairly certain that this guy was going to die a couple of nights ago.

11:55 am: Barbie's eyes are doing well; it looks like she may be able to go home tomorrow. It's too soon to know for sure, but it doesn't seem that there will be any long-term vision problems.

3:50 pm: Very interesting Super Tuesday lecture today. Really, not sarcastic. Our discussion today is on death and dying. Upon walking into the classroom, we were promptly asked, "How do you want to die?" We all responded with ideas such as: at home, without pain, quickly, surrounded by family. Then we discussed the brutality and futility of CPR. We were told that only about 10%-20% of patients who get CPR will live to be discharged from the hospital. Additionally, we were informed that about 75% of people on TV shows survive such ordeals. Yes, I am typing while sitting in lecture. Shh... don't tell; it looks like I'm taking notes. Anyway, talk about false hope and unrealistic expectations!

People with terminal diagnoses, who have time to plan their deaths, have a higher likelihood of dying at home, surrounded by family, compared to those who die suddenly. I wonder whether or not physicians also have a higher likelihood of dying at home because they know the poor outcomes that result from aggressive life-prolonging treatment. Hand is going up...

My professor really liked the question and suggested that I do a research project on the topic. I nodded noncommittally. I do find it interesting, so maybe I'll get to it one day, like when I'm done with my book and my bucket list and my current painting and the ten other things I always have going on at once. First month of third year is not the time to start tacking additional tasks onto my to-do list.

July 10: Wednesday

I experienced my first two rapid responses today. When you're the "on call" team you carry the code pager. When the shrill rapid beeping starts blaring, you immediately stop what you're doing and race toward whichever room is listed. Both turned out to be nothing but it was thrilling to head toward an unknown emergency. When people see you running, with your white coat flapping behind you and your stethoscope bouncing on your neck, they jump out of the way, flattening their backs up against the wall to let you pass while craning their necks to see what medical crisis you're off to fix.

To clarify, neither time did my own pager go off, I just obediently followed behind my team when they started running. There is a fundamental difference between people who get excited when they hear a code pager and those who cringe. Turns out I fall in the camp of people who get super excited. The rapid responses were great distractions from worrying about my Step 1 score and also broke up the monotony of rounding. Turns out that rounding lasts for hours and is pretty darn boring.

10:45 am: Passed my boards! Barely.

While of course I wish I had scored higher, I can't help but be so, so, so relieved that it's over and I am moving on with my classmates. My insightful mentor, The Boss, firmly stated in her email to me earlier today: "Do not be worried. You will excel in the clinical environment." I trust her advice and input implicitly, so I will not worry. We've previously agreed that my strength is working with people and has never been, nor likely ever will be, taking multiple-choice tests.

2:30 pm aka 1430: I removed an internal jugular central line from a patient, which is a large IV that is placed in a patient's neck. This marks the first time this rotation I have touched a patient other than during a physical exam on morning rounds. While the internal med folks are all really friendly (bordering on non-confrontational), I don't see myself being in a specialty with so few procedures. I like getting my hands dirty.

Ms. AI was moved out of Step-down back to the floor. Good.

Turns out many end-of-life studies have been done and a greater percentage of terminally ill physicians die at home with no aggressive interventions compared to the average layperson. I direct interested parties to the article, "How doctors choose to die," published in *The Guardian* by Dr. Ken Murray.[3] Intriguing. I think I will fill out a living will someday soon.

My intern and senior resident both let me draw blood from them. Bloody good fun. We were doing this in the break room and received many odd looks from people passing by in the hallway.

En route to see a new patient, my senior resident shares advice that was given to him upon receiving his own Step 1 score: "Do not let your score influence your level of confidence." I really appreciate hearing that, thanks. It was like he could read my mind and knew I needed a boost.

A patient disappeared today. Kind of impressive considering he is paraplegic and has minimal upper body strength. The patient is well known for screaming, weakly flailing his arms, and spitting at any staff member who enters his room. Additionally, he also refuses to put on a hospital gown, so he has been lying in his hospital bed covered in strategically placed washcloths. To sum up, not just a paraplegic but a naked paraplegic managed to escape off of the floor this morning. Strong work floor staff.

July 11: Thursday

10:11 am: I have so much to learn.

11:42 am: I often ask patients what they understand about their medical conditions. Many of them have never had anything explained to them in terms they can understand and they have no idea what is going on.

4:05 pm: The naked paraplegic was found and returned safely to the floor. Apparently, he wheeled himself to the hospital courtyard where he was eventually found and brought back up to his room. I'm not entirely sure if the goal was leaving permanently or just temporarily so that he could have a cigarette.

My poppa (my dad's dad), the singing NY cab driver extraordinaire, escaped from a hospital once. After one of his many heart attacks, he left the hospital without telling anyone, got into a cab dressed solely in his hospital gown with his ass hanging out, and then had his girlfriend pay for the cab when he arrived at home.

I just realized I never described the patient on whom I removed the central line. Through a series of unfortunate events the patient had both hands amputated, and in their place they now have intricate hooks. The dexterity and speed with which the patient maneuvers their hooks is pretty incredible. You try tearing open a sugar packet, pouring out just half into your coffee, deftly using a stirrer, then picking up the cup and drinking without spilling! I don't know if it's inappropriate to be so impressed. Maybe that is the typical level of functioning for someone with those types of prosthetics?

July 12: Friday

11:43 am: Tried going on rounds today without a stethoscope. Such a rookie.

Mr. BH has been discharged. Alive. Not a celestial discharge. Still in pain, still with a broken hip, but alive nonetheless.

3:12 pm: Ms. AI started throwing up blood. She is in constant pain. I don't know how to help her.

July 13: Saturday

Fifteen days in and my first day off since starting third year.

July 14: Sunday

6:43 am: Back at work. On call again. The internal medicine residents always seem nervous and hesitant to do things. We talk and talk and talk about patients and when we're done talking, we call a consult or two and then talk some more. A consult is when you ask another medical specialty for their opinion about your patient. For example: if a patient has a seizure, you might call for a neurology

22

consult; if a patient develops chest pain, you might call for a cardiology consult; or if a patient feels depressed, you may call for a psychiatry consult. I know these patients are complicated but commit to a choice and do something! I'm guessing their hesitancy is compounded by the fact that it is July, and they are all probably scared to do something that could kill someone. I guess that's understandable.

It's hard to give patients awful news. Every time we do I think I see a dark look cross the patient's face. It's as though they're rethinking all the poor decisions they have made throughout their life that led them to this point in time.

4:30 pm: The intern is too trusting. A patient came in with a pus-filled infection on the dorsum (top) of her hand, which ostensibly developed after she fell off a bike one week ago. She has no other injuries, not a scratch on her. She swore up and down to the intern, and myself, that she does not do drugs. After leaving her room I commented to the intern that I thought she was probably lying about her drug use. Her injury looks suspiciously as if she was injecting heroin into her hand. He replied, "No, there is no reason not to trust her." Sure. We'll see about this one. The intern and I present the patient to our senior resident and our senior agrees with me that yes, she is probably an IV drug user. The intern sticks to his guns. Again, since one else wants her, she has been assigned to me. Let's call this new patient of mine Ms. BA for bike accident.

5:45 pm: The urine drug screen on Ms. BA came back positive for all sorts of good stuff including opioids, cocaine, and marijuana, and that's not even the fancy drug screen that picks up designer drugs. Called it. Another win for the medical student.

July 15: Monday

It's shocking how many people have nasty foot problems from diabetes. The prevalence of diabetes makes me concerned for my dad - the disease is nearly ubiquitous among overweight Americans. My dad is out of shape, a former smoker, and has already had one heart attack. He is the poster child for a future diabetic, and I worry about him constantly.

I just found out Ms. AI is being presented at M&M today. Why? M&M, or, Morbidity and Mortality, is a conference where a patient who had a complication or who died, allegedly due to a preventable medical error, gets presented to all of the medicine teams. The teams then pick apart the case. The goal is to identify the cause of the problem so that it won't be repeated by anyone else.

In theory it's a non-accusatory forum to address life and death errors, but I've heard it can get pretty heated. Not quite like the TV show coming out called *Monday Mornings*, but something to that effect.

Noon: Morbidity and mortality conference. Here we go.

12:55 pm: Sitting in M&M while your patient is being presented is the worst thing ever, and I'm not even responsible for making decisions regarding her care. (I mean, I like to think I am, but really the residents make all the decisions and I just write her daily progress notes). The roomful of docs was provided with a barebones overview of her case, missing many of the details regarding the complexity of her condition. Then they start talking condescendingly about how they would've handled her case differently and perfectly. I wanted to yell out, "No, you don't get it, she is crazy unstable!" but I sat there quietly and watched my team face the firing squad while I hid in a corner.

July 16: Tuesday

7:53 am: Feet smell powerfully bad. Especially right after morning coffee.

9:14 am: Ms. BA is still swearing up and down that she does not use drugs. We keep going along with her story about the bike. No one will confront her. I don't think she should get more narcotic pain meds because she is drug seeking. Her abscess isn't even that big, and it's healing really well. Hopefully she doesn't go home and inject more heroin into it.

2:20 pm: Super Tuesday lectures are made infinitely more bearable by the presence of my closest guy friend, Magnus. We share a dry sarcastic humor and hold similar views on many issues ranging from patient care to football to the importance of bacon.

Magnus and I became close because he dated my bestie Piper all throughout first year. The three of us would sit next to each other every day during lectures and hang out whenever not in class. Piper broke up with him right after first year ended and fortunately, they never once tried to put me in the middle of any of their drama. It was a messy breakup and they did not speak to each other for the entirety of second year. Piper and Magnus are still two of my closest friends; I just have to hang out with them individually now. They've had shared custody of my friendship since their separation.

July 17: Wednesday

This morning I walked into Ms. BA's room to find her lounging in bed, quietly watching TV. She waits until a commercial starts, then looks at me and deadpans that her hand is killing her and she is in 10/10 pain. Not to be insensitive, but if you can calmly and clearly tell me about your pain while watching soaps then it's probably not 10/10. Actually, it's definitely not 10/10; 10/10 is more like childbirth to an extra-large baby without an epidural, or having a broken bone sticking out of your body at some weird angle, or having your leg bitten off by a shark with dull teeth. Those are examples of 10/10 pain in my book. I'm sure it hurts but really, I think she's drug seeking again and I have no interest in giving her more meds.

Ms. BA is getting under my skin because lying is a pet peeve of mine. While growing up, my parents told my sister Olivia and me that they would never lie to us because once you catch someone in a lie, their word can never be trusted again. To this day, I still trust my parents; they're awesome. Ms. BA sucks.

1:00 pm: We have a patient on our service with a three-week-old wound in the back of his head. There were stitches and staples put in initially, staples all down the middle with one stitch at the top and two stitches at the bottom. His staples were removed a week ago, but the stitches were forgotten about for reasons unknown. I offered to remove the stitches because they had been in too long (scalp stitches are usually kept in for 10 to 14 days). My team agreed this was a good idea, but my intern wanted me to consult the trauma surgery team first. Umm, no. Bad idea.

Calling the trauma team for their permission to remove THREE stitches on a well-healed wound would result in me either getting laughed at or yelled at by the trauma team. I explained that I wouldn't call. The intern retorted, "Yes, you have to." The intern then left to go do something else. I normally do not defy my superiors but this was ridiculous. To appease my intern, I called Sophia (my dear friend and fellow medical student), who is currently rotating with the trauma surgery team. That way I could aver that, yes, technically I did call the trauma team. She didn't answer (because the trauma team is always busy, which is why I didn't want to call in the first place) and then I went and removed the stitches anyway.

3:00 pm: My intern is not happy with me. Fortunately, the senior resident jumped in and defended me by explaining, "No, no, no, we do not consult trauma surgery for little things like that." Phew. Yet another example of internal medicine people being terrified to do anything without the explicit permission of as many people as possible. Or another example of July interns being terrified to kill someone. Either way. But really, if you have three three-week-old stitches holding the back of your head together then you have way bigger problems in your life than a rogue med student.

July 18: Thursday

One of the patients got me sick. It hurts to swallow. My throat is on fire. My tonsils are disgustingly swollen. It feels like strep, but it's likely something viral floating around. Ugh.

Night team gave Ms. BA more narcotics. Will people please stop increasing the pain meds on my drug-seeking patient? The senior resident reluctantly admitted to me that he had increased her dose. He explained that it was to make the night nurses lives easier. Fine, I get that, but isn't there any other option?

I would like to have an honest conversation with Ms. BA about her behavior before she leaves. I want to tell her that she really needs to stop using needles, especially dirty ones, because she will get more abscesses. My team informed me that the nature of medicine is to treat and not bother addressing problems for which there can't be follow-up. Ok, but what I don't understand is this: I have the time, I have the training, and I'm still naively optimistic enough to think that I can make a difference in her life. What is the harm if I go over options for treatment programs? Either way she is going home today.

This whole time she thinks she's pulled one over on us. She thinks she is so clever and has successfully tricked the medical team into believing that her abscess is from a bike accident. In addition to paralyzing hesitation to do things, there is also a large amount of confrontation avoidance among the internal medicine people. Beyond frustrating. I'm too action-oriented and straightforward for this specialty.

A couple of weeks prior to coming to The General Hospital, my other patient, Ms. AI, had a nasty infection that almost killed her. She had to be intubated. This involved placing a breathing tube in her throat and connecting it (and her) to a ventilator, a machine that breathed for her. This is akin to being placed on life support. She has extreme anxiety and nightmares about that hospital visit and she is terrified about the prospect of going to sleep, decompensating, and waking up intubated again. Her solution to this is to not sleep. She looks painfully tired and is fighting falling asleep.

Her previous hospital experiences have been pretty traumatic. Another horrific experience was during one of her pregnancies, which resulted in her requiring an emergent cesarean delivery. She shared with me about being whisked away into a bright room, being surrounding by people in yellow gowns and having a mask put over her face. When she awoke, she learned her baby had not survived the delivery. Poor Ms. AI. I want to give her a hug. If you know her, you probably don't want to give her a hug because she's pretty bitchy with the rest of the staff, but she's chill with me for reasons unknown.

July 19: Friday

About an hour ago I received a text from my intern to go check in with Ms. AI because she is in a lot of pain. My mission was to figure out what was wrong and comfort her but offer no pain medication. After about two minutes of chatting she told me that on top of everything else going on, she is having really bad belly cramps and muscles aches from starting her period. She is also suffering from severe anxiety and depression. I talked with her a bit and regretted that I had nothing to offer her. As I was leaving, an idea popped in my head. I randomly asked her if she would like to speak with our chaplain about her anxiety and for some spiritual comfort. She loved the idea. Found a way to support her and no meds required. Take that, intern.

I am feeling more and more ill as the day goes on and my energy is gone. I just want to bury myself in my bed, under layers of warm blankets. How sick do I have to be before I can leave? We were jokingly (?) informed during orientation that we would have to require IV fluids and IV antibiotics in order to be considered sick enough to not be at work.

July 20: Saturday

10:31 am: I kind of have the urge to check Ms. AI's medical records from my home to see how she's doing but I am off for the weekend, so I will resist. It's only my second day off from work in 20 days and my first full weekend off since I started third year.

My head is achy, I barely have the energy to sit up, and my ever-running nose is red and irritated from constantly being rubbed by tissues. I am not moving off my

28

couch today. I wish I felt better so that I can enjoy my days off. Casey is on call, so I have the apartment to myself. I don't think we've spent any real quality time together in days. Or months. It's getting hard to tell whether this can be blamed on our schedules or if something else is the cause.

July 21: Sunday

11:43 am: After sleeping most of the past 24 hours I feel infinitely better and ready to leave the confines of my apartment.

It was so gorgeously bright out today that I decided I needed to spend the day outside. I was in luck. Once a month the LGBT group at my medical school hosts a potluck dinner and as a mostly-straight ally, I try to attend each month. The hosts for this month are the brilliant Dr. Neuro (who I adore) and his partner. Upon arriving to the party, Dr. Neuro took my best friend Jane and I upstairs to the balcony overlooking his pool and backyard. From this vantage point he pointed out each of the physicians and their specialty, so we would know whom to best target for networking. After about ten minutes of playing who's who, two more people entered the backyard. Our professor confided to us, "Oh, look, that's the medicine attending, Dr. Osler. He's started coming out to family and friends last week, but he hasn't come out at work yet. It's been really difficult for him. This is his first time ever attending the potluck. I've assured him it's a safe place where he can be comfortable and open." Well, I guess there's no safer place to run into your own med student than at an LGBT potluck/pool party?

I'm fairly certain Dr. Osler almost ran from the pool deck upon making eye contact with me. We chatted briefly and then each went about our own business of drinking and relaxing.

July 22: Monday

11:35 am: There was a mandatory CPR recertification class this morning resulting in me missing morning rounds again. It feels weird to be away from my patients three days in a row.

11:46 am: Ugh… the chaplain never checked in with Ms. AI on Friday! So much for that idea. On top of that, it turns out Ms. AI had a fall and developed a new infection. Why is she getting worse and not better?

2:35 pm: Ms. BA has been discharged. I wonder how long before she returns with her arm infected and requiring an amputation à la *Requiem for a Dream*.

July 23: Tuesday

6:50 am: We have a new attending today so farewell to Dr. Osler. He was easy-going and laidback, making my transition to third year smooth. I've heard rumors that our new attending is borderline neurotic in how she likes things done and can be a real stickler about pretty much everything.

9:26 am: Many patients seem distrustful when we talk to them. They and their families often query: "Do you know what you're doing?" "Why am I not better yet?" "How old are you?" "Are you sure about that?" "I checked Google and I think I have xyz…" I keep thinking, "We're doing the best we can and don't worry; our attending keeps a close eye on us."

11:46 am: Ms. AI has diarrhea so prolific right now that she has taken to wearing diapers. She tearfully admitted to me how embarrassing this whole situation is for her. We're not that far apart in age. I really, truly can't imagine being in her position; it must be so, so terrible.

2:23 pm: Super Tuesday! Hold the super.

3:12 pm: My personal life is falling apart. Can I keep ignoring that right now?

July 24: Wednesday

11:49 am: We have a patient in his 90s who is likely not making it out of The General Hospital alive. His name is 95. His daughter, who is my parent's age, made this realization while we were rounding yesterday. She broke down crying. Not just crying, but really sobbing. We witnessed the moment where she came to understand that her father is not only mortal but is dying. My team left me with her during rounds to comfort her and I am so glad they did. I let her cry it out for a bit, then encouraged her to talk about

95 and her family. After a while, we discussed coping, strength, and surviving events we believe are insurmountable. After spending so many hours of so many days wishing I could be of service to my patients and my team this felt wonderful. This will certainly be a most memorable patient encounter.

On another note, 95 is one of the healthiest patients on our service: no diabetes, no cardiovascular disease, and no obesity. The senior resident informed me that if someone makes it to their 90s, it's because their life leading up until that point was likely healthy. Evidently his health status is not surprising to anyone else on the team.

1:15 pm: My intern is off today, my senior is at clinic, and my attending is not here. I'm going to be a bad/lazy med student and go home. I really need to go food shopping and take a shower. It's been awhile.

July 25: Thursday

6:52 am: As I pre-rounded today, Ms. AI told me to not be so nervous when presenting in front of the new attending. I was touched to realize that this patient, someone so sick and brittle, had noticed how my bedside presentations changed with the new attending. She is absolutely right. This new attending definitely makes me jittery. I just wish my team could do more for Ms. AI. She appears to be fading before my eyes, every day more pallid and frail than the day before.

11:52 am: My team went into 95's room during rounds. While discussing the plan for 95, his daughter walked into the room. When she saw me, she walked right over and gave me a big hug, then looked me in the eye, thanked me, and told me she'd never forget me. Great way to start the day! It would have been just as wonderful if my team wasn't present to witness her gratitude, but having the team there was a bonus.

7:35 pm: As part of my end-of-rotation evaluation I was scrutinized while taking a patient history and doing a full physical exam. In general, the feedback was positive. My attending taught me how to properly palpate the spleen during the physical exam. From now on I won't have to awkwardly pretend as if I know what I'm doing during that part of an abdominal exam. My attending remarked that I am skilled at quickly developing relationships with my patients. It's nice to feel that I'm good at something since most of the time I am fairly lost. Patients do not act the way we were taught they would.

There's a *NY Times* article about patients developing post-traumatic stress disorder (PTSD) after ICU stays.[4] Patients at higher risk tend to be young females. I wonder if PTSD is plaguing Ms. AI during her hospital stay.

8:36 pm: I am actively ignoring the fact that Casey told me on Monday night that he doesn't know if he ever sees us getting married.

July 26: Friday

11:30 am: Turns out that 95 is a trooper. He's doing great and will be going home tomorrow. Yet another patient this rotation that my team had written off for dead but will be going home very much alive.

2:15 pm: I had a final feedback session with my senior resident today. He said he was pleased with my progress and went on to explain, "I don't want to use the word aggressive... No, your assertiveness in offering to do and watch procedures was great." I told him I tried to keep an open mind during the rotation, but we agreed that internal medicine probably isn't for me. Like in any way. At all. Ever.

I'm happy it's my last night of call with inpatient internal medicine and tomorrow is my last day at the hospital. The next four weeks will be outpatient internal medicine.

Since tomorrow is my last day, I really need to go say goodbye to Ms. AI.

3:35 pm: Timing. Not a minute after typing the previous sentence the code pagers went off. I took off running and was halfway down the hallway to the patient's room before it clicked that I was heading towards Ms. AI room. She was unresponsive, so a rapid response was called.

Then she started posturing, with her arms and legs extended stiffly at her side. The doctor pinched her skin and tried other painful methods to rouse her. I wanted to yell at him to stop. I stood frozen near the doorway of her room and watched her get intubated while the residents discussed whether or not she may have developed a bleed in her head.

The scene played out exactly the way she described to me that she was afraid it would happen. Masked, yellow-gowned docs swarming around her bed and shoving a tube down her throat. She was sent for an emergent head CT, so I went with her, and then I followed her to her new room in the ICU. I kept vigil at her bedside for some time, unable to imagine how I would feel if one of my nightmares came true. One of the attending docs stopped by and asked me if I was ok. He kindly updated me that her CT scan was normal. I'm usually good at hiding my emotions but this was too much to witness. She can't die. She can't. Of all the patients... not her. Please not her.

5:45 pm: Time does not stop and our team is busy. There is a new patient for me and I almost vomited in his room because of the stench emanating from him.

6:50 pm: Lots of new patients are rolling in, including two who are psychotic. Psychotic patients are fascinating to me, and today they are also distracting me from thinking about Ms. AI. One new patient kept yelling at me and calling me Bessy. The other one is intensely paranoid and believes she is part of an FBI conspiracy and film project. She seemed relieved (though I think slightly disappointed) when I told her firmly "no" we are not making a movie about her. Though, she will get a part in my book. I didn't tell her this.

July 27: Saturday

6:45 am: Today is my last day on inpatient medicine. I would've said goodbye to Ms. AI but she is still intubated in the ICU. I will, however, go and say goodbye to 95 and his wonderful family once we're done with rounds.

1:30 pm: Wow, what a great note to end on. I spent nearly 40 minutes sitting with 95 and his wife of forever.

They have many children and even more grandchildren and great grandchildren. 95's wife revealed to me in a conspiratorial tone, "Every time he thought I wasn't busy enough he got me pregnant again." My favorite exchange went something like this:

Wife: "I couldn't have found a better man, I am so blessed."

95: "You could've found a richer man."

Wife: "I guess so."

95: "Eh, but he probably wouldn't have you let you spend all his money the way I let you spend all of mine!"

The two of them busted out laughing.

95's wife asked me if I had a boyfriend. I replied "yes," and she told me that he better be treating me right. She added that he must be worried all the time about other doctors hitting on me. I'm not so sure about that, but I just nodded and smiled and left it at that. There were lots of hugs and well-wishing when I left the room. I am in awe of their relationship. You could see the love between them, radiating from them. My grandparents, my mom's parents, were like that. Hugging and kissing and holding hands up until the day my poppa died. My relationship with Casey isn't like that; it hasn't been like that in a long time. Maybe in the past, but not recently. I'm dreading going home today and discussing the state of our relationship, but I can't put it off any longer.

Before I leave the hospital and officially finish inpatient medicine, I go turn in my pager that never went off.

Outpatient Internal Medicine

Song: Passion Pit. "Swimming in the Flood." *Manners.*
Columbia Records. 2009.
Drink: Bottomless Mimosas

July 29: Monday

7:10 am: I will not cry today. I will not think about my breakup with Casey. I am sitting at the Starbucks at The General Hospital and I will not cry. So far so good but it's only 7:15 am. Off to my first morning at the internal medicine outpatient clinic. Remember, no crying.

7:50 am: There are two other medical students present when I arrive at my first assigned clinic site. A nurse shows us our schedule for the day. Looks like our first patients will be arriving in ten minutes. Ok. Turns out this is the student clinic where we are expected to see our own patients, take a history (the patient's recitation of their illness), and do a physical exam (aka the H&P), then develop an assessment and plan. Just like grown-up doctors. This is all well and good, I just had no idea I would be having my own patients right now this second.

9:15 am: I took my worst history ever. Probably a combination of being caught off guard with this situation of walking into a student-run clinic, having my own patients, it's Monday morning, and I'm still distracted from everything that happened this weekend with Casey. Sad. No, no, no, not going to cry. Not here, not now. This patient's history was made particularly difficult because the patient recently had a stroke and has memory impairment.

Me: "Sir, how long have you had diabetes?"

Patient: "I have no idea."

Me: "Ok, what happened when you had your stroke?"

Patient: "I don't remember."

Me: "Do you take all of your medications every day?"

Patient: "Yes."

Me: "You take every one of your medications every single day?"

Patient: "Well..."

Suffice it to say that the visit did not improve from there.

4:30 pm: I used to live in Chicago and I loved it there. I moved there on a whim after graduating from college. If not for Casey, I never would have left Chicago. I'm aching to go back there at the moment.

6:15 pm: I'm about to leave for dinner with The Boss, my trusted advisor and confidante. When I first moved to my little Midwest city, I desperately wanted a job at The General Hospital to increase my chances of being accepted to their affiliated medical school. Casey searched around the hospital and found out that The Boss, one of the senior attending physicians in the emergency department at The General Hospital, was thinking about taking on a premed student to help her with a new research project.

I emailed her out of the blue and basically wrote, "Hi, my name is Silvia, you don't know me, but you want me to work for you." She wrote back the next day with something like, "I have no idea who you are, but I'm intrigued." Shortly thereafter I began working for her.

We quickly developed a productive and trusting working relationship. She became my premed advisor, helping me navigate the application process, prepping me for my interviews, and even writing one of my recommendation letters. Once accepted into medical school, she became my academic advisor. Years later, our working relationship has grown into a friendship as well. Upon hearing of the breakup with Casey, she immediately offered to take me out for dinner and drinks (aka get me drunk). So, off I go to dine and drink with The Boss.

Midnight: I'm a couple of beers and martinis deep right now. The Boss and I talked for hours and she informed me that when I am ready to date again I will have no problem meeting new men. Her explanation went something like, "It will be just like Zappos, you will have an array of options, and you will pick the one you want." I told her that mostly I am unhappy but a part of me is a little angry, a little disappointed, and oddly, a little relieved. I offered that if she wanted to, she could be a little mean to Casey when she runs into him at the hospital. She immediately declined my suggestion, of course.

July 30: Tuesday

10:30 am: I have no clinical responsibilities today, just afternoon lectures, so I spent the morning moving my stuff into the guest bedroom. My outpatient medicine schedule is noticeably lighter compared to inpatient medicine. I work two half-days at the student clinic, three half-days at Far Away Clinic, and one half-day in a cardiology clinic.

3:02 pm: I'm ok until someone asks me if I'm ok. I feel like a life I had been planning for years just died.

July 31: Wednesday

7:30 am: Back at the student clinic, then this afternoon I'm working at Far Away Clinic, a fair distance away from my little Midwest city. I'm not sure what my responsibilities will be this afternoon.

9:43 am: It turns out that patients frequently do not show up to their appointments at the student clinic. I have yet to see any patients today.

10:15 am: When I'm upset, I lose my appetite. Everything tastes like cardboard. When I went through Hurricane Katrina during my senior year in college I lost almost 20 pounds in just a few weeks. Fortunately, it was right after my junior year studying art abroad, and most of those 20 pounds were souvenirs from my months spent in Rome and Paris. Stories from college are for another time, perhaps another book.

6:15 pm: I didn't sit down the entire afternoon at the Far Away Clinic and I barely had time to write my notes. I really enjoyed the pace as well as the wise Dr. Pearl, the physician with whom I worked.

Dr. Pearl would send me into the patient's room to do an H&P, after which I would present the patient to her and then offer my ideas for what we should do. She would then step into the room for a few moments to greet the patient and clarify anything that was unclear. I was immediately trusted to see patients and give my opinion on their care. This is a first on this rotation. Dr. Pearl apologized for all of the running around, but I loved it. She doesn't know I spent a lot of my days on inpatient internal medicine sitting and studying. Between seeing patients, she offered pearls of wisdom about medicine and life as a female physician.

One of my patients this afternoon was a tall, dark, and handsome man, who arrived in his manly uniform. He was sprawled out on the exam table, nearly naked in just red and blue striped briefs, too tall for the table, his legs dangling off quite a way. He was lying on his side, head propped up on his hand as if posing for the annual Midwest uniformed man calendar. Do you have a nice visual yet?

Unfortunately, his whole body was colonized with the bacteria called MRSA, which left him covered in painful abscesses. Being so big and tough, he didn't come in until the lesions were huge and he could barely get dressed. Some medical terms I used in my note on him include: indurated (hard/firm), fluctuant (squishy), erythematous (red), purulent (pus-filled), and malodorous (smelly). He was lying on his side because that was the only comfortable position for him. Why naked? So that we could drain the larger abscesses on his hips and thighs. Not so sexy. Sorry. At least I'm learning proper medical terminology.

August 1: Thursday

8:45 am: I'm waiting to see the human resources folks at the Cardiology Clinic to get my ID badge. Tonight will be my first time seeing Casey since our breakup last Saturday evening. We... wait, no... now it's "I", *I* need to take myself off the shared cell phone family plan we're on.

The car and renter's insurance need to be separated. He'll be moving out soon and I'm going to need to move on with my life. Not easy. Not fun. I thought he was going to be my husband and the father of my children. Time to delete the Pinterest wedding I had planned.

10:34 am: Finally done with obtaining a Cardiology Clinic badge.

12:45 pm: Back up in Far Away Clinic.

It's noticeably different working for a physician who does not trust you. The doc I'm working with today is a young attending named Dr. Newbie. Just like yesterday, I would go into the room, report back to him, and then he would go in. However, *unlike* Dr. Pearl, Dr. Newbie would then proceed to re-ask every question I had already covered. Patients must get annoyed answering the same questions repeatedly. It certainly annoys me because it means he either wasn't listening to me, didn't care what I said, or didn't trust the information I reported. Every single patient. Not every physician will operate in the way that I, the third-year med student, wants them to. Oh well.

Dr. Newbie lacks a bit in the interpersonal skills arena. For example, a new patient arrives at the office to establish care, she has ripped shoulders and arms, is dressed in workout gear and running shoes, and I'm guessing she will leave the office and head straight to the gym. While getting a history from her Dr. Newbie queries, "Do you ever work out?" Um... really? He couldn't be like, "Oh, I'm guessing you're a runner?" Or something equally appropriate?

The patient and I exchanged glances and then she politely responded, "Yes, I do work out." There were several moments like that with other patients throughout the afternoon.

August 2: Friday

7 am: I miss my family. I need a hug from my momma. My sister Olivia – pregnant with twins – is due to go into labor at any minute. I've been secretly painting a

Winnie the Pooh themed piece for the twins' future bedroom. I wish I could be in NY right now.

11:15 am: Interesting patients today at Far Away Clinic.

Noon: I have a new appreciation of the word hypochondriac. Into clinic this morning walked a healthy-appearing young woman with a multitude of concerns. Her vital signs (meaning her heart rate, blood pressure, respiratory rate, and temperature) were normal, and even though she frequently visited the office, she did not have any actual medical conditions listed in her chart. She ended up getting four referrals to various specialists, all at her insistence, and we addressed several other concerns unrelated to the referrals as well. Several of the docs informed me that with some patients, it's easier to give in and let them have whatever referrals they want. Not sure how I feel about that.

2:13 pm: I'm getting antsy, I can't take it anymore; I have to get out of this city.

5:10 pm: I'm trying my best to not sit around wishing that I had never left Chicago. I loved it there so much. Professionally, I'm in a great place. I love my school and my friends, I'm going to be a doctor, and I know that I can leave this shitty little city in less than two years. That's gonna have to be enough for right now.

August 3: Saturday

4:24 pm: Almost finished the Winnie the Pooh painting for my sister.

August 4: Sunday

10:43 am: I really need to be studying, but I'm still so distracted. It is weird to think of myself as single after all these years. One of my friends asked me if I would be willing to date a guy who has kids. Huh? I don't know, I hadn't really thought about it. Yes? No? I have no idea.

Noon: I will be an auntie exactly 24 hours from right now! Olivia's soon-to-arrive twins have no idea how much they have already helped brighten my life this past week. Every time I have felt sad this week, I imagine her and my little nephews. I can't help but smile and think that one day, with the right guy, I will know that happiness too. Is it possible to have tears of pure joy and abject sorrow at the same exact moment? Let's not find out right this moment, though, as I'm sitting at my neighborhood Starbucks, and it would be really awkward if I started crying right now. I have to stop writing for a moment.

5:44 pm: Interesting article for those so inclined: there's a *NY Times* opinion piece from August 3, 2013 entitled "The Trauma of Being Alive" by Dr. Mark in, in which he mentions the Kubler-Ross stages of grief.[5] The stages include denial, anger, bargaining, depression, and acceptance. In thinking about my breakup, I can see how the stages apply. I think I spent the last year in denial about my relationship being over. I am starting to feel a little angry, but mostly I am still just sad. I don't know how bargaining will play into this, and I certainly am not at acceptance yet.

I have a lot of experience with grief and trauma, but I am already emotionally wrecked about Casey, so I won't torture myself or depress my audience any further right now with thoughts of those other haunting experiences... Stop! Redirect. Babies. Think about my sister's babies and how I will have a photo of them tomorrow. Focus on the happy stuff. See, I'm already smiling.

August 5: Monday

12:30 pm: I'm struggling with how much to include here because I set out to record my experiences as a third-year medical student, not to share the details of my love life. Well, here goes nothing. Casey and I had sex last night. Our evening started off innocently enough but, as tends to happen whenever we are left alone, we can't stay away from each other. He hasn't moved out yet, so I knew I was in a high-risk situation. I couldn't remember the last time he had seemed so interested or passionate. It was incredible. I cried afterwards.

I keep trying to blame myself for our relationship falling apart. I think if I weren't so stressed with school the past two years and so focused on us getting engaged, then maybe we would've kept the fun lightheartedness in our relationship that had always been present. But I remind myself, if he had proposed a year and a half ago then maybe I wouldn't have gotten so down and serious in the first place.

I don't understand what went wrong, or what wasn't right enough for him. We had a fun and happy relationship. He treated me so wonderfully; he was affectionate, cooked for me almost nightly, and routinely helped me study in med school. The sex was always incredible. But, after seven years he still wasn't 100% certain that I was "the one." I couldn't give him any more years of my life. I had to end it. I need to stop. Dwelling on this will only make me mopey and weepy again. I just wish I knew what it was about me that wasn't good enough for him.

1:00 pm: As I sit here, depressed, eating my Greek salad, I am also obsessively checking my phone every two minutes, awaiting updates from New York on the progress of Olivia's delivery. At this precise moment she is in a hospital in Manhattan getting an epidural. Babies will appear soon. Within an hour, perhaps?

2:34 pm: I am creating tracks in my carpet from all my pacing. Olivia went down to pre-op about 20 minutes ago, and her hubby Alejandro was called down to meet her in the OR a minute ago. Here we go!

3:04 pm: Olivia's cesarean should be almost done, right? The babies should be out by now and her ob-gyn should be stitching her up. I want to see their bitty faces and give them kisses and thank them for helping me through the week.

3:08 pm: Two healthy, beautiful baby boys have arrived! Welcome to the world my little nephews Jackson and Henry. They are, in a word, perfect. My momma, now known as grandma, sent me adorable photos. Olivia, now known as mommy, and her babies are doing well.

PS: Yes, I saw patients today at the student clinic. No, I don't really remember what happened.

August 6: Tuesday

8:00 am: Another day with no patient care. Outpatient internal medicine is not what I expected. At least we have a clinical skills lab today.

My friends and family seemed surprised and impressed when I tell them that I broke up with Casey and that I told him to move out. Everyone guessed that I would be the one to move out. As I explained to Casey, I was the one who already did everything. I left my beloved Chicago for him, I worked my ass off to get into the only medical school in this little Midwest City, and I spent every day of the past year and a half trying to figure out how to make our relationship work. I'm done being the one to do things.

So, Casey is the one moving out. He didn't argue; he agreed. His move out date is about three weeks from now. Maybe once he moves out we'll stop having sex? Oh, and for the first time in seven years, he left a hickey on my neck. I feel like such a teenager.

11:18 am: The cow eyeballs squished a bit when cutting into them. Slimy little buggers are slippery. A few almost went shooting off the exam table at our clinical skills lab. While learning about performing eye exams, we were treated to some pretty horrific images of human eyeballs in various stages of injury and infection. I like procedures. As I now have a break until afternoon lectures, I should probably go study.

1 hour later: I did not go study. I talked to my sister and to my mom. Somehow Casey and I are going out tonight for dinner. A non-date, if you will. I guess it's better than ending our relationship with fighting? We're just really bad at not being together. I wonder who will pay the check.

After Casey and I broke up, I tried reaching out to my girls first but everyone was out of town because we all had the weekend off. I then called Magnus, who picked me up within 15 minutes of me telling him that Casey and I had split. He brought me to his apartment, invited over a bunch of friends, and we spent the day drinking beer and watching classic dumb comedies such as *Dogma*.

At some point he apologized for not being good with "girl stuff," but he added that he has plenty of beer for me, and beer is almost as good as girlfriends in these situations. I agreed. The following day I spent with Piper, Sophia, Jane, Maggie and Daria, who were also incredible. My friends showered me with love, hugs, and support. It's not that I'm surprised by how supportive and kind my friends are, but they have gone above and beyond to take care of me. Truly incredible.

I love my friends.

August 7: Wednesday

6:53 am: My heart is still pounding from the nightmare that just woke me. There were blasts and bombs going off all over. I was with my cousin Violet. It was the day of her October 19 wedding and her hair was already done. We needed to get out of the area because we were in danger. Firefighters directed us towards safety. There were blocks and blocks of debris piled high for as far as you could see. We had to climb over the piles because there were no longer any clear roads to walk on.

The piles were made of blasted building bits and body parts. Bleeding and horrifically injured people cried out for us to help them, but we couldn't help anyone because it wasn't safe to stop. The smell of burning flesh and smoke hung in the air.

Four missiles zoomed overhead so we ran into a building for cover. We could feel the heat of the blast. I thought the building was on fire and that we would burn to death. The fear choked me. Back outside, we again began climbing over the piles of bodies. A woman reached out her hand for us to help her, but the firefighters yelled at us to keep moving. I tried to apologize to her for not helping but I was rushed along too quickly. We reached a staircase and started climbing. Violet yells to me "No, I can't do it anymore." I support her back and push her forward as we climb. She faints backwards onto me. I woke up screaming.

Noon: There was only one patient for me to see in the student clinic. I was hoping for a busy day to pull me out of my post-nightmare haze.

I spent my afternoon at Far Away Clinic with Dr. Pearl. Her patients absolutely love her. It's inspiring to see a physician happy and relaxed yet working efficiently.

As much as I love my two-bedroom, two-bathroom apartment, I cannot afford to live here by myself. I'm starting my roommate search by posting my apartment on a website called Rotating Room. It's designed for students in healthcare fields who travel to work at different hospitals and need a place to stay for only a month or two at a time. This seems like the easiest and fastest way to get a new roommate.

August 8: Thursday

I shipped the Winnie the Pooh painting I made for my nephews Jackson and Henry. A relaxing morning so far, then off to Far Away Clinic for an afternoon with Dr. Newbie.

Some days every patient seems to have the same complaint; everyone will have a cold, or back pain, or asthma, or whatever. Not today. I saw a spider bite that resulted in a full body rash, a rare bleeding condition complicated by a blood clot in the patient's leg, and a post-op visit.

In response to the patient with the spider bite, one of the nurses spent a solid hour googling various spiders on her giant flat screen computer monitor. I have horrific arachnophobia and fear paralyzes me whenever I see a spider, no matter how miniscule. Unfortunately, her computer screen faces my workstation so I had to crouch down behind my own screen to avoid seeing the myriad of tarantulas, wolf spiders, brown recluses, and other little horrors. Occasionally she would exclaim, "Oh that's so gross! Look how hairy! It's so big! All those eyes!" My heart is racing and my skin is crawling. I keep telling myself to take deep breaths and not look so visibly freaked out. It's unprofessional.

45

I walk into the room of another patient and notice that his face and ears are speckled with large blood vessels called telangiectasias. He has a rare bleeding disorder called HHT. I forgot what it stands for... Hereditary hema... Something. Basically, it's a disease of the blood vessels which causes both bleeding and clotting issues. He came in with leg pain that is highly suspicious for a blood clot. We sent him for an emergency ultrasound and several hours later got bad news: blood clots filled his leg from his ankle to his mid-thigh. Blood clots in the thigh are dangerous; some can break off and go to the lungs, causing blood clots in the lungs, called pulmonary emboli. Typically, you can give blood thinners to people with clots. But, giving blood thinners to someone like him would likely cause potentially fatal bleeding. Definitely a catch-22; treat the blood clots and risk him bleeding to death or don't treat the blood clot and he will likely get a fatal pulmonary embolism. What to do?

HHT is hereditary. One side of his entire family is affected. While HHT is not fatal in and of itself, it puts you at major risk for bleeding to death from minor trauma. The disease is variable, so some family members will have worse symptoms than others, and there is no way to guess how bad it will be for a particular person. The first sign tends to be recurrent epistaxis... aka lots of nosebleeds. His children have recently begun having nosebleeds. His story makes me wonder if he, someone with a potentially deadly genetic disease, ever thought about not having children. If it were me, I don't know if I'd willingly have children. I say that as someone who may be a carrier of a 100% fatal hereditary disease.

August 9: Friday

Countdown to the weekend.

8:40 am: Two nurses are working today. Let's call them GN and BN for Good Nurse and Bad Nurse. BN sat at her desk picking her nose. GN called patients with test results, while BN made a personal call. Not that I'm against personal calls, I couldn't care less, but BN came across as lazy while GN was working.

8:55 am: GN asks, "BN, why haven't you gone through your pile of papers yet?" GN points to a stack of papers next to BN, a pile of lab results and other things that need follow up.

"Wait, what? Why didn't you tell me earlier that I had work to do?" BN rolls her eyes and sighs dramatically before she stops picking her nose and starts to go through her paperwork.

Another morning with the young Dr. Newbie. He still repeats every question I ask. Today one patient replied to a question with, "I already told your med student..."

To which he countered, "Yes I know, she told me." Awkward.

11:30 am: BN is sitting at her station assaulting my ears with her singing. I can't.

12:38 pm: Off to the Cardiology Clinic.

Today started off with Dr. Heart, a world-renowned cardiologist, offering the opportunity to work with her for the afternoon. Simultaneously thrilling and intimidating.

One of her patients today was a spry 100-year-old man, named 100, who had come in for a checkup. Although he had no complaints, Dr. Heart completed a thorough physical exam. This is going to sound so nerdy, but her exam skills are mad impressive. Using the tips of her fingers and her palm, she felt a subtle murmur, determined not only that the heart was enlarged but specifically which chamber of the heart was enlarged, and she figured out that 100 was in the early stages of heart failure.

Dr. Heart explained her exam findings to me as she went. She tried to have me copy her maneuvers so that I, too, could reach the same conclusions. I don't think I have ever felt more inadequate as a medical student. To confirm her suspicions, she decided that 100 needed a few lab tests and an electrocardiogram (EKG). Of course, all of her suspicions were spot on. Damn, she's good.

August 10: Saturday

I spent the day "cabrewing" with a bunch of classmates and other random people. For those unacquainted with cabrewing, it is basically canoeing while drinking a lot of beer. I am mostly sober now and need to get some sleep. It was great to get out of the little Midwest City and do something different. I also met a lot of people. A super cute blue-eyed guy named K Canoe got my number. I'm not interested in him, or anyone at the moment, but I thoroughly enjoyed that a tall and handsome stranger flirted with me. Flirting and all that is still novel to me at this point in my breakup recovery. Too bad I didn't meet him a month or two from now when I'll hopefully be ready to start dating.

August 11: Sunday

10:30 am: The Winnie the Pooh painting arrived while I Skype'd with Olivia and the twins. She loved it and is going to hang it in their room.

1:24 pm: Blehh... studying. If I studied as much as I painted and journaled, I think I would be a phenomenal student. Every move I make hurts as I am sore and covered in bruises from all the times my canoe flipped over onto me yesterday.

Casey and I ended up going to a super fancy dinner together last night. At least we didn't sleep together afterwards. Progress?

Off to get my hair done. I need a new look. It's time to go from being a bland brunette to a fiery redhead!

August 12: Monday

11:15 am: We had eight patients scheduled for the student clinic today, three showed up. Each student got to see one of them. At least I was done by 11 am. My one patient had stitches on the back of her head, left behind by the trauma team. No, I did not call a trauma consult to ask their permission before I removed them.

It's weird to give nurses orders. Even weirder when they do what I request without question. I've read that some women tend to have a harder time commanding others to do things. Turns out I'm one of those women. Maybe it's because I don't feel like I know enough yet, coupled with the fact that I'm giving orders to people much older and more experienced than me. I guess I'll just have to get comfortable doing it.

Off to go study. For real this time as I am running out of time to procrastinate. At the end of each rotation we must take a final exam. These exams are nationwide, and the scores end up in our residency application, so they are high stakes. The exam is in less than two weeks!

August 13: Tuesday

Studied all morning. Go me. Off to Super Tuesday afternoon lectures.

2:34 pm: My first lecture covered a ton of interesting material in an engaging way. Now, we're halfway through the second lecture and the new lecturer is monotonously reading her slides of black text on a plain white background. My mind is starting to wander, not to anywhere specific though.

I'm thinking about my upcoming test, my gorgeous new auburn hair color, dinner with Casey, my classmates, starting my surgery rotation, and wondering how badly I'll be suffering from lack of sleep. Basically, I'm thinking about everything except my current lecture. I wonder if and how I'll manage to write during my surgery rotation. I guess I'll try to at least jot down a few thoughts each day and go back and expand on them as I have time.

Glancing around the room, everyone seems pretty spacey. A lot of students are typing on their iPads and laptops. I'm guessing they're 'taking notes' just like I am right now. Magnus is sitting next to me, on his iPad, alternating between Facebook and researching players for his fantasy football team. Ok, her lecture should be ending soon. My classmates are squirming in their seats.

Our lecture has already run a couple minutes over. Oblivious to our lack of interest, the professor announced, "You guys seem to get it, I could probably leave right now, but I'll go ahead and go through the next two cases anyway." The crew is getting restless. There may be a mutiny soon. I am trying to keep a neutral, pleasant looking face. Magnus is sitting next to me practically jumping out of his seat. I appreciate informative and engaging lectures. I don't like lectures without any new information, without pictures, and that run long. Oh, the next lecturer just poked his head into the classroom and gave the current lecturer 'a look.' Message received, she just wrapped up. Finally.

3:11 pm: Now *this* is a lecture: clinical decision making tailored for new third year medical students, using a common disease as an example but easily applicable to other medical conditions. Words of wisdom from this lecture: use evidence-based medicine but never betray your gut.

I have no cell phone service in the lecture hall. As soon as I walked out of the classroom my phone beeped with a text from K Canoe, the guy I met cabrewing on Saturday. I was kind of hoping he wouldn't contact me because I feel bad ignoring him, but I'm definitely not ready to date yet as I've only been single for two weeks.

August 14: Wednesday

At the student clinic once again. My patient is a soft spoken and kind young man who has a genetic condition causing high blood pressure, diabetes, and severe heart failure. Clearly embarrassed, he revealed to me that he couldn't afford all of his prescriptions. We sat with the attending and went through every single prescription, picking out the most important ones. The whole time, I felt incredulous that there was not more we could do for him. The attending noted that this is not an uncommon situation for many of society's poorest.

Another patient I saw today also has multiple medical problems. This patient cannot afford his medications either, but it's because he keeps spending his money on cigarettes, alcohol, and cocaine. Sometimes I wonder how to impress upon people that they must take care of their bodies.

6:30 pm: Casey told me he found an apartment. I guess that's a good thing. Back to studying.

August 15: Thursday

1:56 pm: Studied all morning and now I'm back up at Far Away Clinic. I examined a soldier in army fatigues with a mysterious rash. We have no idea what it is or where it came from. Seriously. I have yet to figure out which rashes and skin conditions can be examined without wearing gloves. Dr. Newbie ran his hands over the little bumps covering the soldier's body. I guess he figured it wasn't contagious. I'm going to stick with gloves for now... always. Just to be safe. Apparently, dermatology is not for me.

2:05 pm: I'm between patients, waiting for my 2:15 to arrive. When I look at the patient census for the day, all I see is a chief complaint. For my 2:15, the chief complaint is "butt pain." I have all sorts of ideas as to what could be causing that particular chief complaint. Of course, my mind immediately imagines a guy limping in, looking incredibly embarrassed and refusing to sit down while a faint buzzing sound hums in the distance. I don't really imagine that being a Thursday afternoon kind of chief complaint though. That is probably something more likely to show up in the emergency department on a weekend. I'm guessing it will be something way less entertaining.

2:16 pm: He's still not here so I began thinking about the rise in emergency department visits related to women getting Ben Wa balls stuck in them and needing removal. This problem really skyrocketed after *50 Shades of Grey* was released.

The 2:15 walked in limping but it is most likely sciatica, not a true "butt pain." Oh well. I think Dr. Newbie is also secretly a little disappointed at the anticlimactic visit. Our patient, however, found the situation entertaining as he kept repeating, "I have a pain in my butt, haha." No sir, you have hip pain that shoots down your leg. Let's not exaggerate and get the medical staff really interested for nothing.

6:01 pm: My brain is a bit fried from studying. I'm in a bad mood about Casey finding an apartment. I'm not doing well today.

August 16: Friday

An email popped up a moment ago that someone from New Orleans is interested in my apartment. I'm about to call her. Hopefully it works out.

An hour later: After a phone call, some emails, and a price negotiation, it looks like Zooey will be my new roomie. She is a speech therapy student doing a three-month rotation at The General Hospital, from September 13 to December 10. The timing will be interesting. She will basically be moving into my guest bedroom as Casey is moving out of the master bedroom and while I'm moving my stuff from the guest room back into the master bedroom. I'll be on surgery until November, so I don't even know if I'll see her that much. Who knows? This year is already quite different than I thought it would be.

August 17: Saturday

This time next week I'll be in NY visiting my baby nephews. I am so beyond excited.

August 18: Sunday

10:00 am: Woke up in Casey's bed. Oops, how'd that happen?

7:18 pm: Another one of Casey's married friends is pregnant. I am happy for them but so jealous. My life has been pushed so far away from being at that point. I don't want to be married and having children with someone just for the sake of doing so, but I thought I had found the person with whom I would share my life. Starting over sucks so bad.

August 19: Monday

Every morning at the student clinic I have to walk past the pediatric exam rooms to reach the medical student office. In the pediatrics hallway is a Winnie the Pooh height chart, and every time I see it I smile and think of my baby nephews.

One of my patients gave my attending a completely different history than the one she had given me. Now I look like an ass. Thanks.

3:15 pm: Zooey and I have a Skype appointment at 4:00 pm. She sounds fun and bubbly and I'm excited to meet her. Maybe she'll be my new BFF.

5:01 pm: I don't think Casey realizes that he still calls me 'honey' when he's trying to get my attention.

August 20: Tuesday

Studied outside on my deck all morning. Sunshine felt wonderful and brightened my mood.

Not sure how prepared I am for this final exam. Best go back to studying.

12:24 am: After I finished studying around 10 pm, I sat down with a suture kit and practiced tying knots for two hours. I am getting really psyched for surgery.

August 21: Wednesday

6:44 am: Last day of outpatient medicine. Last day of my internal medicine rotation. Finally.

8:05 am: The heat is suffocating in the student clinic today. Neither myself nor the two other med students are interested in internal medicine and we're all thrilled that the rotation is nearly over. Before the fellow arrived, we started the morning wishing that none of the patients would show up.

11:36 am: Done with the student clinic. I can leave here forever once I get my final feedback. Then off to Far Away Clinic for my last afternoon with Dr. Pearl.

Fun afternoon at Far Away Clinic:

My first patient was a big, badass, heavily tattooed biker here for his annual physical exam. He sat in an itty-bitty paper gown, with a black skull-patterned bandana atop his shaved head. Even the toughest among us need medical care. My favorite part of the encounter was when Dr. Pearl and I informed him that he was due for a vaccine. He gaped at her wide-eyed and whined, "But Dr. Pearl, you know I hate needles!" It was adorable to see this big beast of a man showing trepidation about getting an injection. Especially as I'm pretty sure that tattooing involves needles…

A healthy and fit lady in her early seventies came in for an annual physical. She had been traveling for the past two weeks with her hubby and some friends. During their adventures, she informed us how they all went hiking, biking, and did other outdoorsy activities. In the next week or so she will be off to Europe for a couple of weeks.

Immediately following her was another lady of the same age. However, this patient could barely walk after years of metabolic disease and various other illnesses. It was so striking to see them back-to-back. It made me realize that I need to start working out again. I know I usually eat healthy, but I'm really scrawny right now. I could use some muscle. These women really have me thinking about health maintenance.

A young woman came into the office for an annual physical and I am really jealous of her. She recently returned from a several week around-the-world trip. Next week she is moving to an awesome city to start a new job, and she looks like a Barbie doll. Seriously. Not fair. I hope she realizes how lucky she is. I know absolutely nothing else about her, but I am judging her entire life on those three things because I am jealous of all of them at this moment.

My last patient is a chatty and jovial woman who is a couple of years older than me. Her blood pressure normalized after being high for some time, and she no longer needs any blood pressure medication. Turns out her blood pressure dropped once she finally divorced her husband and stopped dealing with the stress and anxiety of being in a bad relationship. She told me about the years of angst that came with trying to make a relationship work that wasn't right. Now she is finally relaxed.

She talked about starting over in her early thirties with a hopefulness and positivity that I have yet to find. I wanted to thank her, to tell her that she gave me hope for happiness in my own future, but I just listened and congratulated her on her improving health. I find it entertaining when patients share their stories with me, but I have yet to figure out when or even if it's ever ok to share any snippets of my life with them.

I've really enjoyed the wide variety of patients I've gotten to see at the Far Away Clinic. Young, old, black, white, healthy, sick, rich, poor, and from all walks of life. I'll have to keep that in mind when choosing where I want to do residency.

August 22: Thursday

7:30 am: Study, study, study.

The library is blissfully quiet right now but freezing. I'm completely incapable of studying at coffee shops or anywhere there are people walking by or when there is any noise. I have major difficulty sitting still and studying for extended periods of time. On the opposite end of the spectrum, I could paint for hours without realizing any time has passed. And of course, I can sit and journal pretty much anywhere without noticing any chaos going on around me.

7:30 pm: Back in the privacy of my apartment. In the past, my home was more of a clothing-optional type of place. Being proactive, I instituted a clothing-mandatory rule about a week ago to decrease the likelihood that Casey and I have sex again. It seemed logical to me that the more clothes we are wearing the less likely they are to come off. However, Casey is ignoring my rule. Right now, he is strolling around the kitchen without a shirt on and with scrub pants barely covering anything. How can I be expected to concentrate on studying with him strolling around all tanned and half naked? It's asking too much from me. Oh well. I tried.

9:39 pm: Final push. I have one more section to review and then I quit. If I haven't learned it by now it's not happening.

August 23: Friday

6:30 am: Walking out of my apartment this morning the sky was dusky blue and a few stars were still twinkling. It had been raining all night and the humidity in the air was drenching, creating a foggy aura. The crickets and bugs sounded like a large chorus. It was like being in the blue lagoon at the Pirates of the Caribbean ride in Disneyland. I headed off to my exam this morning humming, "Yo ho, yo ho, a pirate's life for me."

Post exam: That exam was terrible. Everyone walking out looks completely shell shocked. Three weeks until I get my score. One of my hardworking and studious friends just came up to me and told me she thinks she failed. At least I'm not alone?

2:34 pm: At the moment I am sitting at the new wine bar at the airport. My flight to NY leaves in about an hour. I'm sipping on a glass of Pinot Grigio hoping it will lessen the pounding stress headache I got from thinking about this morning. I would have been at the airport earlier, but I got stuck behind some slow-moving farm equipment on the highway. Welcome to the Midwest.

My feedback from Far Away Clinic was uniformly positive and I earned excellent clinical grades. The doctors collectively thought I did a solid job presenting my patients and creating differential diagnoses for them. Dr. Pearl told me I should consider internal medicine as a career, which I take as an incredible compliment coming from her.

My feedback from the student clinic was not so great. The fellow informed me that I started out a little scattered, didn't seem enthusiastic, and did not go above and beyond, though I improved a lot over the course of the month. It might be more accurate to say that I was barely functioning during my first day at the student clinic, which was not even 48 hours after Casey and I broke up.

Overall, she gave me average marks and I could not disagree. At the same time, she cut me zero slack for not being on top of my game in my post-seven-year-relationship breakup state because medical students are expected to perform at our highest potential all the time, no matter what. I'm still learning how to turn my emotions off when I walk through the doors of the hospital. I'm not sure if I'll ever be able to do it.

Two months of third year down, ten months to go. Off to surgery.

Thoracic Surgery

Song: Cold War Kids. "Hang Me Up to Dry." *Robbers & Cowards*. Downtown Records, V2 Records. 2007.
Drink: Rhinegeist Zen, Session IPA

August 26: Monday
5:45 am: No other cars were on the road as I drove in. I meet my team at 6 am. It's weird being at the hospital before Starbucks opens. I'm nervous.

It's so disorienting to start on a new rotation.

Four weeks of thoracic surgery here at The General Hospital. Thoracic surgery involves operations on the lungs and esophagus, typically to remove all or part of those organs due to the presence of cancer.

7:30 am: We had a two-minute orientation informing us that we're not supposed to work more than 28 hours in a row or more than 80 hours in a week. We were told to never make evening plans, because we may end up working late and then we'll be pissed. Plan on working until nine o'clock every night and that way if we get off at six o'clock, we'll be happy. Ok...

7:39 pm: I survived my first day, a solid 12 hours. Quite the change from outpatient medicine. As the medical student, my role is pretty straightforward. I'm to read ahead about the surgeries I will be attending, and know the relevant anatomy, reasons for the procedure, complications, and related whatnot. While in the OR, I watch the operation, and if it's appropriate, I close part or all of the incision or do other small tasks, while the attending supervises and points out anatomy or diseased tissue. The attending is in charge and the resident is "first assist," aka the main helper. I would love to first assist because just watching an operation gets a little boring, but, unfortunately for me, the surgery residents always get priority.

Today I learned the elaborate ritual of cleansing one's body and soul in preparation for performing an

57

operation. Surgeons work within a sterile field in the OR. The field includes the patient, and anyone or anything that may come into contact with the patient. In order to be allowed within the bubble of the sterile field, one must go through a series of sequential steps. The procedure, nearly religious in its solemnity and precision, starts with putting on a surgical cap, facemask, and eye shield. This is followed by washing your hands and nails thoroughly for three minutes, drying your hands with a sterile towel (starting at the fingertips and working towards the elbows), then donning an OR gown and two layers of sterile gloves, all without touching anything in the surrounding area. Once sterile, you cannot touch ANYTHING that is not sterile, or you will break the field and piss everyone off. Your hands have to remain between your shoulders and your waist; you literally can't put them down at your sides. Once sterile, you may approach the ceremonial operating room table.

The first case I scrubbed into involved repairing part of someone's esophagus (the tube running from the mouth to the stomach). Almost immediately after scrubbing in and stepping up to the table, I developed an itch on my nose. Trapped in my sterile attire, I spent nearly two hours next to the OR table trying to rub the tip of my nose against my surgical mask in order to relieve the annoying sensation. No luck.

Another case involved placing a trach, or breathing tube, into someone's neck. I learned that bleeding tissue is not always bad, because at least that means there is good blood flow to the area. Unlike zombie movies, dead tissue cannot come back to life. Simple. Logical. I like this surgery thing.

The nurses are really helpful here. In addition to being kind, they thoughtfully taught me about the magic of swabbing a bit of peppermint oil on your surgical mask before beginning a smelly surgery. Oh, and I like when they play music in the OR.

9:15 pm: I'm in bed. My alarm is set for 4:45 am. I'm forcing myself to stop writing and go to sleep early.

August 27: Tuesday

7: 25 am: It's remarkable how differently the surgery team wants their patients presented during morning rounds. The entire presentation takes about one minute and notes are written ASAP. We see every single patient from 6-7 am, have a quick breakfast if there is time, and then we're off to OR at 7:30 am.

My surgery team is as small as my medicine team but we have just as many patients. We round so much faster than when I was on medicine, yet the same amount of work gets accomplished. Everything seems so much more efficient. Maybe I should be a surgeon.

A patient in the surgical ICU keeps yelling, "Ice cream! Ice cream! Ice cream!" Well sir, I would like some ice cream too, but you don't hear me making a fuss.

10:35 am: Every physician has one body part that they can't stand. I have yet to meet a doc without an aversion to at least one type of injury or illness. Popular dreaded subjects include eyeballs, feet, poor dentition, and hand injuries. Mine is mucus, or in laymen terms: boogers. I gag and nearly vomit whenever I see snot. I already knew this but I did not know the extent of my disgust. Today, I learned that my new least favorite thing to do in the entire world is remove nasogastric (NG) tubes. NG tubes run through a patient's nostril to their belly, and can be used for either feeding or for suctioning stomach contents. I will not go into detail about removing them because I will get nauseated again.

11:15 am: The surgery intern hates eyeballs.

2:05 pm: Today is our first day of surgery lectures. One of the surgeons, Dr. Mastermind, someone we have never met before, immediately starts posing questions after we sit down. He then looks at us, and starts calling on us *by name* to answer! Apparently, he memorized all of our names and faces from the medical school directory so that he could look us in the eye and call on us the first day. Oh my.

A student is fumbling to answer one of Dr. Mastermind's questions. After a moment Dr. Mastermind deadpans, "It's ok to make up answers, just say them with confidence."

Dr. Mastermind is teaching us surgery secrets. He just quipped, "When in doubt, take it out." I'm already a big fan of this surgeon. Turns out he works at The Private Hospital, where I'll be rotating next for general surgery.

5:45 pm: I've been awake 13 hours already and my day is nowhere close to being done.

The walls of the operating rooms are tiled a light blue, with the carefully arranged surgical equipment lying on sterile blue towels. The surgical lights reflecting off of the tiles and the array of metal tools gives the room a blue tint. I feel as if I'm underwater when in the OR. Swimming or drowning though? All the surgeons and nurses are gowned and gloved so that only their eyes are visible, making them appear to be in SCUBA gear.

The speed and efficiency of surgeons is daunting and impressive. The threat, no, not threat… the… the *concern* of seeing Casey throughout the day is annoying though. I feel like I'm on his turf.

9:23 pm and off to bed. Alarm set for 4:15 am.

August 28: Wednesday

4:55 am: The only awake people at the hospital are the overnight teams and third year medical students.

In just over two days I have already done more than I did all month on internal medicine. I've scrubbed into several surgeries, made calls, returned pages, given orders, removed chest tubes, done procedures, written progress notes, and completed other random tasks. My intern walks me through procedures or tells me what he wants done and then trusts that I will do it. I am actually being helpful to him and to the team (I think). Very refreshing.

6:03 am: A pale, frail, older female patient is wandering the halls of her floor. Her ethereal, floor-length white dress with flowing sleeves makes her look like a ghost. I wonder if anyone else can see her.

8:56 am: Post rounding. I'm at the thoracic surgery clinic today with the impressive Dr. Thorax. Most of the patients are here because they have new or suspected cancers. The physicians who are able to work in oncology amaze me.

10:58 am: One of my patients is a not-old-enough guy who has two separate cancers. Neither is curable without major surgery but to resect both would likely leave him without the ability to ever speak or eat again. His family asked Dr. Thorax what she would do if it were her. An interesting discussion ensued about the complexity of the operations, the likelihood of complications, and the chance that he would have an acceptable quality of life at the end of it all. He hasn't made a final decision, but his initial thought was to take the pain medications we offered, not have either surgery, and live out the rest of his days enjoying time with his family. I think I'd do the same if it were me.

August 29: Thursday

4:55 am: It feels like I've been on this rotation for way more than three days because so much happens each 11- to 15-hour day.

I never noticed before, but the staff elevators announce each floor in English and Spanish. The patient elevators are only in English. Strange, no?

Today I learned that an entire bagel fits comfortably inside my white coat pocket. Score!

Yesterday evening marked Casey's last night here before he leaves on vacation. By the time I return home tonight he will be gone and he won't return until September 10. After his trip, it will finally be time for him to pack up and move out of my apartment. I'm gearing up for a rough couple of weeks. At least I'll have my new roommate Zooey to distract me. She arrives on the 15th.

There is all of one patient in the clinic today. His lung collapsed a couple of days ago so he is here for a checkup. It's not common for a lung to spontaneously collapse in a young person, but when it happens the patient is typically a really tall skinny male.

Twenty minutes later: Wow, he is a walking example of my textbook description of spontaneous

61

pneumothorax (lung collapse) in young males. In addition to being tall and skinny, he came across as sweet and shy, too.

August 30: Friday

What a relief not to have to worry about seeing Casey throughout the day. All the surgery teams changed today. My new team consists of a senior resident, a surgery intern, and a surgery physician assistant (PA). The senior resident is a friend of Casey's. He is tall, friendly, and donned in classic green surgical scrubs, so his name will be the Jolly Green Giant, or JGG. Everyone seems happy to teach and let me be involved. I already know JGG well because of Casey. I don't know the intern yet, but he is rumored to be kind, smart, and helpful. On a similar note, I have heard that the surgery PAs are excellent. All in all, I seem to have lucked out with my team.

Allegedly there is a 'mystery bug' at a nearby hospital that has closed their operating rooms until next Wednesday. Creepy. Every single operation had to be rescheduled. I can't imagine how bad of a bug it must be to cause the cancellation of five days' worth of operations.

After finishing up at the surgery clinic this afternoon I got lost walking back to the main hospital. In the midst of my confusion I stumbled upon Dr. Neuro, sitting on a bench, eating a red Jolly Rancher. We chatted a bit, discussing my surgery rotation and surgeons in general. Casey was brought up, followed by how poorly I may have done on my internal medicine final exam because I was so scattered in the aftermath of our breakup.

This led to me almost breaking down crying on this random little bench somewhere on the hospital grounds. Our conversation basically turned into an impromptu therapy session. Dr. Neuro has such a calming presence. His polite but gently probing questions about my daily life caught me completely off guard. Out of necessity, I've been keeping fairly solid walls around me at work, but he drifted right through them. It's slowly dawning on me that I've been so busy I haven't really been processing all the change going on in my life. I'm really looking forward to having this weekend off to recoup.

I worked from about 5 am to 5 pm each day this week and totaled about 60 hours for my first week on surgery.

Wahoo! I just found out I don't have to come in on Monday because it's Labor Day and there are no surgeries scheduled. A three-day weekend!

August 31: Saturday

I think it is time to start changing out the photos in the apartment.

September 1: Sunday

11:05 am: Welcome to September.

I had a list of things to do yesterday. Clean my apartment, go food shopping, print out new photos, etc. Instead, I met up with my friend Callie at her apartment's pool. We ran into a group of girls from our class and our quiet day catching up turned into an impromptu pool party.

The fun continued as we went bar hopping downtown. One of the many fun things about hanging out with Callie is that she knows everybody, and she is an excellent wingman. My evening ended with a handsome blond ortho resident getting my number and texting me goodnight. Woke up today in a super messy apartment with no food in the fridge but hungover, tanned, and happy.

4:59 pm: With newly printed photos of friends and family, I began the task of changing out all the happy photos of Casey and me. The first photo I took down had captured an adorable moment from when we saw Arcade Fire in Chicago a couple of years ago. The rush of tears came on so suddenly and forcefully that my hands were shaking and I nearly dropped the frame as I pulled the photo out. I pushed on. One at a time I removed all the photos from our travels throughout the world over the past six years and 11 months. Memories from dozens of cities and events spread over three continents were placed gently in a neat little pile. The oldest photo I came across was a strip of black-and-white photo booth pictures from when we first met in Chicago. In the sequence we're smiling, then kissing, then looking at each other and laughing. We looked so happy. I was all of 22 and he was 25.

Next, down came the stuff on the fridge. It had been covered with save-the-date cards, wedding invites, and baby announcements from all of our friends that met, fell in love, got married, and started having babies. Because that is the normal way things happen. Most people don't just date forever.

Lastly, I replaced a piece of artwork I had painted for him last Christmas called *Fenomeno* by Remedios Varo, with another of my own recently completed paintings. It's a full-scale replica of Picasso's *Las Meninas* that I fell in love with when I saw it in Barcelona. Now I'm done. I can't handle anything else today.

8:37 pm: To cheer myself up I signed up for an online dating service. Why not? I don't think I'm ready to start dating but it would be a nice ego boost to get some attention online.

September 2: Monday

Labor Day. Upon moving into the apartment three years ago Casey painted the master bedroom green. Twenty minutes ago, I finished repainting it a smoky blue.

September 3: Tuesday

5:15 am: Love wearing scrubs to work. Hate not seeing my friends because I work all the time. And today starts my first 24-hour call day.

5:30 am: Unfortunately, the new patient on the census is the young man from clinic last week. His lung collapsed again over the weekend, and this time the surgeons ended up resecting (removing) part of his lung. Now he's got all sorts of intravenous lines and tubes in him, including a chest tube, which is preventing the remaining part of his lung from collapsing again.

7:30 am: Wow the music in the OR today is screaming heavy metal. Of all the possible tunes to be blasting out of the iPod of my super-efficient soft-spoken attending Dr. Thorax, heavy metal is definitely a surprise. In my humble third year medical student opinion, it's waaaaaaaaay too early in the morning for all this yelling!

Normally, I would not be chilling in the OR typing away on my iPad but the current OR patient is undergoing a lung lavage. The patient has a lung disorder called Protein Alveolar Proteinosis, where their lungs essentially collect a lot of crap, making it difficult to breathe. For the procedure the docs repeatedly fill one of the lungs with water and then drain it, over and over again, to help clear out all the material that has accumulated. The process is then repeated on the other side. The result is an almost immediate relief of the majority of symptoms once the patient awakens. Fifty liters of fluid will be used today and the process takes about six hours. It's pretty strange to think about the treatment objectively, though. The docs are essentially drowning the patient repeatedly. So here I am, sitting and studying (and occasionally typing) for a couple of hours. I wish I had a fleece, though; it's freezing in the OR in just scrubs.

Several hours later: I'm an ice cube now.

Just passed Maverick in the hallway outside the surgery department and had a three second conversation. Awkward. Not him, me. He's an emergency medicine resident, a stereotypical outdoorsy climbing type who always looks mildly mischievous underneath his curly brown hair. We met nearly two years ago while volunteering for a medical school event, and I always get stupidly flustered around him. Our conversation back then was nothing Earth shattering, but something about his personality appealed to me. I remember vividly thinking, "If I were single, I would totally go for this guy." The thought immediately struck me as odd because I never had any interest in cheating on Casey. Maybe in the back of my mind I already knew that Casey and I were in a dead end relationship? I wonder if Maverick is single now? Maybe Callie will know as she always has the best resident gossip. The Boss would probably know too, but I bet she'd kill me if I dated one of her residents. There's no point in finding out though, I'm not ready to date yet anyway.

Terrifying Tuesday lecture. The surgeon is telling us about a shooting trend that happened a couple of years ago. A guy would call 911 and report that a man had been shot. The thing is, no one had actually been shot yet. The caller would then wait, with a victim bound at his feet, until he heard the sirens of the approaching ambulance. Upon hearing the sirens, the caller would then shoot his victim in the back of their neck, thus severing their spinal cord, and then run. The purpose of waiting to shoot was so that the EMTs would arrive soon enough to save the victim's life. Instead of dying, the victim would forever be paralyzed from the neck down. My stomach is churning.

10:50 pm: A senior surgery resident came over to me and reports, "There is a patient with burns covering over 90% of his body. He is getting his dressings changed at 11 o'clock. You should go and watch."

11:45 pm: I don't even know how to describe what I just saw. I had never seen a burn patient before. I walked into the uncomfortably warm room and surveyed the unconscious and heavily medicated patient as the nursing team organized the materials for his dressing change. His arms and legs were covered in white bandages, thoroughly soaked with blood and seepage. The toes on his left foot poked out of the bandage, unscathed and healthy pink. His right foot did not exist anymore, having been obliterated in the fire. A white sheet covered his belly, held taut and stapled directly to his abdomen. Layers of white gauze covered his face.

A severe burn causes the skin to contract, which constricts the blood vessels and compromises blood flow. Body parts die without blood. To ensure adequate blood flow it's sometimes necessary to make incisions in the skin to relieve the pressure. Big, long strokes are needed wherever these contractures (skin contractions) take place. Escharotomy is the word. At this patient's hips, shoulders, and peeking out from the bandages on his extremities, you can see where the surgeons have intentionally split his flesh. Along the escharotomy incisions, shiny yellow fat and blood vessels strained to escape the confines of his dead grey-brown skin. The sheet over his belly covered a bag containing his intestines, which spilled out after the escharotomy on his torso.

I put myself in a position where I could be called upon to help if the nursing team needed an extra hand with the dressings. As horrific as this appeared to me, I wanted to help. It was the least I could do. I looked behind me to locate the nearest chair in case I felt faint. As the final preparations with his new set of dressings were finished being laid out, I asked the simple question, "What happened?"

The nurses began unwrapping his many layers of gauze while sharing that he ran into a burning house to look for trapped occupants. Upon stepping into the house, a flashover engulfed him in flames. According to Wikipedia (my source for all things in med school), a flashover can reach over 930°F. His buddy was able to force the door open and pull him out mere seconds later. In those few moments, he sustained burns to essentially his entire body. And now here he lies in the burn unit. A moment after the story concluded, I was asked to help hold his leg while the nurses repositioned him onto his side. It felt heavy and warm in my hands. As I held up his leg, I couldn't help but think that his body already resembled the skin of the cadavers we dissected in previous years in medical school.

I don't have a lot of experience with nurses, but the care they took in changing his dressings amazed me. I don't think I could ever do that on a daily basis. They are the kind of people I would want caring for my own family members.

When I asked about his prognosis, a nurse whispered to me that she hoped his family would choose to revoke life support.

12:16 am: So now here I am, in my bitty little call room that looks like an ancient college dormitory (or a prison cell, depending on the angle). My roommate for the evening, one of my classmates, got right into bed and seemed to fall asleep easily. Not me. I had to process what I just saw. My hope for the burn patient is that he is well

67

sedated and feeling no pain and feels loved and is honored for having his last conscious moments on this earth spent trying to save the lives of others.

4:30 am: I hate my alarm clock. And waking up in a call room is weird.

5:38 am: I already pre-rounded on my patient so just rounds and then home hopefully by 8 am. I'm excited to go home and sleep in my own bed for a bit; away from the cancers, the traumas, and the burns at the hospital.

September 4: Wednesday

Slept in and then spent the rest of the day working on my apartment, purging the rooms of Casey's presence. I didn't move to a different apartment, but I want it to feel and look as if I did.

September 5: Thursday

How is it Thursday already? I'm so confused with these days. So much gets accomplished every day that it feels as if I've been on surgery for weeks already, not eight days.

The tall thin young man may be discharged today. Hopefully no more collapsed lungs for him.

September 6: Friday

5:02 am: Woke up in a weird mood; I think I dreamt about Casey last night. Happily, I will be in the OR all day. Like literally ALL day, as there are big surgeries today. Need to get my game face on and not look mopey!

4:18 pm: I scrubbed into an esophagectomy today on an older gentleman named Professor Z. Basically, the operation is exactly what it sounds like: they take out the esophagus and connect part of the pharynx directly to the stomach. It's fascinating to watch surgeons open people up, rearrange their insides, then put the person back together.

4:45 pm: JGG is planning to go out of town tonight and is practically jumping out of his skin to leave. To his dismay, a patient unexpectedly developed a pneumothorax while at the same time a new ED consult arrived. Just as our clerkship director warned us; don't make plans for 6 pm.

The surgery intern and I bonded today. He skipped lunch because he was too busy, so I shared the peanut butter crackers that are always stashed in one of my 50 white coat pockets. While munching away he confided in me that he doesn't like the days when JGG is trying to run out the door, because he doesn't feel confident enough yet to be left solo. I could see his frustration and underlying concern about being here alone if something bad happens to a patient. I wonder if seven years as a surgery resident will morph him from being a super nice guy into someone cynical and bitter. I hope not.

September 7: Saturday

I love sleeping in and waking up feeling refreshed. I've been getting emails from the online dating site and one caught my eye. A tall, fair, blue-eyed resident name Dr. Spengler struck up a conversation. Seems great on paper. I emailed him back.

September 8: Sunday

10:45 pm: First night in my new bed. When Casey moves out he'll be taking our bed with him, so I had to order a new bed for the master bedroom. My room. I'm sitting with my iPad right now, but it's not the same as writing on paper. I miss my journal. Writing with the knowledge that someone someday may read my words changes how I put them down. I am trying to be clearer and more deliberate with what I write as opposed to my usual stream of consciousness ramblings. Time for sleep.

11:15 pm: Sigh. I'm still struggling and having trouble sleeping. I can't think about Casey yet because I still get angry, sad, and lonely, often all at the same time. Other than working, studying, and redoing the apartment, I am attempting to meet new people. There was the one from the canoe trip and the ortho resident, neither of which I followed up with even though both have been texting. Either could be a fun rebound but I don't know. I'm not ready. I really have to go to sleep. My alarm is set for 4:30 am. Ugh.

September 9: Monday

7:12 am: Professor Z seems to be doing well post esophagectomy. His kind nature and good spirits are already well known and appreciated amongst the surgery team. Walking into his room today I was greeted by an array of stunning, brightly colored bouquets. One bouquet contained a variety of bright orange flowers (my favorite color), another featured red roses, and a trough-shaped vase near the window overflowed with blue and purple flowers accented by a couple of peacock feathers. Clearly, I'm not the only one who enjoys his company. He seems to have quite a few admirers.

3:10 pm: During a free moment, I slipped into a daydream about the random summer I worked at a beach in California. Memories of the warm weather, the sunshine, the sand between my toes, and the cold surf vividly filled my mind. My pager began wailing and jolted me from my reverie. I have to figure out how to obtain a wound vac. Wound vacs (short for vacuum) are suction devices that are placed over wounds and literally suck out fluids like blood and pus. Gross. One of my difficult patients developed a purulent, malodorous, nasty, boomerang-sized infection on her back and now needs a wound vac. Surgery is really good at ruining nice daydreams. Back to work.

I'm sitting awkwardly close to a fourth-year medical student who asked for feedback from a senior resident. The resident coldly replied, "You are very smart, you have a lot of book knowledge, but you need to work on your common sense. You need to learn to think and organize your brain before words come out of your mouth." Oh wow. There was more to that conversation, but not much. Surgeons certainly don't mince words.

September 10: Tuesday
4:49 am: Casey returns today. He will be back in my apartment by the time I get home from work.

I walked down the surgery hallway a minute or so after a gunshot wound victim was wheeled from the ED to the OR. The patient bled so profusely that the hallway the patient rolled through had a vibrant trail of blood traveling down it and a metallic smell clung in the air.

My internal medicine exam grade is in. I'm freaking out. We can ask for our grade through email but I'm going to go check in person because if I failed, I don't want to start crying in the middle of the surgical ICU.

30 minutes later...

Ok so not only did I pass but I scored high enough to qualify for high pass or honors. The secretary at the internal medicine office, Ms. CV, must have sensed my relief and shock because she looked at me quizzically and then asked me if I was ok. My incredibly logical response to her query was to start crying. What is wrong with me? I swear I'm not a crier. She gave me a hug and we chatted while I calmed down. We sat for nearly 20 minutes and discussed life and love while I ate a pack of Smarties from the stash that is always at her desk.

Ms. CV told me about when she was young and naive and dating the wrong guy. She realized he was the wrong man for her, but carrying out the decision to leave him was a terrible experience. But, she added with a grin, she then met the right man. She and her husband are about to celebrate 34 years of happy matrimony. It's remarkable how someone taking a couple of minutes out of their busy day to sit and chat with you can cheer you up.

1:43 pm: Tuesday lectures. A trauma surgeon is lecturing to us about firearm injuries. He added, "I don't know how to take away weapons in our country, but I know how to help trauma victims."

3:28 pm: My favorite quote so far today came from a pediatric surgeon who implored, "You should be passionately connected to the care of your patient."

3:45 pm: Magnus must be bored because he keeps texting me random memes.

September 11: Wednesday

6:11 am: At what point does it transition from being called breakup sex to just having sex with someone you used to date?

8:20 am: I have a rare peaceful hour and a half before I have to be anywhere, so I'm relaxing on the front steps to the medical school, enjoying the sunshine. I immensely dislike being indoors in windowless underwater operating rooms all day. At least I get to do my surgery rotation in the fall. The winter students rotating will arrive before the sun is up and leave after it is down every single day. Can you imagine only seeing sunlight on weekends?

There are a lot of people hurting today and I feel their pain. Most of the day I will avoid watching television, because 9/11 coverage still makes my heart ache. I was 17 years old, sitting in third period math class when an announcement came over the loudspeaker that a plane had struck the World Trade Center. I had a moment of panic, knowing that my father worked mere steps from the Twin Towers. My teacher rambled on about numbers to a progressively uninterested room of students until the bell signaled the end of class.

My fourth period American History teacher brought my class to the library, where a steadily increasing number of students were convening to watch the coverage live. I sat in a daze on the open winding staircase between the first and second floors of the library, unsure what was going on. We silently watched the news unfold, with a collective gasp and cry when the first tower fell, sick with knowing that some of our family members were inside. I couldn't reach my dad but was able to get in touch with my mom. She informed me that my dad was okay but then revealed how his phone had gone dead mid-sentence as the first tower collapsed, her overly calm and measured voice betraying an underlying strain and rising anxiety.

The school tried to corral all the students on school grounds but my friends and I snuck out a side door and drove home. I paced my bedroom, journaled, and called every family member I could think of to see if they had heard anything else from my dad. I felt rage for the first time that day, the event inciting anger and hatred towards those responsible. I also felt fear, but mostly I experienced an overriding sense of helplessness. I had no skills, no ability to help, and no power to do anything useful. After pacing tracks into my carpet for nearly eight hours, my father finally turned up safe and sound at our house on Long Island.

These days on 9/11 I cry not only out of sadness but also out of fear. My parents, my sister and her husband, and now my newborn baby nephews, all live blocks from each other in midtown Manhattan. The rest of my family, including all of my aunts, uncles, and cousins, live in Washington, D.C. and Boston.

Terrorist attacks and other catastrophes are out of my control, so I try not to dwell on them. I'm usually pretty good but sometimes it's hard. I've had nightmares about being inside a collapsing building, seeing the walls shake and debris start falling. I wake up crying and won't be able to shake the post-nightmare haze until I hear my momma's voice. So yes, today will be spent avoiding television. I've been a bit fragile when it comes to triggering the waterworks these days and breaking down about 9/11 while I'm at work sounds awful and embarrassing. I will do a quiet, private reflection and remembrance when I get home later tonight.

8:45 am: The unmistakable sound of bagpipes playing *Amazing Grace* filled the air. Looking around, I spot a 9/11 memorial going on atop the building across the street. There are people lined up on the roof, removing their hats and placing their hands over their hearts. Just lost it. I'm outside the medical school building crying. So much for waiting until later for a private moment.

9:26 am: Back inside the College of Medicine I went to the bookstore to get a snack after washing my face in the bathroom. One of the internal medicine residents with whom I'd become friendly saw me and without a pause commented, "Hi, oh, you look tired."

I simply replied, "Oh yes, I'm on surgery."

No other explanation needed. In reply I got an encouraging, "Hang in there, it gets better!"

Yes, I am tired and my beautiful green eyes are not looking their best at this moment. My eyes have bags under them from staying up too late having sex with my ex-boyfriend, and that fine tint of red and swelling is due to sitting outside crying about 9/11 less than an hour ago. Little-white-lying that I looked tired just because I'm on surgery seemed easier and unquestionable.

It really has been a quiet morning, I'm not used to this on surgery. I've already written so much today and it's only 9:48 am. For having not done much other than go on rounds and make phone calls, this day already feels too long.

In a surprising turn of events, there were more residents than patients at Dr. Thorax's clinic. This means my only job is to take out about a billion staples from an esophagectomy patient, whom I had followed during my first week on surgery. It's nice to chat with him and his wife and to see that he is doing so well after such an intense surgery.

September 12: Thursday

7:01 am: I enjoy starting off my days visiting… um…. I mean pre-rounding, with Professor Z. He is always in good spirits. Each day his voice gets stronger and he gets chattier.

After rounds each morning we visit pre-op patients who are scheduled to go to the OR that day. There is only one patient today. She is an elderly lady named Primadonna, who is having a suspicious-looking lung nodule removed. This may turn out to be cancer, unfortunately. Here she is, lying in her pre-op bed, gowned and ready to go for surgery, awaiting a possible diagnosis of lung cancer, and she is sitting and puffing away on an e-cigarette. Talk about addiction. I wanted to take a photo of this woman. She held onto that e-cigarette until the nurses started wheeling her out of the room to go to the OR, at which time she reluctantly handed it off to her daughter.

I told a resident how much I envied the surgeon's efficiency. He replied, "They don't pay us more to work harder." In terms of being paid, considering how many hours surgery residents work, he told me that they make less than minimum wage if you do the math.

I'm about to leave Dr. Thorax's clinic. There was another third-year medical student at clinic today too. I examined, presented, and wrote notes on six patients this morning. The other medical student saw one patient. One! What was he doing all morning?

Still been emailing back and forth with the online guy, Dr. Spengler. I think we may actually go out on a date soon.

September 13: Friday

While pre-rounding on Professor Z today, I learned that he has recently retired after being a professor for over 40 years. Now that he is retired, he has decided to focus on his writing. We talked about his former job, life in the hospital, and recovery after illness. He does not like being out of control of what is happening to him. Completely understandable. He is most looking forward to a shower and the Starbucks coffee that his friend is bringing him later this afternoon. He joked about his hair being messy from not showering but he supposes that this new look is apropos to his burgeoning career as a writer. I'm thrilled he is doing so well but will miss our morning chats when he leaves the hospital.

September 14: Saturday

Mental asystole.

September 15: Sunday

5:13 am: The hospital is creepily quiet at 5 am on Sunday mornings.

Zooey moved in yesterday, but I'm yet again on call so I won't have a chance to help her get settled.

6:02 am: There is a pleasantly demented man in the surgical ICU that constantly calls for his nurse. I keep hearing, "Nurse! Nurse! Nurse!" Pause and repeat. He isn't exactly yelling; his voice has an operatic quality and he bellows the words as if he's performing an aria at the Metropolitan Opera House. He is closely tended to in the ICU and is not in any distress or pain, he just keeps singing whenever his nurse leaves the room. The overnight team informed us he was like that all last night too. In the most complementary and respectful way possible, I will call him Operaman.

I pre-rounded on e-cigarette-smoking Primadonna and let me tell you, she is the most miserable and nasty patient I have met so far this year. She let me know how bothersome it is to have nurses and physicians checking in on her. Lots of F bombs and degrading comments that always start with, "You people..." I'm pretty sure she believes we are trying to torture her. She is mad that she is coughing shit up, but after chain smoking for 45 years it's really not *that* surprising, yet somehow it's our fault. Her lack of insight and empathy is profoundly shocking.

12:00 pm: I've been here six and a half hours, and Operaman is still going at it.

2:45 pm: Still yelling. It's been busy today but not too busy, and the ICU is calm at the moment. I'm gonna go chat with Operaman.

3:45 pm: What a pleasant man. First, I asked Operaman about his pain. He informed me that no, he wasn't in any pain and that his nurse is wonderful. He told me about where he was from and what he did for a living. He smiled while telling me that he has a lot of children and has lost track of how many grandchildren and great grandchildren he's got at this point. He kept looking at me and repeating, "Thank you for coming in, it gets awful lonesome in here."

6:00 pm: Thirteen hours down, 13 hours to go...

7:50 pm: Operaman started up again so I sat with him for a bit and we discussed football and watched the Broncos-Giants game. I told him I needed to go study but I promised to come back and visit later. He promised not to yell in the interim. Five minutes later he started singing again. As part of his dementia I'm guessing he probably has a pretty poor concept of time.

9:20 pm: I sat with Operaman a bit longer. He wanted to hold my hand while we chatted and appeared sad that no family visited him today. He kindly asked me if I could stay and be his doctor.

September 16: Monday

Zzzz.

September 17: Tuesday

1:36 pm: Tuesday lectures. I spent four hours in the OR this morning. Surrounding the operating table – the intern, the senior resident, the attending, the scrub nurse, and a pulmonology fellow. That is a lot of people doing intricate work in a limited amount of space. Dr. Thorax was nice enough to let me scrub in, but I could not get anywhere near the OR table. I stood nowhere near the operating table for *four hours*. I basically stared at the back of JGG's scrubs, trying to not break the sterile field. Of those four hours, I spent about two and a half of them thinking about what I will wear on my date with Spengler tomorrow night. It's my first *first* date in forever. I'm guessing it's like riding a bike. From an academic standpoint, I learned that I am capable of falling asleep standing up.

1:43 pm: Trauma lectures have the best images. Evidently not every student in the room is looking at the gory images from the PowerPoint because the surgeon is currently screaming at my classmates, "Make sure you look at that picture. Look! Look at it!" These surgeons are way too intense for me. Relax man. Take a deep breath.

2:15 pm: A calmer surgeon is now lecturing. He is stressing the importance of asking the right questions in order to reach a diagnosis. He claims that 80% of diagnoses can be made by history alone. Interesting.

3:01 pm: The third out of four lectures just started. I am so painfully tired today. I slept all day yesterday because I was post-call and then couldn't sleep last night.

4:05 pm: My favorite surgeon, Dr. Mastermind, is lecturing again today and offering some gems of advice. "Whenever there are two ways to do things, that means neither one is perfect." Plus, "Sometimes surgery doesn't work out perfectly, but as long as you do the right thing, it's ok."

September 18: Wednesday

7:28 am: I can't help but feel mildly insulted when the JGG is surprised that an exam finding I report to him is actually present. Today he remarked, "Oh look, there really is a small air leak with cough on Ms. Primadonna's chest tube." I swear I don't make things up. I really do arrive at five in the fucking morning every single day to pre-round on my patients.

Hand hygiene is super important. Number one in terms of preventing the spread of disease. That being said, it is excruciatingly painful to use alcohol-based hand sanitizer upon entering and leaving every single patient room on rounds when you have a paper cut. Ouch.

The highlight of rounding today involved being pimped and randomly knowing about Takotsubo cardiomyopathy (aka Broken Heart Syndrome), which led to Dr. Thorax announcing that I am "one of the smart ones." I didn't reveal that I learned about it from watching Scrubs.

My new roommate Zooey texted me, "I haven't seen you in a couple of days, everything ok?" I responded, "Yep, just been practically living at the hospital." Zooey seems so sweet; I wish I had time to get to know her better.

On the flip side, I can't believe Casey hasn't moved out yet. Ostensibly, there are some delays in finishing the new apartment into which he is moving. I still like having him around, so I haven't really been forcing him out the door either. I know I can't move on until he leaves though. What's worse is now that Zooey moved in, Casey and I are both sleeping in the master bedroom. Great planning, right?

4:43 pm: I'm exhausted. Been falling asleep on rounds and in lectures all day. I'll be rushing home soon to change for my date with Dr. Spengler. Fortunately, Casey is on call tonight, so I don't have to awkwardly leave my own apartment wearing a skirt and heels on a Wednesday night.

11 pm: Great date, must sleep now.

September 19: Thursday

5:15 am: How is it already September 19? Last time I checked it was the end of August. I caved and went to work today for the first time ever with zero makeup on. I needed five extra minutes of sleep. I feel like a true third year now.

7:20 am: At some point I'll write about my date last night with Dr. Spengler, but I have to focus on prepping my presentation on Barrett's Esophagus that I am giving tomorrow night.

8:25 am: I'm back at Dr. Thorax's clinic for the last time.

Today marks the first time I've cried with a patient. I requested to see this particular patient because I had worked with him in clinic two weeks earlier. On entering the room, I found an anxious looking patient with watery red eyes sitting on the exam table. I hesitantly ask if he is ok, (which by now you know is the easiest way to make someone cry), and the patient immediately bursts out sobbing.

I sat with the patient for a while and once he calmed enough to talk, he told me that his child died yesterday. The patient sobbed and cried out for his lost child. Stunned and shocked, I regretted that I had nothing to offer my patient, no words of solace or comfort. What could I possibly say to a parent who lost a child not a day earlier? I simply sat there, held his hand, and cried too. The patient was so distraught that he didn't think to cancel or reschedule his appointment. After I informed Dr. Thorax of the situation, she too went and sat with him for a bit.

1:08 pm: As I packed up my bag and got ready to leave, Dr. Thorax thanked me for my help, told me I have solid surgery skills, offered that her door is always open, and suggested that I come speak with her before the end of the rotation. Success.

7:30 pm: Home from work, ate a quick dinner, and now it's time to put together my presentation for tomorrow. My goal is to be done by midnight. That gives me four hours of sleep... again. Can people die from exhaustion?

September 20: Friday

5:30 am: Today should be my last day on surgery, but since I'm on call, technically my last day will be tomorrow. I can't believe I've survived half of my surgery rotation already. I'm absolutely wiped.

I stayed up all night writing and editing my Barrett's Esophagus presentation. I haven't gotten much sleep any night this week. Once again, I'm too tired to put on makeup. I'm not talking about a lot here, a little under eye concealer, a swipe of Urban Decay Sin eye shadow primer potion, a thin line of bright eyeliner and some mascara, totaling about three minutes of my morning. It's not much but I enjoy spending three out of the 1440 minutes in my day focusing on myself.

7:00 am: My presentation got pushed back because Dr. Thorax isn't here today. I don't mind, though I wish I had known last night because I'm going into a 28-hour call day running on fumes.

1:05 pm: I now have a random free hour (because I no longer have to practice my presentation), so I'm sitting with my pumpkin spice latte, catching up on emails and paperwork. An email arrived from Ms. CV, the secretary from internal medicine, letting me know that she was thinking about me and asking how I was doing. Another email featured a ton of adorable photos of my chubby baby nephews. This afternoon turned out so lovely! Too bad I can't leave the hospital for at least another 17 hours.

A couple of minutes to talk about my date with Dr. Spengler. I experienced instant relief upon seeing him, as he actually resembled his photo. Overall, he is tall, cute, super sweet, nerdy, and quite chatty. Throughout the date, I sat there obsessively thinking, "Oh wow, I can't believe I'm on a first date with someone" and wondering if people would look at us and think, "I bet they're on a first date." Weird, weird, weird to be on a first date! We totally hit it off and had a great time. He didn't kiss me goodnight. Wuss.

I ran into another medical student and he immediately commented, "You look tired, you must be on surgery." I give up. I will wake up three minutes earlier in the morning and resume wearing makeup. I made it a whole two days without makeup. As an aside, please don't ever see someone and tell them they look tired. Seriously. Just stop.

4:00 pm: My day is getting better and better. Since the patients are all calm and stable I can take a nap. It is blissfully quiet and cool in the call room... Zzzz.

5:15 pm: Hands down the best nap I have EVER taken. I feel mildly human again.

I can't believe this part of the rotation is almost over. Way more my speed than my internal medicine rotation. I did a ton of suturing and stapling, improved my surgical skills, and took the chance to get my hands dirty as much as possible. I love doing procedures, though I do miss having time to sit and chat with my patients. The surgeons were welcoming and encouraging, if not a little high-strung at times.

September 21: Saturday

4:10 pm: The rest of call wasn't particularly busy or exciting. I scrubbed into an appendectomy and passed out in my call room bed by 1 am. Unfortunately, I awoke at 5 am to pre-round, and couldn't leave until after rounds concluded, sometime around 9:30 am. So that made for a 31-hour shift, clocking in at a grand total of 96 hours this week. Wait, I thought I'm not allowed to work over 80 hours a week? Don't worry, as long as my weekly totals *average* less than 80 hours then the occasional 96'er is kosher. Fucking loopholes.

Next up, off to The Private Hospital for general surgery. All I've heard about rotating there is that the hours are worse.

General Surgery

Song: Miike Snow. "Cult Logic." *Miike Snow.*
Columbia Records. 2010.
Drink: Moerlein Emancipator Doppelbock

September 23: Monday

5:15 am: Due to unfortunate scheduling, Casey is the senior resident on my team this week. Whoops. When I originally requested my schedule, it looked as if I would be at The General Hospital while Casey rotated at The Private Hospital, then we would switch locations. I didn't realize there would be a week overlap, where he would be my senior here at The Private Hospital. Since it's only for the first week he won't have any influence on my grade, for better or worse, anyway. He's an excellent teacher and we're completely professional at work so I don't mind working with him.

6:20 am: Casey just pawned me off on the vascular surgery team instead of keeping me on the general surgery team. Am I supposed to be insulted? Maybe he knows something I don't about the general surgeons. As I understand it, general surgeons mainly do surgeries on organs within the abdomen such as the gallbladder, the appendix, and the colon.

6:20 pm: Waiting for Magnus to drive me home from The Private Hospital. This is my first time sitting in nearly 13 hours. Spent the entire day in the OR. Being way busier with longer hours here, I'm glad Magnus is at this site too or else I don't think I would see any of my friends this month.

The attending vascular surgeon Dr. Vascular performed the first case, a complicated and intricate procedure called an aortobifemoral bypass. He made sure I could see the operating field and would point out various anatomical landmarks, though he didn't seem particularly interested as to whether or not I was present. Towards the

82

end of the case he casually asked if I could tie knots, to which I replied, "Yes."

Dr. Vascular's face betrayed a fleeting skepticism. "Ok good, come here and tie this knot."

I tie some knots. He nods approvingly and then offers the suture and needle driver as a follow up test. I take the tools without hesitation and begin suturing. As I continued to close and adjust my handiwork at his suggestions, some of his comments included, "Good technique," "Excellent," and "You seem to really be enjoying this, aren't you?" This culminated in the statement, "Ok, you should be a surgeon." Followed immediately by, "What are you doing right now? You should come into my next case..."

Vascular surgery is so cool. All those tiny little vessels, coursing through the body under high pressure. Maybe I'll be a vascular surgeon.

September 24: Tuesday

7:35 am: This rotation is so different than my previous ones. Barely any notes or direct patient care for me to do (at least while the patient is awake). I'm expected to be in the operating room all day long. I pre-round from 5 am to 6 am, round with the team from 6 am to 7 am, then I'm in the OR from 7 am until about 6 pm, which is when the night team arrives.

Casey warned me about Dr. Gump. She is a chief surgery resident, which is a senior resident in their last year of surgery residency. Her reputation of having poor technical skills, medical knowledge, and leadership ability are well known amongst the surgery folk. I'll try and stay on her good side and learn what I can from her.

7:45 am: There are only size small scrubs available here (men's small, mind you), and they are comically big on my petite five-foot-two-inch frame. The residents and nurses were, rightfully so, laughing at me tripping over my pants. Sigh.

8:01 am: I didn't notice yesterday, but the views overlooking my little city from some of the patients' rooms are really beautiful.

11:45 pm: Well that was simultaneously terrifying and exhausting: three straight hours of hardcore pimping by a militant surgery attending. Time to run back to The General Hospital for afternoon lectures.

5:05 pm: The über-impressive Dr. Mastermind gave me props today for being well prepped for his lectures and knowing my shit. Time to run back to The Private Hospital for my overnight call.

7:10 pm: Nighttime rounds. Two patients already stated to me variations of "This all happened so quick, I became sick and then I was in surgery, what happened to me?" Patients arrive in pain, scared, and overwhelmed. They are whisked off to surgery and wake up in a hospital sedated and confused. I spent a lot of time providing basic education and support tonight.

9:01 pm: This is my first night on call... and it's with Casey. Now, I could have scheduled this differently, but my goal is that I can help him (finally!) GTFO of my apartment tomorrow.

12:45 am (now September 25): Saw some consults, wrote notes, and helped out with various patient care tasks. Time for a couple of hours of sleep.

4:02 am: I'm not saying I want to be in the hospital as a patient, but some of them look so cozy in their beds.

6:30 am: I miss talking to patients. Like today, I saw a patient on rounds that happened to be missing most of the fingers on one of his hands. His hand is completely unrelated to his current admission, but out of curiosity I wanted to hear his story. There have been other patients with whom I've wanted to chat, but no, surgery is all business and prizes efficiency. Patients are parts that need to be repaired, replaced, or removed, not individuals.

After much thought and scrubbing into some pretty cool operations, I realized that I don't want to be a surgeon. I miss spending time chatting with my patients. Surgery is not for me. Just like internal medicine is not for me. There is a saying in medicine that when you find the right specialty you 'have found your people.' I love the efficiency, the pace, and the procedures, but surgeons are not my people. I will keep looking for my people.

6:55 am: Is it time for me to leave yet?

7:30 am: Twenty-six hours since arrival and almost no sleep. Time to go home!

8:20 am: Rocking out to LMFAO's "Party Rock Anthem" kept me wide-awake on my drive home. Goodnight my friends.

September 25: Wednesday

3:25 pm: Woke up from my post-call nap. Studying and cleaning my apartment are on the agenda for today, then another date with Dr. Spengler tonight. Starting to meet and date new people while Casey is still living in my apartment has been an interesting navigational challenge. Him continuing to live here feels like a strange sort of standoff. As if he's waiting for me to cave and ask him to take me back. Well, it's not going to happen. Though admittedly, it is hard to move on when you're spending the day working with your ex and then sharing a bed with him at night. Why is this the slowest breakup ever?

September 26: Thursday

4:40 am: Even at 4:40 am the elevators are slow as shit here. My second date with Dr. Spengler ended terribly. We chatted, laughed, enjoyed a delicious meal, and then decided to check out a nearby wine bar because we were having such a fun time. But then disaster struck. In the midst of the flowing conversation he casually mentioned doing something fun on my birthday, which is in January, and I began to get antsy and flustered. Like, semi-panic attack. Well, actually, full on panic attack. I don't want a boyfriend – I just want to start dating again. Clearly, I'm not ready to reenter the relationship scene.

This whole dating thing was a terrible idea. Spengler is out having a fun night but I'm still processing the fact that the guy with whom I'm having dinner is not Casey. I came home from my date to find that Casey still has not yet moved out. The annoying and frustrating aspect of the evening is that the date went really well. By the time we finished our glasses of wine, all I wanted was to be hiding in my apartment. Sorry Spengler, I can't right now.

5:24 am: I will never again take sleep for granted.

10:39 am: I scrubbed in with Dr. Mastermind and chief resident Gump this morning. Dr. Mastermind is wonderful; he teaches throughout the whole case, pointing out anatomy and other interesting findings, yet still works efficiently. As the lowly med student, my job today alternated between holding the laparoscopic camera and the retractors. The laparoscopic camera is a small, flexible camera used to see inside the body during surgeries. Retractors hold tissue and body parts back so that the surgeons have a better view of what they're operating on. While holding the camera, Gump repeatedly leaned her hefty body against my arm, causing my arm to move. She would then sternly remind me not to move the camera unless she instructed me to do so. Uh, I'm trying but I can't hold up your ginormous body weight! It's as if she has no proprioception. Her general tone is condescending. In a patronizing voice she'd bark stuff like, "Good job holding that retractor, don't let go now." As much as I would like some coffee, I'm not about to let go and go grab a latte, but thanks for the advice. Her acid tone of voice is grating my psyche.

10:24 am: The residents seem unhappy and stressed all the time. Perhaps because the two chiefs rotating here right now are idiots. Maybe surgery residents in general are just miserable. Dr. Gump is my chief and Magnus is stuck with Dr. Arse. Dr. Arse is notorious for screaming at and humiliating medical students. Some of the junior surgery residents confided in us that the more condescending, short tempered, and berating a chief is, the greater the likelihood that they are overcompensating for being poor surgeons both in terms of knowledge and technical skill. The junior residents then added that Dr. Gump and Dr. Arse are prime examples of this type of behavior. Magnus and I exchanged looks of dismay; we've got several more weeks with these so-called chiefs.

1:20 pm: Dr. Vascular is bringing me back to his OR this afternoon! No offense to general surgery but vascular surgery is so freaking cool. Besides, Gump has yet to teach me anything, or really to speak to me at all. I am certainly not her primary concern, nor should I be, but all the other residents manage to make teaching points, ask me questions, or at least engage me in some sort of medically relevant conversation.

One of the nurses noticed me shivering in the OR and brought me a scrub coat to wear. Both here and back at The General Hospital almost all of the nurses I've worked with have been enormously helpful to me. Starting a rotation at a new hospital is extremely disorientating and as med studs, we really don't know anything so their guidance is so appreciated. Thank you nurses for being kind to us!

8 pm: At 5 pm I was about to walk out the door... then the team got a consult. Instead of being given to the student on call, Gump gave it to me. Nearly three hours later I am now finally heading home. If I were Gump, I would give 5 pm consults to the student on call (because they have to be there anyway) and send the other student home. My feet are throbbing with every step I take as I walk out. I'm really enjoying a lot of aspects of surgery, but the hours are physically painful and, from my lowly med student perspective, Gump seems to be managing the team astonishingly poorly.

September 27: Friday

No energy left for typing. Must sleep now.

September 28: Saturday

Sitting outside, enjoying the cloudless sky and fresh fall air at the coffee shop next to my apartment. I didn't have time to write on Friday because I scrubbed into two long cases that spanned a total of 15 hours. Not only did I not have time to write, I didn't even see the sun yesterday. Being in darkness both going to and leaving the hospital is depressing. In my grand total of 20 free minutes I ate lunch while getting feedback from a resident, did paperwork, went to the bathroom, then went straight back to the OR. But here was my day:

Case 1: femoral popliteal ("fem-pop" in surgeon-shorthand) bypass surgery with Dr. Vascular.

Love, love, love. Vascular cases with Dr. Vascular are awesome. I'm not saying that holding retractors isn't important, but it's way cooler to also be allowed to make the initial incisions, open the body, place clamps, remove diseased tissue, and do all the stuff that residents get to. For this case, we removed the saphenous (leg) vein and cleaned it so it could be used to make a new connection between the femoral and popliteal arteries. By making a new connection, we can restore blood flow (and oxygen flow) to an oxygen-starved leg. A good blood supply is crucial and means a happy healthy leg. Little to no blood supply means a painful dead leg and amputation. I'm not even supposed to be in his cases because it's not general surgery, but he's so awesome.

In this patient, her (or his?) native artery became damaged by years of high blood pressure and high cholesterol, resulting in compromised blood flow to her leg. I say 'her' with a question mark because I was fairly certain of the patient's gender, but really, not 100%. As much as I'm enjoying vascular surgery, I'm not getting enough face time with my patients. Pretty much the only thing I know definitively about my patients is whether they've recently been on blood thinners or if they have heart disease.

One of the many critical points in the operation is creating the anastomosis, i.e.: suturing together the femoral artery and harvested saphenous vein. The two ends must be connected perfectly in order to successfully transform the vein into a makeshift artery. I watched intently as a senior resident began connecting the two vessels. Dr. Vascular, watching me gawk at the senior resident, offers "Silvia, would you like to put a couple stitches in?" A stunned and excited "yes" escapes my mouth. The scrub nurse handed me the micro tools so I could get a feel for them and practice a bit. I then stepped in where the senior resident had been working a moment earlier. With all my concentration and steady hands, I begin stitching the vessels together. In one smooth movement, a small bite through both the femoral artery and saphenous vein brings the vessels together. I did three stitches and if asked, I don't think I'd be able to pick my favorite one.

After the anastomosis is completed it is, of course, thoroughly tested to make sure there are no leaks. During testing, Dr. Vascular and the senior resident add additional stitches until there is a watertight (literally, blood tight) seal. As soon as the clamps are removed, two little squirts of blood pop up like miniature red water fountains, identifying where the anastomosis needs reinforcement. Once the holes are patched, Dr. Vascular informs me that my area held strong, and both leaks were on the opposite side of where I worked. Success! It may sound silly but I don't care, I beamed with pride at my three little throws.

While chatting with Dr. Vascular at the end of the case my favorite comment from him was, "I don't want to ruin your life, but you really should consider vascular surgery." Oh Dr. Vascular, if ever I were to be a surgeon, I would totally follow your footsteps!

At the end of the case, I closed almost the entire incision by myself. Before I threw a single stitch though, he put me on a surgical stool and had me perfectly set up with proper body position, view, and lighting. I started on the deep layer first, and then moved to the skin, which was friable from both age and poor blood flow. I worked slowly and methodically to bring the edges of her paper-thin dermis together smoothly. After completion and inspection, the resident told me it was the best closure he has ever seen by a third-year medical student. I *might* have had a visible skip in my step when leaving the OR.

Twenty minutes for lunch and feedback then back to the OR for case two.

Case 2: sigmoid colon resection with Dr. Gump.

My arms are aching from steadily holding the laparoscopic camera the entire case. I stood as still, silent scenery for nearly five hours. They might as well have just put the camera on a pole. My real job during the case involved ignoring Gump as she teased me about wearing makeup to work and about my purple frames. Yes, I am 29 years old and another adult made fun of me about my glasses.

At the end of the case, Gump asked me to close the laparotomy incisions. These are tiny and require only one simple stitch at the skin. The bed was at my waist, so I couldn't see well. I started to lean down. "No, stand up, back straight now," she barked.

Ok... But I can't see. I put the stitch in, but it doesn't close well so I cut it out. She explains to me in detail how to suture the skin and then tells me to try again. I still can't see so I do another poor stitch that needs to be cut out.

At this point, I thought of three logical things that could happen: 1) we could raise the bed, 2) I could sit down (similar to how Dr. Vascular had me sitting in the morning case) or 3) I could bend down a bit. The fourth option, which was the one Gump went with, involved me trying again.

Gump could ask me to put in a hundred stitches, but if I can't see the surgical field, then none of them are going to go in right. I throw a third stitch that does not close the skin well. Gump sighs, cuts it out, *leans over (!)*, and then puts the stitch in herself. She then goes on to explain to me in excruciating detail about the importance of suturing and on and on about how I really need to work on my technical skill. "Fuck you, Gump!" I screamed (in my head). Frustration seethed through me and my skin crawled at the sound of her voice, but I merely smiled subserviently and focused on all my earlier accomplishments with Dr. Vascular. My heart is starting to race and I am getting twitchy as I sit here thinking about yesterday. I can't talk about this anymore.

September 29: Sunday

5:45 am: I've been here since 5 am and haven't seen a resident yet. I'm kind of dreading today. Turns out one of the junior surgery residents saw photos of Casey and me on Facebook and decided to tell all the other residents and the chiefs at The Private Hospital that we dated. As gossip in and of itself I don't care, but "Chief" Arse is on call today and I don't want him to have any reason to start shit with me.

My fem-pop patient is doing well. I'm keeping an extra close eye on her.

I'm listening in on a conversation between Dr. Arse and an attending surgeon dubbed Dr. Angry Little Hobbit (a name surreptitiously given to her by the junior surgery residents). I'm a little nauseous hearing them speak. In over three months of rotations, this is the first time I have heard physicians speak rudely about patients. I don't want to write what they are saying because they're being so horrifically offensive. The overwhelming majority of surgeons that my friends and I have met are much kinder than we had anticipated. The old school mentality – work, work, work and torture your underlings – is fading. Looking at The Arse and Dr. Angry Little Hobbit, they seem like misfit holdovers in this setting.

The other residents laugh at them and brush it off by saying, "Oh, they're always like that, we don't take it personally." I don't get that type of behavior. I wonder if they knew I was writing about them if they would still speak so... what's the word... so freely?

9:00 am-ish: Every time I look out the window I long to be outside. Not sure why I am so antsy today, usually I am pretty content to be at the hospital. On rounds, Casey and I noticed that Gump would not talk to either of us. Gump even made a point to greet the medical student standing next to me, loudly stating, "Good morning med student Jade, how are you today?" Casey and I stayed at the back of the team during rounds and laughed about it because we dislike Gump so much anyway. But I have a new nagging concern. The chiefs are in charge of grading the med students. Gump will determine my grade. I'm so screwed.

10:13 am: It took nearly a week of searching, but I finally found a stash of extra-small scrubs. They're still too big for me, but at least I'm not as ridiculous looking now.

2: 20 pm: A nurse kindly offered me a stool to stand on while in the OR so that I could see the operating field more easily. Everyone started laughing when I replied that I was already standing on one.

5:15 pm: I survived rounds, laid low, and am now chilling with the junior resident on call and listening to Hendrix. So far, so good. Still feeling antsy though. On Magnus's way out for the evening we traded horror stories of working with our respective chiefs. As bad as Gump is, The Arse appears to be living up to his reputation, too. He has been word-vomiting an endless barrage of belittling remarks and screaming condescending statements at Magnus.

5:55 pm: It's too quiet here. It's busy, and there is a ton of work to do, but all of the surgeries are scheduled, predictable. The atmosphere is lacking the chaos that I enjoyed at The General Hospital.

8:15 pm: It's always mildly concerning taking down a wound dressing; you never know what you're going to discover underneath. Imagine watching a scary movie. With each layer of dressings removed the suspenseful music playing in the background creeps louder. Bloody and sticky gauze piles up on the bed, and the patient begins to shift uncomfortably as you get closer to their surgical wound. You're possibly going to find something gruesome, but you can never predict the extent of the visual assault your eyes are in for. A suspenseful pause in the orchestra just before removing the innermost layer of dressing that directly covers the wound... then, the music booms and reaches a fever pitch as the oozing surprise underneath is revealed! Full exposure! Shield your eyes! Blood, pus, ulcers, raw skin, bone, muscle, a smelly hot mess! Umm... Not really. Usually it's a "clean, dry and intact wound" (written "c/d/i" in the charts) held together by some combination of stitches and staples. So much for the buildup.

10:15 pm: Casey ordered me to unpack a patient's wound so the team could inspect it and put fresh packing in. Packing involves putting strips of sterile gauze inside a wound so that the wound closes slowly over time from the inside out. If you close a wound too soon you can trap bacteria inside which may lead to an infection, or abscess. Unpacking is the corollary process of removing packing that has been previously placed. I removed the soft and dry outer dressings to find an unremarkable oval shaped wound below the patient's left rib cage.

A tail of packing was visible, and the wound did not appear particularly deep or angry looking. I pulled at the end of the strip of gauze, starting to unpack the wound. As I kept pulling, I felt like a clown tugging an endless string of scarves out of a mysterious abyss. It kept going and going and the pile of gauze on the bed grew larger and larger. Fascinating. Where will it end? I had to focus on keeping a pleasant neutral face so that the patient would not get concerned. Foot after foot of bloody, purulent gauze kept coming out. Occasionally I'd come across a knot where two strips of packing had been tied together. Hand-over-hand, on and on it went. Twenty-four feet of packing later, I finally reached the other end. Twenty-four!

The surgeons inspected the wound and my next job as the lowly medical student involved repacking the chasm. In order to properly pack the wound, I needed to place fresh gauze inside, starting from the deepest crevices. To reach the furthest depths, I ended up having my fist and a third of my forearm inside the patient.

I immediately went and ate my dinner afterwards. I think I have reached full desensitization.

September 30: Monday

10:00 am: Got a solid night of sleep and woke up feeling great, which was quickly overshadowed by Casey telling me that Gump and The Arse took it upon themselves to inform Casey's boss and my surgery rotation supervisor that we used to date. WTF. Not sure what their goal was in doing that. Getting us in trouble? Gump and The Arse are ridiculous. Either way, the residents all rotate tomorrow and Casey will be heading back to The General Hospital. Unfortunately, the chiefs do not switch so Magnus and I still have nearly three more Gump-and-Arse-filled weeks.

2:00 pm: Of course, once my med school discovered that I was 'involved' with a senior resident they had to follow up. An email popped up from my supervisor asking me to come to her office immediately. I had to assure her multiple times that our relationship both started and ended before my surgery rotation and that I had no qualms about seeing him at work. I left out the part that we're still living together and occasionally having sex. Whatever.

October 1: Tuesday

2:49 pm: "You had it right, but then you backtracked because I tricked you. I made you question yourself," Dr. Mastermind laughed while addressing a stumbling medical student attempting to answer a question. His goal is to get us to stick to our guns and be confident when we answer questions, even if we may be wrong.

8:32 pm: Back home. Zooey has been a fabulously cheery addition to my apartment and the few hours I've been away from work have been great. We spent most of the evening talking about New Orleans and cooking dinner together.

October 2: Wednesday

7:05 am: My newest patient, Lady CRC, exudes an aura of calm, peace, and hope. She has colorectal cancer. Yesterday, I scrubbed into her OR case and we removed the diseased part of her colon. Unfortunately, due to time constraints typical of being on surgery, I can't spend nearly as much time with her as I would like. I want to hang out in her room and discuss her life and adventures and learn her story. Not today.

3:15 pm: I'm hiding and eating lunch. Well, hiding makes it sound bad... Rather, I'm eating lunch in a place that is not readily visible. By not readily visible, I mean the hospital's roof. It's not like I can't be reached between my cell phone and my pager.

I used to think it pretty rude when Casey would put his feet up on chairs when out in public. A moment ago, right as I sat down to quickly eat my lunch and type out a few words, I put my feet up on the bench next to me and contentedly sighed because of the blissful relief. No more judging surgery residents who immediately put their feet up while sitting down.

A classmate of mine is finally getting to see her fiancé tonight. He has spent the last seven months deployed to Afghanistan. She is not allowed to leave the hospital early to be there to greet him when he arrives.

October 3: Thursday

The surgery team walks into a patient's room during rounds and I immediately start to take down the patient's dressing so the team can assess the stump of his recent amputation. Having seen one recent amputation, I was not especially concerned about what I would find under the many layers of gauze and Ace Wraps. However, seconds after I pulled back the first layers of gauze the patient began moaning in pain. An uneasy feeling about what would be found beneath the dressings quickly took hold.

Blood and fluid had soaked through many of the deeper layers of gauze, making the dressing sticky and difficult to unwrap. Pulling at the adherent layers caused my patient to cry out, begging for me to stop and let him take a few breaths before continuing. I worked as gently as I could, getting increasingly concerned and curious about what sort of mangled mess existed under there. The smell worsened as I worked. Suddenly, the remaining clump of soaked, sticky gauze fell to the bed, and I stood staring at the cut-off end of the man's tibia and fibula, macerated and infected muscle, and a bit of loose, ragged skin attempting to contain everything. It looked like a piece of meat that had been left to rot.

I collected the pile of used dressings from his bed and tried to look nonplussed as I turned to throw them away.

At that moment, the senior resident received a call that one of the vascular surgery patients needed to be seen ASAP. I felt a mixture of gross fascination and disappointment yet sweet relief when the resident chose me to go off and see the vascular patient. I turned and quickly left the man and his stump behind to be re-wrapped by the resident and another student. I guess I'm not fully desensitized yet?

The week is almost done.

Man, do surgeons love to gossip! The med studs are generally ignored to the point where residents do not think we are even still in the room. I'm randomly eavesdropping on multiple conversations around me. The attendings are talking about residents and nurses. The residents and nurses are talking about the chiefs. They're griping about how horrible Gump is, how inefficient she is, and how she is a terrible chief. Amen to that.

I'm now listening to the scrub nurses talk about Dr. Angry Little Hobbit. OMG. The nurses have a technique they use in the OR to try and protect the residents from her. They repeatedly question her, distracting her from screaming at the residents. Wow. I had no idea the extent of the selflessness of the nurses here.

9:00 am: An attending was lightly pimping me today about my weakness: liver anatomy. As I hemmed and hawed about the name of a particular ligament, a nearby resident leaned in behind the attending and mouthed the answer to me. It was a sweet gesture. Unfortunately, he was wearing a surgical mask so mouthing the answer did little to help me out.

5:15 pm: My initial excitement about leaving work at 4:45 pm instead of the usual seven or eight pm was hampered by the realization that I still worked a 12-hour day.

While watching Glee I started laughing at some funny nonsense scene. Zooey ran out of her bedroom with a look of shock and amusement on her face and exclaimed, "It's nice to hear you laughing!" I didn't realize how rarely I must seem outwardly happy between working all the time and the breakup. I'm not *unhappy*, I've just been feeling a little numb recently. A little affective anesthesia.

October 4: Friday

11:20 am: Six cases back-to-back-to-back-to… You get it. I even first-assisted in two cases. Usually the correct type and size of surgical gloves are only ready and waiting for the resident and attending surgeon. Today, I was thrilled to discover that my gloves and gown were laid out in the OR, ready and waiting for me!

3:32 pm: Sitting and waiting for my next case, hanging out with Magnus. While chilling in the surgeon's lounge we began discussing his name in this book. For reasons still unknown to me, his knee-jerk response when asked what he wanted his name to be was to enthusiastically exclaim, "Magnus!" I offered many other less absurd options, but none of them was as random, or made him as happy. So, inexplicably, my closest friend was christened Magnus for the pages of this book.

4:44 pm: An hour later, I'm still waiting for my next case. Fortunately, Magnus is on call tonight and offered to cover the case so, I'm going home. I may be imagining this, but I think Magnus was hitting on me today. Whatever. Home I go for margaritas and tacos with Zooey.

October 5: Saturday

My first full weekend off in a month. I plan to sleep for most of it. Today, in theory, is the day that Casey finally moves the remaining 1% of his stuff out! Golf clubs, a painting I made for him, his medical school diploma, and the remainder of his kitchenware. I bet 50-50 odds he actually shows up today to complete the transition out of MY apartment.

11:15 am: Thank you surgery rotation for teaching me about efficiency. Instead of studying at home, while holed up in my bedroom, I planted myself at a nearby Starbucks. I chose this particular locale because it is a veritable meat market of young professionals forced to spend their weekends prepping for an array of qualifying exams, comps, and board exams. Efficiency = picking up men while studying.

October 6: Sunday

Casey finally moved the last of his possessions out of my apartment. We looked at photos, went through old vacation scrapbooks, had breakup sex (again), talked for a long time, and still couldn't figure out exactly what about our relationship wasn't right for him. But if it isn't right, then there is nothing to be done. Moments after his car pulled away, I dialed my mom and bawled to her over the phone. I wish she lived closer so I could get a hug. Momma encourages me to keep looking forward, not back. She's happy he is gone. And way deep down, so am I.

I put out word to my friends that I could use a little love and support right now. Zooey gave me a great hug that also helped.

"Confidence, passion, and emotion." Words to live by. Ok so that phrase may have just been uttered by Drew Brees in the pregame huddle before my Saints took the field against the Bears, but I think it can be applicable to life outside of football. Magnus and I spent the rest of the evening rooting against each other, as he's from Chicago and I'm a Tulane graduate.

October 7: Monday

5:02 am: On call again.

It is freezing in the ORs at The Private Hospital. I now wear a full base layer, usually consisting of leggings and heavy shirt, every day under my scrubs. Still shivering today, even wearing multiple layers.

I'm oddly psyched about scrubbing into my first limb amputation. You know it's gonna be a bloody surgery when (after you've already scrubbed in and can't alter your attire) you notice that the surgeons and nurses are all wearing large face shields. My nerdy little oval glasses will provide minimal coverage against massive splatter. Oops.

I'm jealous that nurses get to take breaks during surgeries; surgeons, residents, and med students do not.

12:23 am: The call rooms for the students and residents are on the tenth floor of The Private Hospital. Only one of the 15 elevator banks goes up to the tenth floor. I'm so tired and bleary eyed that it took me three tries to find the right bank of elevators.

4:30 am: My alarm is blaring. Where am I? Oh right. At work. I slept at work.

9:20 am: People do all sorts of ridiculous things to avoid going to the doctor.

9:23 am: When can I go home? I really want to sleep.

11:14 am: I picked up my thoracic surgery evaluation. It was far better than any internal medicine evaluation. I had near perfect clinical grades coupled with an excellent assessment. The closing comment from Dr. Thorax summarized, "I would love for her to consider a career in surgery."

1:15 pm: Tuesday lectures. I'm sitting in class (even though I'm post-call and should be sleeping), getting the feeling that I need a hug. Sleep deprivation is not good for my mental well-being.

2:30 pm: The lecture I'm in right now is dragging on painfully. Thing is, it's not her, it's us. She is engaging and going at a good pace, but when she asks questions, there is nothing but crickets. I don't know if it's burnout from constant fatigue, the mental and physical exhaustion, or purely not caring, but seriously, she must feel like she's pulling teeth with us. I am certainly not helping the situation as I sit here, in my own head typing about my life.

2:43 pm: There are studies showing that when people spend too much time together they tend to find each other more attractive. Is that some sort of cabin fever? I wonder if any of my classmates are hot. I've never really looked at any of them that way. Would I hook up with any of them? There is a slew of good-looking guys but mostly they're young, and things could be super messy if I dabbled in my class. Either way, more fun to think about than focusing on the surgery lecture.

5:05 pm: Finally home! I'm too tired to do the math, but I think I stayed at the hospital for 36 straight hours.

October 9: Wednesday

5:42 am: Ungrateful patient. Ugh… Sorry that my post-op check is disturbing your slumber. He's lying in bed whining and bitching. "You guys aren't doing anything. If this is what surgery is always like, I am never getting another one." The team saved his life last night. And we're monitoring him constantly in case he crashes and dies.

3:20 pm: Excellent feedback from Dr. Mastermind.

Working with Gump is pure torture ever since she found out that Casey and I dated. She is constantly condescending. She never addresses me by my name and keeps me out of the loop on any updates about our patients. On the other team, The Arse is routinely screaming at Magnus. Magnus told me that he has a baseline level of anxiety and fear when at work. Earlier this morning I heard The Arse shriek, "Magnus, if you ever fucking present a patient like that again I will fucking kill you." Yep. Death threats at work. You know. The usual. At least Gump doesn't yell at me. I think I prefer being ignored. On the bright side, as Gump now actively ignores me, I have a little bit of freedom to choose which cases I attend each day. Obviously, I try to work with Dr. Mastermind and Dr. Vascular as much as possible.

8:40 pm: Carrying my iPad and journaling throughout the day has been extremely therapeutic. I can rant and rave on paper (well, not real paper – digital paper), so it doesn't inadvertently get turned on my patients, friends, family, classmates, or any other innocent bystander. I wonder how my classmates are dealing with the stress.

October 10: Thursday

1:30 pm: Last call day. At 7:28 am I had to make a tough call, 2 minutes to go pee before a long OR case vs. 2 minutes to buy and inhale a muffin. No, I couldn't do both. I opted for peeing. I went into the all-morning case running on empty – no food, no water, and no coffee. I could feel the ache in my head about halfway through the case and it kept building.

To beat down the worsening headache and stave off a migraine I downed a cup of coffee, a bottle of water, a sandwich, and a handful of ibuprofen a minute ago. A guy tried hitting on me while I was at the cafeteria desperately seeking antidotes to my headache. Flattering? Yes. Good timing? No. I hope I didn't come across as rude. This is not the healthiest of specialties. I am chronically sleep deprived and suffer from an aching back and feet. To avoid having to pee during long cases, I often fluid restrict myself all day, resulting in a constant state of dehydration.

6:14 pm: Dr. Mastermind cheerfully pimped me for nearly three straight hours during a colorectal case this afternoon, all in Gump's presence. Being well prepared for the case, I missed almost no questions. When I am intimidated by an attending or resident, I tend to freeze up. But there is no paralyzing fear when working with him. He is brilliant and brings out the best in the people with whom he works. The nurses even joked that he could ask me any random fact and I'd come up with the right answer.

I was on a roll. At one point, he asked me about tumor markers for different cancers around the body. I responded correctly to questions about CA-19-9, CEA, Alpha-fetoprotein, and on and on. He then went way off course and randomly asked me to name the bacteria responsible for causing the plague. I look up at him from behind my mask and protective eyewear and without hesitation responded, "Yersinia." Even Gump had to be impressed. I have no idea from where that little bit of information popped into my head. I love working with Dr. Mastermind as much as I hate working with grumpy frumpy dumpy Gump.

When it was time to close, Dr. Mastermind positioned me to help Gump, who appeared taken aback by my newfound surgical skill. She stated that I had clearly been practicing at home, a lot. In reality, I hadn't practiced a single stitch at home. Nearly 100% of my free time has been spent studying surgical texts to improve my knowledge so that I can rock cases like the one we just finished with Dr. Mastermind.

As miserable as I am working with Gump, she is still my chief and tasked with grading me. I've gone with the tactic of killing with kindness. I still mostly get ignored but I figured it is the safest route and gives me the best chance of getting a decent evaluation. I wish Dr. Mastermind could grade me. It's becoming clear that my issues with Gump are not entirely mine; apparently it has been noticed that she favors male students and residents.

Unlike internal medicine, I've done everything I could possibly do to make the most of this rotation. I arrived at the hospital by 4:30 am every day to pre-round on my patients, prepped for every case, studied every night, and in general worked my ass off every single day. I'm trying not to get too down and frustrated about the fact that I probably won't get recognition for all the work I put in because my grade is at Gump's mercy. It also hasn't escaped my notice that working and studying nonstop every day is a great way to stay distracted from my personal life.

5:48 pm: I received a sketchy text from my mom, "So are you on call...?" This cannot be good. After many texts back and forth she finally admitted that my dad is going to the emergency department with weird chest pain.

8:19 pm: After a negative EKG and several rounds of normal labs, it is determined that my dad is ok. It seems most likely that he has costochondritis (sore chest muscles) from being out of shape and repeatedly lifting his chubby grandsons, rather than a heart attack.

12:01 am: The view of downtown from the roof of The Private Hospital is stunning. I love the efficiency and pace of surgery. I suspect I will miss that on my next couple of rotations.

8:00 am: I fell into my own cozy bed as the church bells across the street started ringing in eight o'clock. Last surgery call is over. Goodnight.

October 11: Friday

Remember K Canoe from the cabrewing trip two month ago? The one with the blue eyes? I texted him.

"Hi, sorry I went MIA, I've been on surgery the past 2 months and practically living at the hospital. I'm around now if you're still interested in chatting."

I heard back six hours later. We started texting back and forth and planned a date. Should be fun. Hopefully better than my last few dates that were all so awkward/bad that I don't even think I mentioned them. I have a feeling he's not a relationship type of guy, which is pretty much what I want right now... no relationships. Just fun.

Other than Saturday night, most of the next six days will be consumed with studying for my surgery final exam. Three hours after the test ends, I'm hopping a plane to NY for my cousin's wedding.

October 12: Saturday

Study, study, study.

Date tonight with K Canoe.

October 13: Sunday

My date last night started off great though ended kind of blah as we each went home to our own separate beds. I have a sneaking suspicion that he is a relationship seeker like the others.

I am so close to being done with surgery I can taste it. I'll finally be done with Gump and no more hearing The Arse ream Magnus all day. No more painful exhaustion, aching feet, throbbing back, shooting neck pains, being pimped all day, listening to shallow gossip, 30-hour call shifts, being surrounded by Casey's friends, no more. So close!

Have I mentioned yet how much I love my new roommate? Even with working all the time we're still becoming good friends.

Tonight will be a Mexican fiesta at my apartment with Piper, Maggie, and Sophia. Beer and guacamole all around.

October 14: Monday

9:15 am: The rooftops at The Private Hospital are so peaceful. With the fall weather approaching, it's crisp and cool outside (and also deserted). I'm only going to one case today, so I'm able to sneak in a real breakfast and collect my scattered thoughts.

10:15 pm: I'm so excited to finish surgery tomorrow that I can't sleep. Which is bad, because I still have to be awake at 4 am. I don't have any patients to say goodbye to because I didn't have the time to connect with any of them, and I don't foresee a tearful farewell when parting with Gump. Basically, I'm going to make it through rounds then escape The Private Hospital as soon as humanly possible.

October 15: Tuesday

4:01 am: My last day waking up at 4 am. Wahoo.

9:07 am: I bailed as soon as rounds were over and my notes were finished. I had to refrain from running across the lobby and out the door. The moment I passed back through the door to my apartment I threw off my scrubs. It felt like ripping off a layer of unhappiness.

10:25 am: So content right now. Studying while relaxed and cozy at my favorite Midwest bagel shop, savoring lox and cream cheese on a toasty warm everything bagel and a pumpkin coffee before heading off to Tuesday lectures. Even while rapidly approaching a notoriously challenging surgery exam, I feel my body relaxing.

1:05 pm: At Tuesday lectures, sitting next to Magnus as usual. We're so happy surgery is over.

My sweet, hardworking classmate Jade approached me during our lectures and asked me to share the following story. Jade's lifelong best friend is getting married on a Friday night during our upcoming family medicine rotation. On that rotation we have lectures all day on Fridays instead of Tuesdays. Jade requested to be excused early from Friday lectures and offered to make up the coursework. The family medicine supervisor replied, "Why did you decide to go to medical school if you just want to be in weddings?" Jade repeated the quote several times to make sure I had it written down correctly. She looked shell-shocked while she talked to

104

me, about to either cry or laugh at the absurdity of the response she received.

I'm stunned that the knee-jerk response by the department was to question her dedication to the medical profession. We give everything to be here. After all we've been through. How are we supposed to be caring and empathic towards our patients when we're not allowed to be that way in our own lives? Talk about a recipe for bitterness. Funerals are considered valid excuses for missing work, but I believe weddings should be too. Living people matter in this world; it's too late for the dead ones.

On another note, I'm touched that she thought of my writing as a venue for her to get her story out into the world.

2:35 pm: A student tried answering a question but did not use the proper medical terminology so the surgeon snarkily remarked, "You need to answer my questions using grown-up doctor words." Oh fuck off. Two more hours and then no more surgeons in my life for a long while.

11:36 pm: The best thing about getting into bed tonight involved changing my alarm from four am to half past seven. Even after two straight months of waking up at four am, I never became a morning person. Every painful morning I would swear that I'd start going to bed early, but I never did. Speaking of going to bed, I should probably try to sleep, but I'm lost in my thoughts at the moment.

October 16: Wednesday

Spending an uneventful day at the med school studying with Magnus for the surgery exam. We vented about our respective chiefs for a bit then got to work.

Um… I was emailed an urgent request to go talk to my surgery supervisor. I'll be back.

30 minutes later.

During the surprise meeting with the supervisor, I was pointedly asked if Gump worked primarily with the male students. I didn't verbalize anything but cautiously nodded my head. She cocked her head to the side and replied, "Ok, that's what I thought." I'm not sure of the details, but I was then informed that Gump will NOT be completing my surgery evaluation! How did this happen? Even better, my review is now going to be left in the capable hands of Dr. Mastermind and one of the other senior residents. I feel a weight has been lifted!

I thanked her and merrily went on my way. If I do well enough on the exam, I'll be eligible for high pass or honors, which provides renewed motivation to study.

October 17: Thursday

7:30 am: Dreams of Casey all night. There were different scenes but all revolved around seeing Casey either with another woman or him alone, refusing to talk to me or even look at me. The scenes played over and over, once at a beach, once at his apartment, once at a restaurant, incessantly. I no longer existed to him. I woke up dejected, lonely, and defeated. I wonder why my brain likes to torture me.

There are many things about the rotation that I valued and that I will miss. I really enjoyed the pace, expertise, and technical skill of the surgeons. I have a new appreciation for efficiency. In terms of independence, from now on I will try to figure out two or three solutions to a problem before asking for help. On the contrary, there were many aspects of the rotation that I can't wait to leave behind. The main issue though is I didn't get enough face time with my patients. I barely knew who any of them were.

Final bout of studying.

October 18: Friday

Oh, sweet relief. Back at the airport, sitting at the little wine shop, sipping on the wine bar's current flight of white wines. I feel the tension melting away. The exam was rough, don't get me wrong, but it's over. I hope I did well enough to get honors, but there is nothing I can do about it now.

As I sit here sipping on my wine

Something interrupted me while writing the sentence above. I have zero recollection of what I was about to type. Surgery has clearly fried my brain.

Time to board for NY. Time to see my family. Farewell surgery, farewell Casey, farewell shitty little Midwest City. I'm on my way to New York for the wedding of my cousin Violet and her fiancé David.

Intersession II

Song: Metric. "Help I'm Alive." *Fantasies*. Last Gang Records. 2008.
Drink: Grande Pumpkin Spice Latte

October 18: Friday

11:58 pm: I greeted my mom at the airport with a calm, "Hi, I'm ok." As I got closer, she pulled me into the biggest bear hug imaginable.

While holding me in her momma bear arms she gently encouraged, "Let it out, baby." Her words felt like permission to totally lose it and release every emotion I had been bottling up for the past two months so that I could function. The floodgates opened. I broke down and let it all flow out of me. I felt like a pressure cooker finally getting the release valve pressed. The tears flowed, mostly mine, some hers, until finally I calmed, then smiled, then laughed.

I feel extraordinarily better now. Thanks mom.

October 19: Saturday

11:15 am: Today is filled with wedding prep and bridesmaid responsibilities, such as getting my hair and makeup done. The stylist gave me awesome sexy beach curls. Sweet. Time to party!

1:30 am: As I was leaving the wedding celebration, one of the groomsmen tried dancing with me. He should have tried hours ago when I was sober and more awake. I haven't had sex with anyone since Casey and am looking to break the seal. If he had tried earlier, he probably would have been successful. Too little, too late though. I'm going to bed.

October 20: Sunday

My surprise wedding gift to Violet and David will be a painting of The Bethesda Fountain in Central Park, NY. David proposed to her there and I love the idea of memorializing such a special moment in their lives.

7:20 pm: This weekend went too fast. I'm back at the airport. I so do not want to leave NY. But at least I'm getting to a good place: Casey is 100% moved out, Zooey and I are having a blast, and I'm done with two of my most difficult rotations.

October 21: Monday

9:25 am: Today kicks off our second intersession week. My classmates are all smiling and joking around, blissfully relieved to be done with medicine and surgery. Since the first block of rotations is over, we are now officially starting block two. This gives me a chance to regroup from the exhaustion of surgery. Block two consists of four weeks of family medicine, four weeks of neurology, six weeks of psychiatry, and then a two-week elective rotation in radiology.

My class is already being encouraged to talk about feelings and whatnot. Clearly this is a much more touchy-feely set of rotations.

9:53 am: As my classmates are sharing tales from medicine and surgery, it's clear that every one of them is slogging through struggles and growing pains. Each of their stories could be a book. The group leader suggested that we should journal about ten to 15 minutes each day to record this 'transitional period' in our lives. I'll keep it to myself that I'm currently doing that. Like right now. This second. As she is speaking.

7:30 pm: Magnus and I hang out pretty often and on this particular Monday decide to go for drinks to watch Monday night football at a bar, instead of at one of our apartments. He paid for my dinner and drinks, unnecessarily, and while pulling his car keys out of his pocket, what looked like a folded receipt fell from his pocket to the floor. On a split-second closer inspection I realized it was a condom. I eyed him suspiciously but chose to let it slide without comment.

October 22: Tuesday

9:27 am: I'm not used to going to work at a normal time and seeing other cars on the road in the morning.

Glancing around the classroom it looks as if no one is really paying attention. We have no responsibilities and no assignments during the intersession week, so most of our class is partying every night and then bleary-eyed and hungover each morning through the mandatory boring lectures. I'm not going to question it though, I'm just going to enjoy.

7:43 pm: One of my new favorite evening activities is cooking dinner with Zooey. She's so awesome; I love that we're living together. Even though we couldn't hang out much while on surgery, I immediately felt comfortable having her in the apartment, as if she was always meant to be here with me.

October 23: Wednesday

10:05 am: Today is our neurology review day.

11:15 am: So far, the neuro folks are mainly repeating lectures we've already had during first year and second year. I'm spacing out. Hmm... K Canoe is texting me.

Lunch: Anytime Magnus and I start ranting about surgery we just stop and gleefully yell, "It's over!" and start laughing.

11:30 pm: Just got home from my date with K Canoe. Sigh. I confirmed that my beer-guzzling former frat boy met cabrewing is somehow also in relationship mode. I am nowhere near that land. He chatted casually about several dates into the future and about cohosting my upcoming Halloween party with me. Dude. It was our second date! Too much. I once again felt itchy, panicky, and increasingly uninterested while he talked to me. At the end of dinner, I politely requested that he return me home under the pretext that it was late and I had to be up early for class.

I'm recalling season two, episode two, of *The Big Bang Theory* where Leonard talks about a peripheral character stating, "She's not interested in dating as much as using men as tools for stress release." I find that quote to be quite apropos.

October 24: Thursday

11:43 am: The lecturer is engaging, but they have yet to cover anything new. After the constant pimping on internal medicine and surgery, most of this stuff is seared into my brain and now seems like review. However, after the intensity of the past four months, I'm appreciating the chance to mellow out this week. Maybe these intersession weeks will help stave off third year burnout?

10:54 pm: Dinner tonight with my close friend Leann brightened my whole day. We bonded almost instantly while working for The Boss and have stayed close for years. The majority of dinner was spent planning my Halloween party. We also discussed how disappointing things turned out with K Canoe. As for Halloween, I'm thinking about going with a *Dexter* theme for my party this year, perhaps decorating my apartment with blood and guts and other props reminiscent of a grisly murder scene.

October 25: Friday

2:15 pm: Today our whole class is having an afternoon dedicated to disaster medicine training. I love it. Since surviving both the 9/11 attacks and Hurricane Katrina, I have a vested interest in disaster medicine and disaster preparedness.

Most of my class is grumbling and wondering why this is relevant to medicine. God forbid they have to learn about emergencies and disasters; they're only going to be doctors. Fucking shortsighted idiots. I think it for a flash but then settle. It's subtle I know (ha), but you may be able to tell that these are my twin professional passions.

An annoying small-town classmate of mine, who unfortunately for her was sitting right behind me, complained loudly at the end of the lecture, "Ugh, I got nothing out of this."

I stood up, turned around and retorted, equally loudly, "Well I hope you're never in a terrorist attack or in a natural disaster because I have lived through both."

I stared at her dumbfounded pudgy little face until she mumbled some apology and slunked out of the lecture hall. When the city you live in is under attack and the phone lines go down and you don't know where your father is, you become concerned about disasters. When you get evacuated from your home during a hurricane and come home four months later to find that home destroyed, you begin to rethink the power of Mother Nature. I hope I ruined her day.

7:05 pm: I went to the grocery store today. Exciting, right? Well, it was for me. While picking up toiletries, I noticed an aisle that I hadn't been down in years. For the first time in eons, I ventured down the personal care aisle and picked up a box of condoms.

The rest of my night will be spent decorating for my Halloween party.

October 26: Saturday

My apartment looks fantastic. I hung cheap clear painter's drop cloths on all the walls and then splattered them heavily with red paint. The streaks, splatters, and handprints made the apartment look like the scene of a bloody massacre. Incidentally, throwing red paint around all night and turning my apartment into a bloody murder scene was an insanely therapeutic art project.

I also laid out a ton of borrowed props: body parts are hanging from chains and dark purple Christmas lights provide eerie lighting. I baked red velvet cupcakes topped with white frosting. Into the frosting I placed little candy knives and decorated them with red gel, making the cupcakes appear to be bleeding. My Dexter costume features a green Henley shirt, black gloves, tiny black booty shorts, a short black apron, knee high black leather boots, and a fake bloody knife. One of my friends asked why I didn't dress as Dexter's female counterpart by wrapping myself in plastic like one of his victims. Umm... because I'm not a victim and I would never play the role of helpless dead female. I'm the effing lead in my story.

8:30 pm: I scheduled my party for 8 pm, knowing full well that my friends will likely show up around nine and everyone else will start showing up around ten. That being said, I am sitting by myself in a fully decorated apartment, in full Dexter costume, drinks out, mood lighting set, with the mounting fear of, "Oh my God I threw a party and no one came!"

October 27: Sunday

1:15 pm: OMG, the party rocked! Though of course now I'm nursing a hangover. The variety of costumes amazed and impressed me. Piper (as blonde and straight-laced as can be) showed up in full Goth makeup and attire. Daria and Jane showed up as Daria and Jane. Sophia came as Einstein, hair perfectly coifed in a gray pouf, while Maggie proudly walked around in a Hilary Clinton mask and pantsuit. There were a handful of Marios and Luigis, Buddy the Elf, a sexy pirate, some sexy male cats, a couple of fancy 1920s flappers, among many others. At one point a banana burst through the door, carried in on a gorilla, which really is the best way to make an entrance to a party. The Most Interesting Man in the World graced us with his presence, leaving some extra Dos Equis in my fridge (which I greatly appreciated). I also spotted a Spartan warrior, several iterations of Miley Cyrus, and I don't remember the rest. There were people coming in and out all throughout the night. After the main event died down, we all went out downtown, and I think we ended up at a gay bar? The end of the night is a little fuzzy.

10:20 pm: Sophia and I went to see the ballet *Swan Lake*. It was a stunning performance and the last show for their troupe. At the end of the show, the lead ballerina, Odette, appeared to take her bows. While on stage, her Sig O arrived and presented her with flowers. A moment later he bent down on one knee, proposing to her. She broke her calm and elegant character's personality and started jumping up and down on stage in excitement and of course received huge applause from the audience. Very sweet to watch, though honestly, witnessing someone else getting engaged really kind of stings a bit.

Family Medicine

Song: Coconut Records. "Nighttiming." *Nighttiming.*
Young Baby Records. 2007.
Drink: Chili Mango Margarita, or any other drink
featuring Tequila

October 28: Monday

7:45 am: For one afternoon every other week,
starting in January of first year of medical school, we work
at primary care offices around the city. I worked with a
young physician, Dr. Red, at a nearby primary care office. I
had almost zero clinical knowledge when I started with her,
because by January of first year all we had covered was
biochemistry and some other basic science topics. Starting
from day one she let me see her patients, stumble through
presenting them to her, and answer my questions. I learned a
ton about medicine and improved my history taking and
exam skills. My experience was excellent so when time
came for my family medicine rotation I requested to be
placed at her office. Dr. Red and I chatted last night and
arranged to meet at her office at 8 am today. So, here I am
right now, sitting outside her office waiting for her to show
up.

1:00 pm: OMG that was the most embarrassingly
ditzy morning I have had in years. I don't even want to share
because it was such a dumb move. I met with Dr. Red and
we went over expectations and goals for the rotation. Just as
Dr. Red's first patient arrived at 8:10, I received a text from
Magnus asking, "Where are you?" It took about a split
second for the panic to set in. I was supposed to be at The
General Hospital for mandatory family medicine orientation,
NOT already at my site. After texting back many expletives
and asking him to tell the course director where I was, I
booked it back to The General Hospital. Of course, the door
to the small classroom where orientation was being held
opened in the front of the room, allowing everyone to look at
114

me and (silently?) judge as I slid into an empty seat as quickly as possible. That, my friends, is how you make a great first impression on day one of a new rotation.

12:05 am: It's after midnight so technically it's the 29th. Magnus just left my apartment. More specifically, he just left my bed.

I feel as if I just hit a milestone. I don't know if Magnus realizes but I haven't slept with anyone since Casey and I broke up. I haven't been with anyone else in ages. I generally felt that the situation was more of a "when" not "if," though it happened a little earlier than I would have guessed. I think I managed to mutter a "Thanks, I needed that" before he left.

October 29: Tuesday

9:40 am: Lying in bed, before becoming fully conscious, my thoughts lazily replayed scenes of my drunken tryst *hier soir* with Magnus, and I couldn't help but laugh. Good times. It's strange to have someone else's scent lingering on my sheets.

Dr. Red does not work on Tuesdays so I find myself with a precious day off. I plan to edit some of my ramblings, as well as start painting Violet and David's wedding present of The Bethesda Fountain.

Whenever I go back and edit parts of the book, I frequently have the urge to tamp down whatever I was ranting about. It takes incredible effort not to change my words to reflect what I would write now while looking back at an event, versus what I wrote in the moment. I already feel that I have over-shared.

4:20 pm: I sketched some mockups for the wedding present painting for Violet and David. It is a stunning and quite complex fountain! The base is 96 feet wide and the central sculpture of a beautiful bronze angel is atop layers of pedestals that reach an impressive 26 feet high. I think I'll use a lot of soft blues and grays to resemble twilight, because I think David proposed in the early evening and I want to personalize the painting as much as possible.

7:04 pm: Crap. One of my close friends is rotating at The Private Hospital with the Arse. She texted me that she came home today crying because of him.

9:25 pm: I've returned from Piper's house. I had to tell her in person about what happened with Magnus as they used to date. I figured she wouldn't mind because she had been the one to dump him nearly a year and half ago, and she has been involved with someone else for a while now. I never would have done anything if I thought it would hurt our friendship, she is too important and special to me. Not surprisingly, she found the whole thing hilarious. She busted out laughing when I told her what happened. Amused, she joked "I kind of want to ask for details, but I kind of already know what it's like, but I kind of want you to tell me anyway."

October 30: Wednesday

Noon-ish: Tons of patients all morning. I'm on my lunch break. I love that I actually get a real lunch and don't need to go off and hide on a nearby roof in order to be able to eat. Family medicine is definitely onto something here.

For each patient, Dr. Red lets me see them first. If it's going to be a potentially difficult visit she'll be like, "Well, see what you can accomplish in there and then we'll go over everything." Her teaching skills and bedside manner are enviable.

3:45 pm: Examining a physician is terrifying. My most recent patient is a retired doc and I felt so self-conscious when doing his physical exam. I imagine they must be judging every move I make and thinking how they'd do the exam differently, or that I look so young that I must not know what I'm doing. In reality, the physicians have only ever been kind and encouraging. Still, I feel like a stumbling novice.

One patient reported leg weakness, so I checked his pulses and he stated, "Oh, you'll never find a pulse on my leg." Upon examining his lower leg in search of a posterior tibial pulse, I felt a gentle, steady beat under my fingertips. He looked skeptical. I felt it with different fingers to make sure I wasn't just feeling my own pulse. Even though I found it easily, I convinced myself that I must have imagined it. When Dr. Red entered the room to do her exam, I was relieved and happy when she reported, "Oh yeah, here it is." I need to work on building my confidence and trusting my exam findings.

4:15 pm: I met with a patient grieving the loss of a family member. The patient is now having some difficulty with depression and anxiety. After talking for a bit, they looked at me and kindly remarked, "You should really be a counselor." I responded that I enjoy talking to people and I'm glad they felt comfortable opening up to me. I really do relish chatting with people and hearing their stories. I left out the part that I used to be a counselor and quit my job in order to go to medical school.

October 31: Thursday

10:07 am: Dr. Red is consistently respectful of her patients, treats everyone with the same courtesy, and never talks about them behind their back. The exact opposite of the Dr. Angry Little Hobbit and The Arse!

Noon: On my lunch break. Telling my friends that Magnus and I hooked up has been entertaining. Reactions have ranged from surprise to confusion to amusement. The most frequent questions regarding the encounter were: "Are you going to start dating?" (No), "Did you use protection?" (Yes, of course), and "Is it going to happen again?" (Probably).

7:00 pm: Since we only have class on Fridays and no patients, Callie and I are going out to celebrate Halloween. Normally, I would never go out and party on a work night, but I can chill out in the lecture hall tomorrow and nurse my coffee so it's all good.

November 1: Friday

7:50 am: Walked in today expecting to have lectures all day from 8 am to 4 pm but, surprise! Standardized patient at 8 am! Wait what?? Shit. Half the class was out partying for Halloween and arrived hungover this morning. Magnus and I exchanged looks and quickly tried to figure out what we're supposed to be accomplishing during the encounter.

9:52 am: Break time. Standardized patients are fake-patient actors used to simulate a real medical encounter. We have an entire simulation center, full of patient exam rooms, replete with all the medical equipment you'd find in a real doctor's office. Each exam room also has video and audio monitoring so our professors can record, supervise, and grade the interaction without actually being in the room with us. Patient encounters are usually my thing. All my previous sim encounters have gone great. Today was different. Perhaps it was because I've been seeing real patients for the past four months. Maybe it was being hungover and unprepared. The ridiculous overacting from my fake patients annoyed and irritated me. Either way, I couldn't get into it. It all felt overly staged.

During the feedback session following the encounter, the fake patient informed me that I said all the right things during the encounter, but I didn't seem to really be 'into it.' The fake patient bluntly described me as emotionally sterile, and told me that I need to work on my ability to connect with people. Emotionally sterile! Yep. Maybe third year of medical school is succeeding in turning me jaded and bitter. Maybe I don't feel like playing their games today. I thanked them for their feedback and mentally assured them that I would work on my ability to connect with overacting fake patients in the sim center.

12:32 pm: Having lunch with Magnus, who admitted that he's mildly terrified that Casey will find out he nailed me and will punch him in the face. They had been friends; Magnus had even gone to him for advice when he went through a rough patch during second year. I'm sure Casey would consider it a betrayal of their friendship. Magnus stated that he would take the punch and not even pretend to make a move to hit back if that were to happen. I don't think Casey would care about me being with any other guy in the world, but I have a feeling he'll be pissed at Magnus if word spreads through the residents. Hmm... was that a subconscious motivating factor for my behavior?

2:45 pm: Magnus is sitting next to me in lecture and he must have gotten bored because he started sending me memes, followed by a few suggestive texts, and then some outright dirty text messages.

Back on a plane. As soon as classes ended, I hopped in my car and headed for the airport. My parents live in Manhattan and are hopeful that I will move back to the East Coast after I complete medical school. I do not want to move back to NY, so my parents instead suggested that I look at Philadelphia as a potential place to do residency. Game to check it out, I am meeting up with my parents in Philly for the weekend.

November 2: Saturday

11:15 am: Med school is flying by.

My parents and I are sitting on a red double decker bus taking a tour of sunny Philadelphia. While rounding a corner we approached the Philadelphia City Hall building where there is a statue of William Penn on top, holding his hand out before him at waist height, in a gesture of blessing the city. Unfortunately, from the angle we approached at, my immediate thought was that his hand appeared to look like a penis. My mother must have read my mind because she then stated aloud, "Ooh, it looks like he has a weak erection!" Yep. That's my mom.

We spent the day strolling city streets, seeing the Liberty Bell, and eating mouth watering local fare. I enjoyed seeing my parents at Violet's wedding, but there was so much going on and so many other family members around. Having some quality alone time this trip was both needed and appreciated.

November 3: Sunday

Back at the airport. Weekends go too quickly. My parents hoped I would love Philly and consider moving there for residency. It is a great city... but it's not for me. My mother is understandably disappointed, but I feel this pull towards the West Coast.

November 4: Monday

7:08 am: This week Dr. Red and I are working at a hospital called The Cardinal, instead of working at her clinic. There are several physicians in her practice and each week they take turns going to The Cardinal and rounding on admitted patients. We're functioning more like a two-woman internal medicine team than a family medicine team.

10:15 am: One of our lung disease patients was not in his room, or off getting an x-ray, or with physical therapy, or anywhere walking around. A nurse tracked him down in a stairwell where he was smoking a cigarette and chatting with Jesus about his prognosis. Turns out these chats happen often, and according to Jesus, our patient is doing quite well. On closer review of his chart, we learned that he has an extensive psychiatric history including schizophrenia. In terms of hallucinations I suppose it's better to believe you have frequent check-ins with Jesus than the accusatory, demanding, and berating voices that are more typical for a person with schizophrenia. Jesus clearly wasn't a doctor, though; this guy's prognosis is quite poor.

12:30 pm: Turns out that rounding in the morning means no clinic patients in the afternoon. This translates to working half days all week long.

Just received news of my grade from the surgery final exam. I barely passed. I am livid; I want to jump out of my skin right now. How is it that I did so much worse than internal medicine when I studied so much more and went into the test so much better prepared? I read nearly every night, did nearly 200 practice questions, and learned so much more while at work. So frustrating. I earned glowing, nearly flawless surgery evaluations, and now I will only get a 'pass' for the rotation because I didn't meet the minimum exam score to qualify for a higher grade. My class rank will likely drop because of this. So mad.

5:45 pm: Magnus is on his way over to watch football.

November 5: Tuesday

120

8:10 am: The group of smokers outside the main entrance to the hospital each morning, hospital gowns flapping in the wind, are sadly entertaining.

Doing inpatient family medicine seems as contradictory as doing outpatient internal medicine.

The Cardinal is not a teaching hospital so there are no teaching teams, no residents, and no medical students scurrying about. The hallways seem so empty. I don't like it. Occasionally, we'll pass a nurse or attending walking alone to take care of their business.

12:45 pm: Success! Dr. Red offered that I am welcome to hang out with her and her friends once I am no longer rotating on her service.

Zooey works out every night and I've recently started going with her to the gym. I used to work out every single day. I am a former gymnast and I fenced competitively throughout high school and college. I don't really know what happened after college, but I stopped being active.

Since I started working out again, I feel as if my body is coming back to life after years of being asleep. Brushing cobwebs off my stiff muscles, forcing greater blood flow through my stagnant cardiovascular system, clearing out the stale air from my lungs. I enjoy lifting until my skin feels tight around my muscles and my limbs are shaking. After my run last night, I worked out my arms so intensely that I had trouble lifting them to wash my hair afterwards in the shower. Granted, I'm so weak right now that it didn't take that many reps, but still, it felt good. There is no way I can make a full emotional and mental recovery without also attending to my physical well-being.

November 6: Wednesday

10:25 am: A suicidal patient on our service feels worthless. He hates himself every day. He's spent years feeling hopeless and depressed. No medications are helpful to him. He also has multiple medical problems, contributing to both his physical and psychological pain. Dr. Red and I have a duty to put him on a 72-hour psychiatric hold, which we did, but then we discussed, "Why not let him go home and kill himself?" He is completely miserable, in terrible pain every day, and he's tried all the meds available. I suppose if he didn't want any help, he would not have come in seeking our assistance, though. Maybe there is still hope for him.

1:23 pm: Part of medical school is learning how to interact with patients at a level that is beyond purely treating their medical conditions. I often mimic the phrases and techniques used by my attending physicians to see what feels right and to help develop my own style. As much as I'm learning medically, Dr. Red is really modeling the type of doctor I want to be to my patients. Her patients adore her and today alone there were several patients who expressed their appreciation and gratitude to her for the care and comfort that she gives them. She is always respectful, straightforward, and kind. Her ability to tease out what the patient is really worried about is a skill that I hope to develop one day.

7:03 pm: Zooey and I have started to take turns cooking dinner for each other.

10:39 pm: I'm struggling with my book. My goal was to focus solely on my third year of medical school and specifically to record experiences about challenging, entertaining, or otherwise memorable patient encounters. I didn't expect my personal life to implode and it is impossible for me to journal without including that information. In my 25 years of paper journaling, I have never thought about censoring myself. I am instantly mortified when I imagine my father or The Boss reading any such details. Any thoughts revolving around my dating life or sex life have been deleted and replaced at least four times. I keep removing passages and storing them in different files, then pasting them back in days, or sometimes even hours later.

Working 80 hours a week and practically living at the hospital lent itself to focusing on my patients. Working all the time provided a welcome reprieve from dealing with my personal life. Now that I'm working so much less, I can start dating and trying to be a normal adult again. At least for this rotation, we may end up far from medicine.

November 7: Thursday

Today was comprised almost entirely of patients with altered mental states. Patient Three on the census made us aware that he was having trouble with his thoughts. We encouraged him to try and express himself. In the explanation of how he felt today he incorporated the words: container, saws, and footballs. Upon finishing his sentence, he looked at us and sighed, so visibly frustrated and disappointed.

A couple of patients later we entered the room of Patient Eight, who was sitting next to her hospital bed. When we asked how she felt this morning, she beamed cheerfully, "They put me in a chair!"

Soon we were with Patient Fifteen. He has metastatic cancer and is entering hospice this week as there are no treatments left that can cure his disease. During our conversation his scrambled speech was unclear and he answered questions we didn't ask. He seemed to have little concept of his surroundings, he was unsure if his family had visited him, and he had no idea how long he'd been at the hospital. At least he didn't report being in any pain. He was only lucid for a couple of seconds, and that was when Dr. Red inquired whether or not he understood that he had terminal cancer and was entering hospice. Nodding quietly, he responded, "Yes, *that* I remember, but I wish I didn't."

Time for my mid-rotation feedback already. Dr. Red gave me a perfect score on my evaluation. In areas to improve, she encouraged me to keep studying and learning. Expanding my knowledge base will be a lifelong pursuit.

November 8: Friday

9:54 am: Sitting with Magnus and my cohort of bored classmates in all-day family medicine lectures.

I enjoy when professors go off on tangents and start throwing life lessons into their talks. The professor just went off on a rant about a resident doing something stupid, which culminated in him exclaiming, "Medicine is a thinking profession. You cannot practice anencephalic (brainless) medicine!"

Magnus is successfully (and frequently) keeping me distracted and away from Casey.

November 9: Saturday

I love my life right now, I feel as if I am slowly reemerging as my old self.

12:49 pm: While studying for my family medicine final exam Zooey inquired, "So, what are you reading about?"

I look up and deadpan, "Gonorrhea of the eyeball."

"Eww, I'm sorry I asked."

Yep. You'd think she'd know by now not to ask.

Piper, Sophia, Maggie, and I bought season tickets to see all the Broadway shows traveling through my little Midwest City. Tonight, we have tickets to *Flashdance*. I have no idea what the story is about other than being familiar with the image of the main character dancing on a chair with water cascading onto her. When I was on medicine and surgery, I barely had any time to see my friends so our night out is long overdue. Part of me wants to stay nestled on my couch, because I recently developed a sore throat but it will be a fun evening. My voice is cracking like a teenage boy who is unsuccessfully navigating puberty.

Zooey is moving out in a little over a month's time and it's time for me to post my apartment again. I couldn't have imagined a more perfect roommate. It felt as if she was always meant to be with me during this time in my life. I can't imagine who will replace her when she departs.

7 pm: While Zooey cooked dinner, I sneakily employed a penis shaped cookie cutter (a relic from my sister's bachelorette party) on her biscuit dough when she wasn't looking and left little dough penises all over the counter for her.

1 am: Such a fun night! The musical was great and afterwards we grabbed a cocktail at my favorite restaurant. Time for sleep.

November 10: Sunday

8:30 am: I awoke screaming from an overly complex nightmare in which a man who was missing parts of his face broke into my parent's home. Once fully conscious, I realized that I hadn't been yelling so much as mouthing a scream and not producing any noise. I mouthed "good morning" to my empty bedroom. Nothing came out. Oh. Well hello laryngitis. Farewell voice, it's been fun. I hope to see you again soon.

Noon-ish: I have taken to communicating with Zooey via charades.

2:02 pm: I can still only occasionally produce whisper-like noises. I routinely talk aloud to myself and I keep being surprised when I try to speak and no sound comes out. I can't remember if I've ever had laryngitis before, maybe once way back in middle school? Other than a three-week bout of crippling bronchitis and pneumonia during first year of medical school, I rarely ever get sick.

4:50 pm: I'm almost completely aphonic (soundless) right now. I'll have to rely on other forms of communication tonight at dinner with Piper, Daria, and Jane. The greater problem is going to be tonight when the Saints play the Cowboys because I always shout at the television during football games.

November 11: Monday

9:24 am: I still have no voice. I can barely make a sound. Instead of seeing patients primarily, I am now relegated to watching silently from the shadows. Dr. Red informed me that she has seen laryngitis a couple of times already this year. She also let me know that it tends to linger for up to a couple of weeks! Ugh I can't be like this for weeks. And there is absolutely nothing I can do about it.

Once again I have observed that if you make it to your nineties, you're probably pretty healthy.

1:30 pm: In all the patient encounters today I've been channeling my inner Silent Bob to provide appropriate facial expressions. I want to demonstrate to the patients that I

125

am involved in the scene even though I am not contributing any vocals.

There was a patient in the most fantastic eighties outfit today. Her look incorporated scrunchy socks, loads of neon, big hair, and a fanny pack. Her persona made me so, so happy.

6:54 pm: Zooey is out of town tonight and Magnus can't come over because I *allegedly* got him sick (oops). My apartment is too quiet. I'm dreading Zooey moving out.

November 12: Tuesday

8:12 am: Woke up today to the first snowfall and by 'snowfall' I mean there is a light dusting of powder that will likely melt by noon. I hate the snow.

12:20 pm: My voice is still in hiding. I'm home today studying and relaxing my inflamed vocal cords.

November 13: Wednesday

7:39 am: My voice has returned!

5:15 pm: There is a geriatrics component to the family medicine rotation curriculum. My class spent today on the memory disorders unit of a nearby nursing home. The woman in charge of our visit clearly loves her job. She is borderline euphoric in her enthusiasm for working with geriatric patients.

Walking through the pristine hallways, we see many nursing home residents serenely sitting in rocking chairs and contentedly rocking babies. One elderly lady is cooing and rocking away, then she suddenly lifts the baby and hurls it! A baby goes flying across the unit and crashes to the floor. Shock and horror. What the hell? The staff didn't even flinch. Turns out that the baby she threw was a doll. Per our tour guide, rocking babies calms many of the residents, though for obvious reasons they do not get to care for real babies. On a closer inspection, I spotted dolls strewn all over the floor in various states of disarray. Ok, now it's kind of creepy here with all the discarded babies scattered around the ward.

The first geriatric resident I visited hugged me hello and thanked me for coming. She seemed content to be at the facility and excited to have a visitor. Shortly after starting to speak with her, her dementia surfaced. She asked me my name several times and repeatedly told me the same few stories about her family. At the end of my time, she asked me to come see her again.

We all came together to talk about our patients. One of my classmates visited with a red headed woman in her nineties. The elderly lady reportedly has a boyfriend on a different unit within the nursing home. She frequently tries to sneak off the floor to see him. I lean over to the classmate sitting next to me and whisper, "That's so gonna be me at 90."

Without hesitation she replied, "I knew you were going to say that."

During our wrap-up session I began hearing faint baritone music in the background. On closer acoustic inspection, it turns out there is a patient singing in the halls. The man singing in the background reminded me of Operaman from my night on surgery call.

5:10 pm: Zooey just left for Chicago and won't be back until Sunday night. Boo.

November 14: Thursday

10:48 am: Working and seeing lots of clinic patients today.

11:19 am: I get a feeling of satisfaction when I see a patient and come up with a plan that is accurate and then implemented by Dr. Red. However, family medicine is pretty repetitive: hypertension, diabetes, a cold, anxiety, a rash, repeat. Dr. Red is amazing, but family medicine folks are not my people.

3:15 pm: A physically abused pregnant lady came in today for a checkup. Police are already involved. Frightening.

November 15: Friday

As I packed up to leave work last night, I received an email from Casey. It started out friendly, mentioning being on surgery and asking how I'm doing. He then directs my attention to the attached excel spreadsheet. Upon opening the file, I am confronted with columns detailing our utility bills for the past year including energy, cell phone, and cable. He had the gall to demand that I pay him back for half of our bills for the past year.

I began shaking with rage. Why drag this out? We never had any agreement about splitting the bills. All of them were in his name and he had a paying job, so he paid them and occasionally I would contribute. I paid for our renters' insurance, his car insurance, and usually his gas. It's not like he asked me to pay or we had an arrangement, verbal, written or otherwise. It's not like he needs the money. He bought himself a BMW last year and has gone on several international vacations in the past couple of years. He even bought, and then returned, a $12,000 diamond to be the center stone for my would-be engagement ring.

Fuming, I called my girls and met up with Piper, Jane, and Daria at the nearest bar to discuss and vent. We debated various ways I could respond, including to reply that he should have broken up with me a year ago, when he knew he wasn't going to marry me. Or, inform him that my emotional distress cost $1,666 and change so we were now even. Jane suggested emailing him back the excel file that only has the word "NO" typed into the columns.

By the time we left the bar I felt a smidgen better. We went over to the nearby undergraduate campus for dinner. At the restaurant we had a cute, friendly waiter so when we got our check, just for the hell of it, I scribbled my name and number on the bill. After dinner, we walked down the street to a tattoo and piercing shop. After a quick visit, I left there sporting a double forward helix (piercings ten and 11) to add to my collection. From the piercing shop, I headed over to Magnus's apartment. I ended up spending the night at his place, marking my first night sleeping away from my apartment. By the time my night ended I was much, much calmer. A little quality time with friends does wonders.

Magnus and I walked into lecture Friday morning as the professor is asking the class, "Who would like to present first?"

Um... present what?

"And don't forget to turn in a hard copy of your papers in addition to submitting it online."

WTF? Surprise!

Half the class seemed unaware we had anything due. How was it that so many students were unprepared? Apparently, the assignment was hidden somewhere within the 30-page syllabus that hardly anyone read and the professors didn't feel the need to remind us of the assignment.

Being the smart medical students we all are, Magnus, the other classmates and I, were all able to present various topics on the fly and then we wrote the papers during our lunch break. Not my finest academic moment but it all worked out. I guess part of being a doctor is being able to improvise and go with the flow. I'm sure part of it is also being prepared for class, but whatever.

I found out there is an underground music festival tonight so I'm going to check it out with a bunch of classmates. It's taking place in a tunnel somewhere and my friends are pretty sure it's essentially going to be a rave. I've never been to one and have no idea what to expect. I have high hopes for house music and lots of glow sticks.

November 16: Saturday

10 am: So yeah... my first rave. The experience was fun, though not something I ever see myself repeating. I found out that there are miles of giant tunnels running underneath the city that were originally part of a construction project to create a subway system. The project got scrapped but the deserted tunnels still exist.

After Ubering downtown, a group of us headed underneath an overpass and down some sketchy side streets, to where we found a nondescript entrance to a tunnel. There were a few large guys casually guarding the entrance and checking tickets. We walked past them into the massive space, unable to hear the music from the entrance. We strolled deeper and deeper into the depths, walking slightly downward, watching it get darker, while the pulsating music got louder and louder. There were vendors and food trucks on either side of us selling water and snacks. In the middle of the tunnel appeared a skate park, with skateboarders cruising up and down the makeshift ramps. Past the skate park, a stage materialized from deep down in the depths of the tunnel. DJs A-Trak and Mike Posner blasted EDM and house music from the speakers, people danced all around, and there were glow sticks aplenty.

After dancing and getting a little (very) tipsy, one of my classmates offered me Molly. It was new to me but in my drunken state I carelessly thought, "Hey, why the hell not?" After wetting the tip of my pinkie, I dipped it into a little baggie filled with white powder. I was instructed to place my finger under my tongue to let it absorb into my body. Very gradually, I felt a calm, mellow energy building. I didn't even notice it at first, but then I realized I was dancing in the middle of a huge crowd without any anxiety. It was like taking an anti-anxiety pill that makes you energized instead of sleepy. Being able to hang out and dance and party without any of my usual worries surprised me. I didn't do enough to have any hallucinogenic effects but enjoyed it all the same.

I crashed at a friend's house and woke up thinking, "Well, that was fun but what the hell was I thinking?"

2:30 pm: The waiter from the restaurant Thursday night texted me. I can't believe that actually worked.

5:45 pm: Magnus is on his way to pick me up. We're grabbing dinner with some friends from school then going out downtown.

November 17: Sunday

11:20 am: Just got home from Magnus' apartment. After dinner last night a group of us all went bar hopping downtown. I've really missed having a social life! Being single is starting to feel like a gift, not a disaster. I'm finally having fun again.

6:30 pm: Uh oh... the tornado sirens started blaring.

6:35 pm: My county is under a tornado watch for the next 30 minutes. Perhaps I should relocate to the bathroom?

130

6:45 pm: Holed up in the bathroom with my electronics and some snacks. Everything is charging in case the power goes out. While I know this is probably an unnecessary precaution, after having my house destroyed during Hurricane Katrina, I'm a bit paranoid when it comes to extreme weather.

6:56 pm: Ok, Mr. Weatherman is reporting that my area is all clear now. Unfortunately, several adjacent counties didn't fare so well.

8:30 pm: Zooey is back home. Upon hearing tales of my weekend and the rave, and then seeing my new piercings, she joked that she shouldn't leave me home alone unsupervised. Clearly my behavior has regressed since breaking up with Casey. It would be a pretty boring story, though, if I were the type of woman who sat in her bedroom crying and eating ice cream after a breakup.

November 18: Monday

Christmas carols everywhere.

I saw a chain-smoking wife at clinic today who won't quit smoking, even though she is worsening her husband's lung disease. I wonder, if the husband dies from his lung disease, is she a murderer?

A child came in with symptoms of a constant cough for months and no other symptoms. Per the parent, they have tried everything to make the kid's coughing stop. When we distracted the kid by asking about unrelated topics, such as school and sports, the coughing stopped. Is this a psych case? There is something weird going on here. We referred them to a therapist.

Zooey and I cooked an *Iron Chef* inspired dinner together and then hit the gym.

November 19: Tuesday

Today was exceptionally boring yet productive as I spent most of it studying.

November 20: Wednesday

1:13 pm: Last day rotating on family medicine. Dr. Red took me for lunch near her office and we made plans to hang out after Thanksgiving. Our lunch concluded by her informing me, "Now that you're not working for me anymore, we can hang out."

Casey and I have been exchanging emails since he contacted me last Thursday with that ridiculous Excel spreadsheet. This culminated with him stopping by this evening. He seemed lonely. He managed to drop into the conversation that he doesn't have furniture in his new apartment, still hasn't unpacked boxes, and has to do laundry via a coin machine. Maybe he doesn't want me to know that he is doing well without me so he is playing up the less than ideal parts of his life. Maybe he really is unhappy. I don't know which I'd prefer.

It's strange but I'm happier without him. He left after a pleasant but uneventful visit. An hour or so later he texted me, trying to make small talk. I'm aware this is a slippery slope. I've decided I will politely answer any text he sends but will not initiate any conversations or contact.

November 21: Thursday

Just studying.

November 22: Friday

11:35 am: Post family medicine final exam. Casey texted about going for lunch. Why does he want this? What is he up to? We cannot be friends. Not yet. Certainly not right now. Things were going so well, why did he just pop up again out of nowhere? To yell at me for not paying him back the bills I didn't owe him? To tell me he's dating someone else? To tell me he knows about Magnus? To tell me he loves me and wants me back? There's some saying about a dead cat and curiosity, but I can't think of what it is right now.

5:10 pm: I have the best intentions coupled with the worst coping mechanisms. Casey and I went for brunch at one of our favorite places and had a nice time catching up. Towards the end I asked why he contacted me and he shrugged, claiming it was simply to say hi and with no ulterior motive. I told him it would be difficult for me to be 'just friends' with him at this point, so we probably shouldn't see each other again for a while. He also agreed with me that if we hung out, we would have to be under the supervision of our other friends to prevent us from hooking up. As he dropped me off, he invited me to come up to his new place to hang out since it was early. I politely declined and told him that although I wanted to, I didn't want to make any impulsive decisions. I headed up to my apartment, proud of my choice to turn down his proposition.

Ten minutes later my surgery evaluation popped into my email inbox with a lowly 'pass' as my final grade. I was flooded with anger and disappointment. I was fuming, and almost crying. I knew it was coming but it hurt to see it cementing into my academic file. Only getting a 'pass' on surgery and on medicine has dropped me a whole bracket in my med school class ranking. Applying for a competitive residency program just became a lot harder.

After 15 minutes of rapidly pacing my apartment, I called Casey back. "So I thought about it, and I changed my mind." Minutes later I headed over to his place. Turns out he only moved a block away. One block. That's probably not good to know. Afterwards, during pillow talk time, I told Casey the reasoning behind my quick change of mind. He laughed and replied that he was glad to be my coping mechanism. So now, several hours later, I feel much, much better and more relaxed but a little conflicted about so quickly hopping back into bed with him. Good for me, I managed to make it a whole six weeks without having sex with Casey.

November 23: Saturday

10:18 am: Good morning. I love weekends where I have absolutely nothing to do. I should probably work on the wedding present painting for Violet and David, but I'm just so cozy on my couch right now I don't want to move.

November 24: Sunday

Casey spent the night with me. This is probably a bad idea. What am I doing?

To zone out and unwind, I spent the next several hours painting. The wedding present for Violet and David is starting to transform from random shapes and colors to resemble the image I'm envisioning in my head.

I'm going to miss working with Dr. Red as I see her as an excellent physician role model, but I'm not going to miss her patients. I miss being at a hospital. I miss the chaos, I miss the noise, I miss the messiness of the dressing changes, and the excitement of code pagers going off. I even miss the fatigue and exhaustion and stress and pimping in a weird way. Sorry family medicine, you are not my people.

11:20 pm: In a surprising turn of events, Magnus texted me about an hour ago that he thinks he met his future wife. I don't know the details exactly, but I feel like I just lost my partner in crime. Of all the random texts he could have sent me, I never saw that one coming. I guess he won't be coming over tomorrow night for football? Talk about this weekend being the crash from last weekend's high. Between Casey reappearing, Magnus leaving, and getting my surgery grade, today totally blows. I should go to bed, I have to be up at the ass crack of dawn tomorrow to start my neurology rotation. Because remember, it does not matter what is going on in my personal life, I have to perform 100% at work all the time. Cue the fake smile.

Neurology

Song: The Shins. "New Slang." *Oh, Inverted World.*
Sub Pop Records. 2001.
Drink: MadTree Thunder Snow Scottish Ale

November 25: Monday

? am: It's sometime after midnight so I'm technically on my neurology rotation. It's too quiet. I can't sleep. I have no idea what's going on in my life right now. I had settled into a safe, fun, happy, comfortable place for the first time in months, and it all just got completely effed up again. I feel like screaming and banging my head against a wall. In a couple of hours I have to pretend as if everything in my life is fine. As well as I had been doing post-breakup, I still have bad days and nights. This happens to be a really bad night. Fuck me.

7:15 am: A little bit of sleep and a hot shower did wonders. I feel much better. I don't know how to explain being upset with Magnus last night. I think it was mainly based around the fact that I was finally, finally feeling happy and settled into my new normal life, and he goes and changes things up. I think I want a little routine in my life right now. Just for a little while. By routine I do not mean boyfriend; I mean I want stable and predictable surroundings. No wrenches. I've had enough upheaval for the time being.

11 am: Neurology orientation was so logical. Our professor, Professor X, explained that medical students tend to do well on the rotation because they are told exactly what is expected of them. And not just what is expected, but also when, and why, too. How simple! How logical! Professor X openly admitted to us that he has refused to make the course more difficult than is logical or necessary simply to ensure that most students don't get high pass or honors. On top of that, since everything is straightforward, the students tend to score well on the final exam. He refuses to do things with no

135

basis in logical sense. He further explained, "Torturing medical students for fun falls under the category of being nonsensical."

It's not officially on my transcript yet, but I found out I scored high enough on my family medicine exam to earn honors for the rotation.

1 pm: It's my first afternoon on the floor. For this rotation I have been assigned to work at the local children's hospital, aka The Kiddie Hospital, as a member of the neurology consult team. I would have preferred working with adults but whatever, how bad can it be?

Each patient here is managed primarily by a general pediatrics team. Fortunately, another medical student, named Padma, is also on this rotation. As the consult team, we are called to assess any patient who appears to have a neurological complication in additional to their primary illness. Since we are at a children's hospital, we are most often called in to assess seizures or seizure-like behavior, though consults may also involve traumatic brain injury, stroke, or an array of other neurologic illnesses.

1:48 pm: My first patient is a child dying from a fairly common, usually nonfatal illness that for some reason caused her brain to swell.

2:33 pm: My second patient is a quadriplegic with a history of being sexually abused. Are you frickin' kidding me? What is this new hell?

It's been two and a half hours, I already do not want to be here.

3:19 pm: In another room there is a mother rhythmically swaying back and forth in her rocking chair. The dark bags under eyes overshadow her young face. As she talks with us, she is trying to incorporate recently learned medical terminology into her questions and comments. It's pretty impressive, she is mostly using these new words correctly and she almost sounds as if she works in healthcare even though I know she does not. Status epilepticus (non-stop seizures). Leukocytosis (high white blood cell count).

Hypokalemia (low potassium level). These are words that she never knew would be in her everyday vernacular.

4:05 pm: Another critically ill child. It's simultaneously uncomfortable and heart wrenching to be present while parents are arguing over how to best care for an ill child. There is often no right answer. This one has severe contractures in their hands, causing their little fists to curl up against their inner wrists. The kid reminds me of my brother and my other sister before they died.

9:00 pm: I spent the afternoon cranky and wishing for this rotation to already be over. I chatted with several friends to help cheer me up and bring some levity to the day. Due to one of their suggestions, I have joined Tinder.

November 26: Tuesday

11:00 am: There are always babies and small children crying and yelling in the background here.

NAT is the worst thing to see on a chart. It stands for Non-Accidental Trauma. It means the child you are seeing is here because someone purposefully abused and injured them. I feel sick to my stomach when I see these patients.

There is a new neurology consult for a young adult with cancer. The patient is dying, and the family and team have been discussing different options for interventions and care. His prognosis is terrible. He is a young guy who will die nearly a lifetime before he should. I hate this place.

5:30 pm: In addition to the depression the rotation is inducing, there is a terrible amount of inefficiency. Lucky me, our team is being headed by the notoriously slow attending neurologist, Dr. Sloth. We'll spend over an hour in a room going over the same information repeatedly. It's so frustrating. I would not mind at all if it were the parents asking questions, but it's the attending being super chatty.

In one room, I listened to Dr. Sloth explain the same information using three different analogies, even though the parents verbalized that they understood the first time. I wanted to yell, "We covered this. Move on!" Dr. Sloth also explains every possible outcome in detail, no matter how unlikely. This leads to a monumental amount of irrelevant questions and generally ends with the parents being extremely confused about what they can actually expect. We saw four patients yesterday. Four! We took nearly two hours per patient.

8:54 pm: I cannot believe it took me four months of being single to join Tinder. I have several potential new friends throughout my little Midwest City. There is a business systems analyst, a pilot, a special education teacher, and another resident. I have no plans yet to see any of them but it's fun right now to chat with all these different people.

November 27: Wednesday

I ran into Casey at the hospital Starbucks this morning and he asked how I was enjoying my neurology rotation. I made a particularly expressive face of disgust mixed with disappointment to which he responded, "Yeah, I hated it. It was my least favorite rotation of medical school. I was miserable on it." We were always spot-on with the non-verbal communication.

I'm in the Neonatal Intensive Care Unit (NICU) for a baby neuro consult. The parents are smiling and cooing at their baby but there is a distressed look in their eyes. More than distressed, their eyes have a kind of blank, empty, glazed over appearance that is completely detached from their smile. The smile is forced, really. It's just a show. For their baby, for the residents, and for the nurses. At night they'll go home, put away their fake smile and cry. At least these parents are trying to still smile at their child and at each other. Rumor has it that there is about an 80% chance that parents will divorce in the aftermath of a child dying. I haven't personally researched that depressing statistic. My parents staying together after losing two children is remarkable. They've set a wonderful example of how strong and steady a marriage can be in the face of disaster. I wonder if this couple in the NICU knows the odds of their marriage failing.

12:15 am: I'm sitting in the noontime pediatrics conference. I glanced over and spotted Dr. Spengler sitting at the next table. I forgot he was a peds resident and that I'd possibly be running into him this month. Oops. This could get weird.

1:50 pm: Halfway through the conference, Spengler came and sat down next to me. We chatted throughout the rest of the presentation and then he up and left. It took me a minute to figure out why I lost interest in him, but I easily recalled the issue: he is looking for a wife. Maybe in another lifetime it would have worked out between us. I'm too busy being irresponsible and selfish right now to be able to contribute anything of substance to a healthy, adult relationship.

3:46 pm: My tolerance for inefficiency is nearly nonexistent since rotating through surgery.

6:45pm: Around four pm, the senior resident was about to send Padma and I home but then a consult came in. As I learned on surgery, a four pm consult is never, ever a good thing. This particular patient was clearly in need of a psychiatrist, not a neurologist. We knew this about five minutes into meeting the patient. For reasons inexplicable to me, we spent an hour and 45 minutes in their room. AN HOUR AND 45 MINUTES! Why? What a phenomenal waste of time.

I thought maybe the neurology resident had a suspicion of something neurological and was thus being super thorough. However, moments after leaving the patient's room she called the resident who had requested the consult and exclaimed, "Do not admit. Do not order any labs. Do not MRI. He *obviously* needs psych." She declared it with such autonomy and authority. Where was that voice when we were in the room? She let the patient walk all over her. Then, she looks at her watch, turns towards me and exclaims, "Oh, we were in there so long! Why didn't one of you say something and cut him off to get us out of there?" Seriously? Because you're the senior resident and I'm a medical student and I would never interrupt and cut short one of your consults.

At this point it was 5:45 pm. Yes, I know, I'm a medical student on rotations and should never leave before my resident, but seriously, the time wasting by these people is absurd. Who spends an hour and 45 minutes with a patient that they know they are not going to intervene on, take on their service, or otherwise see during this hospital visit?

While typing up the note from the consult, the resident suddenly commented, "You guys can leave if you want." Her statement was presented with a straight face and with no voice inflection. Her words did not come across as an offer, or as a threat, but more like a test. Padma and I exchanged quizzical looks.

With a slow and measured tone I answered, "If this were a neurology consult then I would be happy to present to the attending to demonstrate that I can do a proper neuro exam and present a neuro consult, but this was clearly a psych case and neither of us is experienced with this kind of patient."

Without waiting for a response, we grabbed our bags and left as quickly as possible without outright running. I imagine that I am not doing justice in describing the painfully slow nature of days on neurology. And it's only been two days! Oh, this is going to be a long rotation. At least I have a long weekend because of Thanksgiving.

As Padma and I ran from The Kiddie Hospital and celebrated our long-awaited freedom, I texted Zooey to open a bottle of red and have a glass of wine poured by the time I got home. She texted back that by the time I got home not only would a glass be poured but that her chocolate chip cookies would be done baking. Zooey brightens even my worst days.

10:11 pm: Packing for Thanksgiving. More specifically, packing for Thanksgiving while drinking wine and enjoying delicious chocolate chip cookies.

OMG, Zooey gave me the best Hanukkah present ever! It turns out Zooey was once an actress. She told me about all of the cheesy B movies she acted in and we watched the trailers for all of them on YouTube. Hahahahaha. She's wonderful but the movies themselves look terrible!

November 28: Thursday

8:20 am: Happy Thanksgivikkah! I'm en route to New York and my flight should begin its initial descent shortly. Uniquely, this year Thanksgiving coincides with the start of Hanukkah, creating a new hybrid holiday called Thanksgivikkah. The next time this will happen is something like 70,000 years from now. Truly a once in a lifetime event. My family is creating recipes that will incorporate flavors from both holidays. So far, they came up with sweet potato latkes and pumpkin ruggelach.

November 29: Friday

Hanging out with the family all day. Last night's Thanksgivikkah was filled with warmth, love, and quality family time.

November 30: Saturday

My mom's annual Hanukkah party is in full swing. The house is decorated top to bottom and filled with family and friends. People are enjoying latkes, brisket, ruggelach, and other holiday favorites. Children are running around, the menorahs are lit, and I'm contentedly watching the scene.

December 1: Sunday

8:35 pm: Back in my little Midwest City. I'm recovering from a nasty case of food poisoning courtesy of some chicken I had at the airport last night, while waiting for my flight. Ugh... I can't move. I can't type anymore.

December 2: Monday

10:04 am: We have already run the patient list four times and we have yet to leave the resident lounge to actually see a real live patient. Four times. Running the list is when you quickly review plans for every patient on the team's list. Usually this is done quickly, hence the nickname RUNNING the list. Not jogging it. Not walking it.

We started at eight am and discussed everyone. Another resident walked in, so we reviewed the list again. I'm not entirely sure why, but then we ran the list a third time, perhaps to make sure everyone was on the same page after the first two times? The neuro attending strolled in at nine, so of course we needed to review the list once again with her.

I think what I found most frustrating was that the senior resident pointed out all the people that we wouldn't need to discuss or see during the day because they were stable or being discharged. Her message however, did not make it to the other residents, or the attending, who plodded through the minute details of every patient on the list every single time we reviewed it.

I left to go see a consult and came back to the news that a young adult patient died, leaving behind a spouse and small child. So far this rotation seems to be 90% seizures and 10% devastating, irreversible brain injuries resulting in vegetative states and eventual death.

Is the rotation over yet?

We're back in the resident lounge. A junior resident offered to the senior resident that he could go check on a patient. Her response? "Why? Are you bored?" Really? How about a "Yeah, thanks, that makes more sense than all of us sitting around doing nothing." Or, "Yeah, thanks, that will save time later." Or, "Yeah, thanks for taking initiative to get things done." No? Am I being unreasonable? I'm screaming in my head but sitting here with my pleasant-neutral expression, looking as if I'm studying.

It's super awkward to realize some of the parents of the patients are my own age.

There are too many sick kids haunting the halls: bald, pale, shuffling along and dragging IV poles behind them. I look at the children and I see my siblings, slowly dying alone in the hospital. I need to mentally escape from here. Tinder?

9:11 pm: I'm thoroughly enjoying meeting people on Tinder but it turns out my pet peeve is grammar. If you are unable to utilize verbs properly, then please don't message me. I know I'm not the most eloquent writer. I wish I had greater control and skill at expressing myself. But at least I usually construct sentences containing subjects, verbs, and nouns.

142

December 3: Tuesday

8:41 am: I tend to do things that are logical. On surgery, I generally had the freedom to do whatever appeared to be logical. On neuro, it remains to be seen how they interpret logical behavior. Padma and I chose to not wake a sleeping patient during pre-rounds. The patient had been exhausted from being awake for days due to pain. If the patient is sleeping that must mean her pain medication probably worked. Why would we wake her just to check if her pain has improved? From my calculations, that would be illogical. Though I am poor at math, so we'll see.

4:45 pm: Residents are constantly busy and sometimes forget that we, the medical students, are still present. There is a phrase that med students employ at the end of the day, which is typically some variation of, "Is there anything else I can help you with?" At which point the resident will either give the student something to do, or, what usually happens, is they send us home. From what I've seen, 90% of residents are clued in to the fact that this question is code for, "Can I please go home?"

Padma and I posed this question to the neuro resident because we've been sitting here since 3:00 pm with nothing to do. Her response? "No, I don't have anything but stay a little longer just in case." Sitting in a small room with nothing to do for hours seems unproductive. And mildly like torture. Maybe it's just me.

9:02 pm: Watching *Legally Blonde* for the 500th time. One of my favorite lines is, "If you're going to let one stupid prick ruin your life, you're not the girl I thought you were."

December 4: Wednesday

Professor X opened up to us today about a patient dying from his actions back when he was a young physician about 103 years ago. He appears to be haunted by this ancient mistake. His face showed the pain he still carries from that event. Sometimes I think about the fact that, statistically speaking, I will likely kill someone. My hope is that they will be nearing the end of their life anyway, and that my actions do not cause them pain.

The attendings tell lots of stories on rounds. Some are relevant. The ones today are not.

As with all rotations, I analyze and assess what I have been learning. My main insight thus far is that I do not want to specialize on a particular body part. This is not particularly groundbreaking but still good to confirm. I find myself being curious about all the conditions a particular child has been diagnosed with, in addition to focusing on their neurologic complaint. I want to know a little bit of everything about the body. Jack (Jane?) of all trades, master of none (well, maybe master of some).

5:36 pm: One night last week, while waiting at a bar for a drink, I ended up chatting with a petite brunette standing next to me, named Kylie. She is an artist and we chatted all about painting and sculpting, which was a refreshing change from always talking about patients and work. We ended up hanging out at the bar for a while, drinking and goofing off, and eventually she got my number. Kylie and I had made plans to hang out tonight, but she cancelled a moment ago. We rescheduled for an unspecified time this weekend. I thought it was just a friendly thing, but her texts are getting flirty. Maybe she was hitting on me?

December 5: Thursday

10:10 am: Depressing discussions about palliative care and do-not-resuscitate (DNR) orders came up today on rounds.

11:46 am: I have perfected the pleasant-neutral stare. This facial expression makes it look as if I'm paying attention but allows me to totally zone out.

6:28 pm: I'm leaving shortly on a date with a guy from Tinder. My goal was to meet people outside of medicine but it turns out this guy is an ortho resident. He's got a cute photo and must be smart. Almost every ortho guy I've ever met has been tall and jacked so I have high expectations.

9:45 pm: I'm home. To start, the guy looked nothing like his photo. But more than that, he came across as super awkward and had long greasy hair. After barely two drinks I called it quits and told him I had to go home to help Zooey pack. That's an almost true statement.

December 6: Friday

I dread being around the parents with the dead glaze in their eyes. They look so pained and are suffering so deeply.

A snowstorm hit the Midwest, blanketing my city. Since the roads are so bad, Zooey and I walked half a block to the nearest Chinese food restaurant for our last dinner together. The rest of the evening will be spent drinking wine, watching movies, and reminiscing about her time here.

December 7: Saturday

10:15 am: Zooey is packing up to leave. I am too sad to think about it. We enjoyed our last breakfast together and she'll need to get on the road before the snow starts again. I need a new roommate. Maybe she'll be another new best friend? How could my next roommate possibly be as fun and cheerful as Zooey?

3:12 pm: As Zooey departed on her drive back to New Orleans I too left the apartment, so I wouldn't have to be there all by my lonesome. There may have been some tears during our farewells to each other. I headed straight to the nail bar to get a manicure to cheer me up. At the salon I traded in my vibrant fluorescent pink nail polish for a more subdued black polish with sparkles.

Kylie and I are gonna grab dinner and hang out.

December 8: Sunday

10:42 am: So... Kylie and I went for dinner, opting for Thai food. The conversation flowed easily, we chatted about our friends, families, how we got to where we are in life and such. It was phenomenally refreshing to hang out with someone who is not in medicine. We discussed art, covering everything from sculpting techniques to plein air painting to lithography. After dinner we stopped for drinks at an Irish pub, which led to drinks back at my apartment,

145

which kind of led to her spending the night... and then making plans to go out again as she got dressed and kissed me goodbye this morning.

9:59 pm: Starting tomorrow I will have two weeks of outpatient neurology at different clinics around the city. Each morning and each afternoon I will report to a new site. There is a headache clinic, seizure clinic, tic and movement disorder clinic, a sports concussion clinic, and some others. The current medical student rotating through the clinics forewarned me that, in general, the attending physicians at the various sites have no idea when the medical students are scheduled to be there. He added that I should not be surprised or insulted if I get ignored or pawned off on a different staff member. Well, anything will be better than working at the Kiddie Hospital.

December 9: Monday

8:00 am: I arrived at the pediatric headache clinic. To my surprise and disappointment, I will be working with the slowest attending in the world, Dr. Sloth. Off to see patient number one...

While speaking with Patient One and their father, Dr. Sloth's explanation about the child's condition was so convoluted that he lost me. I found this impressive, as I am familiar with the disease process plaguing the patient. The explanation involved an elaborate M. Night Shyamalan movie plot, which involved an evil queen, canons, a fortified castle, and an army siege. By the denouement of his story the patient's head was cocked, their mouth slightly ajar, and the expression of someone about to mutter, "Huh?" was etched onto their face. After the thrilling conclusion, which involved a several week battle, he ended his explanation with, "and those are your options for treating your migraine."

The parent slowly nodded and straight-faced claimed, "Yes, I understand."

Sure you do.

Dr. Sloth is incapable of making a statement without a lengthy explanation attached. While standing in the corner

146

of the patient's room, already thinking that this is my least favorite attending ever, Dr. Sloth concluded the patient visit by announcing, "Not to toot my own horn, but..." Wow he really thinks highly of himself.

9:47 am: We just left the first patient's room. We spent an hour and 47 minutes with them.

Working with teenagers is really frustrating. There is a female teenager here who recently had a head injury, and her father is letting her call the shots about her treatment plan. The more time I spend with children and teens the less I want to have any of my own. Even the perfectly healthy ones are a nightmare.

Been texting with Kylie and making plans to hang out again.

Dr. Sloth seems to enjoy pushing medications. He frequently states, "Now I don't like to push medications on children, but..." Then he'll launch into a lengthy explanation as to why the patient should be on one or more medications.

He even had a patient today counter, "My migraines aren't bad enough or frequent enough to want to take a daily medication to prevent them."

In my opinion, this seemed to be an insightful and logical reply from the patient. The response did not matter though; Dr. Sloth still took it upon himself to list every single option for preventative medication, in painful detail, including how it works, cost, and side effects.

10:45 am: We're about an hour and 15 minutes behind schedule. Dr. Sloth looked at me suddenly with a surprised expression on his face and gasped, "How'd we get so behind?" I employed the pleasant-neutral expression I mastered earlier in the year coupled with a shrug.

When meeting with Patient Three, Dr. Sloth introduced me by the wrong name.

Our current patient is completely incapable of answering questions without first looking at her mother. The patient has no identifiable medical problems based on several extensive work ups. According to the mother, the patient is anxious, has depression, suffers from attention

147

deficit hyperactivity disorder (ADHD), and most likely has a learning disability. I guess Dr. Sloth wasn't looking too convinced because at one point the mother exclaimed, "This is very severe anxiety!"

Umm... no. In reality, the patient appears to be experiencing normal stress due to the big adjustment of being away at college. Never before have they had to do their own homework, do their own laundry, cook their own meals, or wipe their own ass. Your child will be fine, they do not need to be medicated or diagnosed with a learning disability. They need to learn time management and coping skills, as they slowly break free from your smothering grasp. It's time to cut that umbilical cord.

Dr. Sloth recognized this behavioral pattern, and even though he spent an hour covering every option for medication, he recommended that the patient not start anything yet. He suggested that the patient keep plugging away at school and come back if things do not improve. Upon leaving the room Dr. Sloth slyly whispered to me, "I wanted to tell [the patient] to take a pill of suck it up."

Way to go Dr. Sloth! My opinion of you has jumped several notches.

In stark contrast, there was an adorable tiny child in the next room who was quite independent and well spoken. With each of our questions the patient took a moment to think and then looked straight at Dr. Sloth to give him an answer. Toward the end of the appointment, which lasted a *long* time, the tiny patient climbed into their parent's lap, but still answered questions without seeking direction from their parent.

Great job parents, my hat goes off to you. Your child clearly adores you and is comforted by you, but they have been taught to speak for themselves. On the off chance that I should produce my own offspring, I hope they are as independent and adorable as your child.

It's now 1 pm, and I am just leaving the morning clinic. I have not yet had lunch, and I was supposed to be at my afternoon clinic an hour ago.

5:00 pm: Just left afternoon clinic. I was only scheduled to be there until 3:15 pm, but since I arrived late, I felt that I should stay late, even though no one was expecting me or really seemed to notice when I showed up or departed.

This imaginary letter sums up my afternoon clinic:

Dear parents,

Please stop giving your toddlers caffeine. This includes energy drinks, soda, and Starbucks.

Sincerely,

Silvia

December 10: Tuesday

10:11 am: Kylie and I are hanging out tonight.

I saw one adorable patient this morning. The kid had started getting migraines, so we were asking them questions about their symptoms. About halfway through the appointment the patient suddenly looked terrified and squeaked, "Is there a migraine surgery?" Oh, you're so cute! No, do not worry little child. We don't need to do surgery on you. I wanted to give the patient a hug. They looked so incredibly relieved when we told them that they would definitely not need surgery for their migraines.

12:50 pm: Off to afternoon clinic.

Teenage boys are horrifically smelly. As part of a complete neurologic exam one must remove shoes and socks to have reflexes tested. Seconds after this particular teen removed his footwear the stench of rancid feet filled the entire exam room. He sat there, his feet dangling and swinging off the exam table, wafting the smell throughout the room. It filled every corner, leaving no space for me to hide from the acrid scent. My eyes are still watering.

In another exam room, we met a helicopter parent trying to convince us that their child has ADHD. The neurologist explained to the child about the symptoms of ADHD, such as feeling restless and inattentive, and asked gently, "Does that sound like how you feel?"

The child listened calmly to the explanation and pretty quickly responded, "Nope, that doesn't sound like me. I just don't like math and I get bored."

Good job kid. Don't let your parents put you on medications that you don't need.

Some pediatric neurologists are wonderful at adjusting their explanations to the age of the child with whom they are speaking. Others are not and speak to all children as if they are seven years old. From my point of view, it's pretty entertaining to hear a 17-year-old be spoken to as if they are in second grade, but I'm guessing it's not entertaining from the point of view of the patient.

6:45 pm: It's increasingly difficult to keep up with my writing. When each day is a combination of depression-inducing cases, wondering why people move so slow, seeing dying babies and parents in despair, it's a struggle to want to whip out the iPad and jot down all the painful and effed up tragedies. I'm feel as if I'm complaining ALL the time. I hate it. And, I hate that I'm filled with hate about my complaining. Mostly, I want to bang my head against a wall.

December 11: Wednesday

10:13 am: Totally irrelevant neuro lectures this morning. The lectures detailed how neurology fits into the expansion plans for the hospital. I'm sure it was interesting for some people, but why the third-year medical students needed to attend is not quite clear to me. When irrelevant lectures occurred on surgery, we were instructed to instead use our time being productive and seeing patients. The word efficiency does not exist in neurology land. Except in Professor X's corner of Neuroland; his part of Neuroland is orderly and logical. Unfortunately, I don't think I ever get to work with him directly as I've been relegated to pediatric neurology.

Immediately upon arriving to my afternoon clinic site I was pawned off by the neurologist onto one of the psychologists. The psychologist was in the midst of prepping a patient for a biofeedback session. Biofeedback involves using a computer to measure and track a person's response to various relaxation techniques. I myself was not hooked up to the sensors, but I treated the session as if I were the psychologist's patient. I followed along as the psychologist went through her relaxation techniques. We started with deep breathing, then moved on to progressive muscle relaxation, and finished with guided imagery. By the end of the session, I had been transported to a serene beach. I left the biofeedback session feeling peaceful, calm, and the happiest I've been since starting this rotation. I also left with the thought that maybe I should do residency in California, or some other place near a beach.

My happy mood continued when I realized that my parents and I are departing on a Caribbean cruise 11 days from now.

December 12: Thursday

6:30 am: I awoke in the middle of the night with a painfully sore throat, unable to swallow. On inspection of my tonsils this morning, I found them to be grossly enlarged, stretched, and distorted, appearing as if about to burst. Additionally, they were covered in nasty white spots. Add in some bilateral cervical lymphadenopathy (aka swollen lymph nodes), coupled with lack of a cough, and I'm thinking there's a pretty good chance this is strep throat. Damn kids. Walking germ factories.

9:06 am: A trip to the student health clinic and one rapid strep test later, and here I am, sitting on my couch after having taken the first two pills of my z-pack (antibiotics). I'm banned from the hospital for 24 hours while the antibiotics kick in. I guess I'll catch up on my studying today.

2 pm: Very productive morning studying. If anyone out there is feeling really bored, then search Google images for "purulent exudate tonsils." Scroll through the images for the nastiest, most disfigured set of tonsils you can find. That is what mine look like at the moment.

6:34 pm: The perk of not being able to go to work yet not feeling too crappy is that Casey and I got to go for a late lunch and hang out all afternoon until he had to leave for work around five pm.

P.S. Stop judging me.

December 13: Friday

11:20 am: Worse day of lectures yet. My throat hurts. I want to go home.

6:05 pm: I left work early and came home to sleep. As far as I could tell, no one noticed or cared that I was leaving. My body aches. After a nearly three-hour nap, I feel much better, but I'm still not up for working out tonight.

December 14: Saturday

10:52 am: Study, study, study.

Off to lunch with Casey.

December 15: Sunday

9 am-ish I think: I'm barely awake and am still lying in bed. I can hear Casey in his kitchen cooking me breakfast. Lunch yesterday turned into hanging out, which turned into dinner and going out last night.

2 pm: I'm home from Casey's apartment. I know, I know. We spent way too much time together the past few days.

5:39 pm: I had planned on seeing Kylie tonight but she just cancelled. Oh well. It was fun while it lasted.

December 16: Monday

9:30 am: This month is half over already?

Most of the neurology clinics are on the top floor of The Kiddie Hospital. The huge windows lining the far wall of the physician's work area frame the flurry of fluffy snowflakes falling outside.

This morning I am working with a neurologist who looks like Jackie Chan but sounds like Javier Bardem. It's baffling.

I'm frequently impressed by the kindness of the physicians with whom I work. Take Dr. Bardem-Chan for instance. He had absolutely no idea I was assigned to work with him today. I walked up to him while he sorted through paperwork and interrupted him to introduce myself and inform him that I would be spending the morning following him around as he tried to do his job. Instead of making a face, ignoring me, or pawning me off on someone else, he just asked for a minute to finish what he was doing. After only a few moments he seemed to have mentally rearranged his plan for the day. He offered a friendly smile and jumped into a mini-lecture on reading electroencephalograms (EEGs) and taught me the two most common EEG patterns that I am likely to see on my neurology final exam. From there, we started seeing patients. Throughout the morning he offered clinical pearls (of wisdom, not the type cast before swine), invited me to ask questions, and chatted with me about medical school in general.

I think that many a physician would be surprised, or jostled, in some way by a student popping in to shadow all day, but he was impressively collected and unfazed by the whole thing. It's not hard to imagine how different, possibly even enjoyable, my neurology rotation could have been if I had the opportunity to work with Dr. Bardem-Chan the whole time.

10:53 am: Some of the language translators at the hospital are wonderful. They are able to translate in such a way that the patient encounters flow naturally. Other translators however, I really wonder exactly what they're saying to the patient.

11:15 am: As politely as humanly possible, Dr. Bardem-Chan explained to our most recent patient's parents that their child's weight gain is not a side effect of medication. On the contrary, that particular medication is usually known for causing weight *loss*. Basically, he was explaining to them that their child was getting fat because of poor diet and inactivity.

5 pm-ish: While on the phone with my mother, she vented a bit about work and a particularly stressful coworker. Instead of getting upset or angry though, she told me she simply reminded herself that we will be sailing on a cruise in less than a week. In response to the coworker, she tuned him out and began playing calypso music in her head while picturing a tropical drink, topped with a fresh fruit skewer and bright little umbrella, in her hand. I'm going to start employing this trick at work, thanks mom!

11:00 pm: On page 200 of my neurology review book, question number 275 is about Canavan's disease. The question is quietly lurking there, surreptitiously mixed in among the other questions about rare demyelinating disorders. Most third-year medical students would answer the question and move on. Most students will likely forget that question, focusing instead on more common diseases. I imagine that most medical students will incorrectly answer the question on Canavan's disease on the final exam, if there even is one, because it's so rare. You know who would get the answer correct? Me. You know who else would be able to answer most any question about Canavan's disease? My parents.

December 17: Tuesday

10:43 am: While on the phone and completely engrossed in a conversation, Magnus approached me and mouthed, "Do you have a needle and thread?" while simulating the motion of holding a needle and sewing. I distractedly replied yes, and when I was put on hold, made the mistake of asking why he needs such materials. The little shit smiled and replied, "because I am ripped." After which he abruptly turns and saunters back to the library table at which we were studying.

12:20 pm: Heading up to my last afternoon of neuro clinic!

I drove 35 minutes to the distant neuro clinic, and upon arriving I found out that the doc isn't coming in today. Why bother telling the medical student? I turned around and drove home. That's the anticlimactic end of my clinical responsibilities for the neurology rotation. No more sick children and devastated parents. No more painfully slow consults and hours of sitting around wasting time. No more patients reminding me of the slow deaths of my brother Isaac and sister Leia.

I suppose it's finally time to introduce you to the rest of my family and stop with the vague references to my 'other siblings.' Isaac and Leia were my older brother and sister. Isaac was six years older than me, and Leia was four years older than me. Leia and Olivia were twins.

154

My brother, my parent's eldest, seemed healthy at birth. However, he never developed the ability to hold up his head up, and he never learned to crawl. After going to several doctors, one of the specialist determined that he had a progressive illness called Canavan's disease. It's incredibly rare, autosomal recessive, 100% fatal, and at the time there wasn't even a prenatal test for it. Isaac died when he was ten years old, Leia died when she was 20 years old. I was four when Isaac died, and 16 when Leia died.

I don't know yet whether or not I'm a carrier of Canavan's. It is recessive, so not everyone who has the gene will develop the disease. I can't have children until I know my genetic status, because if I marry a man who is also a carrier than our children would be at risk. I can't turn into one of those parents with the glazed eyes, not if I can help it.

December 18: Wednesday

Last day of neurology lectures.

Still chatting with people on Tinder. There is currently a pilot, a grad student, a teacher, and a businessman floating around. I have no plans to meet up with any of them in person yet, but it turns out the pilot flies through this city a lot. Maybe we'll meet up for a drink some day on one of his trips through here.

3:58 pm: My suitcases are out and I've started packing for my 12-night Caribbean cruise. This year marks the first holiday and first vacation in about two and a half years where I will not be expecting, and then disappointed, about not getting an engagement ring.

December 19: Thursday

12:38 pm: Back at the library, studying with Magnus for our neuro final exam. My brain is already on vacation mode.

December 20: Friday

Post exam! I am ecstatic this rotation is over. It was legit painful. I left the College of Medicine exam room and went straight to the salon to get my hair done, followed by a trip to the nail salon. I think that bright auburn hair and fuchsia nails are appropriate colors for my upcoming trip to the Caribbean. I am thrilled to end this chapter of the book. I want to offer some meaningful insights into what I learned on neurology, but I was so miserable the whole time. The last thing that I want to do right now is to relive it in my head and on paper.

After my hair and nails were done, I went to an ugly sweater Christmas party hosted by some of my friends. After the house party we ventured downtown. While out celebrating with all my classmates, I ran into Kylie. She appeared happy to see me and apologized for being flaky. We had a few drinks together and as she was leaving, we kissed goodnight, promising to make plans to hang out when I get back into town.

Halfway through third year. Hopefully I'm not too much worse for the wear. I am so very much looking forward to a vacation. Now, where is my fruity drink with the little umbrella?

December Break

Song: Ratatat. "Loud Pipes." *Classics*. XL Recordings. 2006.
Drink: Veuve Clicquot Demi-Sec Champagne

December 21: Saturday

9:45 pm: My parents and I are watching *A Very Harold and Kumar 3D Christmas*. I'm not sure which of us is laughing the hardest.

December 22: Sunday

12:11 am: Momma just went to bed. I let her read a chapter of my book and then we discussed it. I couldn't watch her reading, though; it was too nerve-wracking for the both of us. After pouring my thoughts into my little blue-covered iPad day after day, I feared that her only response would be, "I'm so happy this has been therapeutic for you" without any encouragement for me to pursue publication. She clearly feared that my adventures in journaling would not be an enjoyable read or promising venture. I know she's biased, but I still value her opinion and her honesty.

Back when I was going through the arduous process of applying to medical school, I remember calling her and asking if she thought I would ever get accepted anywhere. Her response was simply, "I wouldn't be encouraging you if I thought I was setting you up for failure. I know you can do this." In case I haven't been clear enough, Momma rocks.

Her response tonight was similarly positive; I'm encouraged to continue writing. Surprisingly, after finishing the section I gave her, she shared with me that last week she had a nightmare about Isaac, causing her to relive the intense pain and suffering of losing him. He died 26 years ago this coming February yet she still dreams about her baby boy. I never knew she had bad dreams. Have nightmares ever been classified as a heritable disease?

12:56 pm: Our cruise ship sails from Brooklyn and we will be away for 12 glorious days. Sailing from New

157

York is fantastic because of the short commute. There are no airports, no flights, and no hassle. We left my parents' midtown apartment, hopped in a cab, and within an hour we were stepping onto Cunard's elegant Queen Mary 2.

During boarding, everyone over 18 must fill out a health questionnaire, an effort to curtail the spread of Norovirus. Norovirus is highly contagious, causing nasty vomiting and diarrhea. One of the crewmembers asked my age to determine whether or not I would need to fill out my own form. Passing for a 17-year-old? Really? That's a little extreme, even for me. I know I can easily pass for being college-aged but looking like I'm still in high school? Come on.

This is my first time being single and on vacation in years and years and years. I found myself checking out the other passengers in search of a handsome man with whom I can have a tropical vacation fling.

7:15 pm: The Verrazano-Narrows Bridge, connecting Brooklyn to Staten Island, is one of my favorite bridges. The double-decker bridge features two simple and elegant arches, which appear to be floating over the water below. My parents once informed me that it is the longest suspension bridge in the United States. When cruising from Brooklyn we get to sail right under it, so I was able to see it in a whole new way. Once past the bridge, we made our way into the vast expanse of the Atlantic Ocean and began heading south towards the Caribbean.

Momma and I routinely chat in French when we're together. She is fluent, and I used to be fluent. At this point I'm pretty bad but it's still fun. In general, my father ignores us when we're babbling away but if we start laughing, he'll be like, "What? What's happening?"

Within minutes of perching myself on a bar stool in the cruise ship nightclub and sipping on my Bombay Sapphire and tonic, a handsome young man alights on the bar stool next to mine and strikes up a conversation. Black hair, blue eyes, and well dressed. Turns out he is from New York and his goal is to become an actor. I can see myself easily being entertained by him for the duration of my voyage. But it's only the first night, and there are a lot of passengers. I wonder who else I will meet.

December 23: Monday

I am never happier than when I am on the water. The ship booked it south overnight so we're already passing the Carolinas and the air is starting to feel noticeably warmer.

12:45 pm: According to the steel drum band rocking out at the indoor pool right now, "every little thing is gonna be alright." Sometimes I need a gentle little reminder.

2:16 pm: This is the most elegant ship I have ever seen. Pure luxe. There are dark woods and rich fabrics all throughout the ship. Old paintings of British royalty and antique maritime equipment dot the hallways but it's neither overdone nor stuffy. It's absolutely lovely.

If ever you can't find me on a ship, look in the library. For as long as I can remember, cruise ship libraries have always been my favorite place to curl up and journal. At this moment I am sitting at a dark wooden desk, nestled next to a large window, located in the nicest library I have ever seen on a ship. The library is on the starboard side of the ship, towards the bow. Rows of bookshelves are aligned at the rear and there is a beautiful wall to the right, which curves inward as it approaches the front of the ship. The windows along this curved wall provide excellent views of the endless expanse of ocean outside. Love it when I can't see land. This will be the perfect spot to begin editing the first half of my book.

December 24: Tuesday

9:21 am: Last night was a formal and everyone dressed impeccably. My actor friend from the first night chose to spend his evening with a much younger blonde, so I once again perched myself at the bar. Not long after sitting down, a gorgeous blond-haired blue-eyed stud in a kilt with a killer Scottish accent bought me a drink. He looks like he wandered out of a Scottish Abercrombie & Fitch catalogue. A couple drinks later, I nearly choked on my martini as he revealed that he's 18. No! Ick. Fucking Brits. As an

American, I didn't consider that on this British ship the drinking age is only 18. Oh my God. Aside from the fact that he looks about 25 years old, it never occurred to me that he wasn't at least 21.

3:12 pm: There are loads of people in their 20s and 30s aboard the ship and I've become part of a friendly and chill group of young travelers.

Sitting in the library and thinking about the rotations I've completed. Given that I enjoy procedures, appreciate talking to people, and do not want to specialize in a particular body part, I think that emergency medicine may be my chosen specialty. The Boss has never pushed me one way or another regarding EM, she has only ever told me to keep an open mind. I still have half of my rotations left. We'll see.

December 25: Wednesday

10:13 am: I'm far away from medical school and any worries back home. I can't remember the last time I felt so well rested.

2:35 pm: Sitting in the library. It's strange to go back to the beginning chapters and edit. Rereading and reliving those fall days is dredging up memories of my post-breakup pain. There are also so many patients and stories from the hospital that I had already forgotten about.

December 26: Thursday

Happy Christmas! Happy birthday Zooey!

St. Thomas: Sitting at Coqui Beach, sipping on a Presidente beer brewed in nearby Dominican Republic. The water is pristine and perfect for jumping little waves. I feel awkward sitting here and whipping out the iPad at the beach. Usually, I'm curled up under my beach umbrella with an old-fashioned journal and pen. I kind of can't wait for this year to end just so that I can go back to writing on paper.

My little iPad has long ago stopped trying to correct 'fuck' to 'duck' or 'muck' or 'yuck.'

December 27: Friday

We're in Antigua today. My lunch of fried conch (pronounced conk) at Hemingway's Caribbean Restaurant &

Café hit the spot. I have yet to find such delectable conch fritters in the States.

In case you were wondering, Tinder does not work on the ship.

I absolutely adore this ship and its passengers. This is one of the only large cruise lines left that still strictly enforces an evening dress code. On the formal dinner nights, you will only see tuxedos and gowns. It's a spectacular sight to behold.

December 28: Saturday

10:36 am: Today we're in St. Kitts, driving around the island in an open-air cab, about halfway through a three-hour tour (a three-house tour, a three-hour tour...). This island is absolutely stunning. It's lush and fabulously gorgeous here. We visited a monument of a famous massacre and explored one of the island's ancient forts. We also viewed an area covered in gorgeous black lava rock and went to a batik-printing factory.

11:42 am: It always saddens me to see the tee shirts claiming, "Same shit, different island." Nothing could be further from the truth. Each island has its own history, its own flavors, its own accent. My parents always try to explore each island and only buy crafts from local artists to help support the community, as opposed to buying tchotchkes from the chain retail suppliers.

1:49 pm: My beach chair is pulled right up to the surf and I'm listening to the rhythmic sound of waves crashing ashore. There is calypso music playing faintly in the background. I am in the happy place I envisioned during my guided relaxation exercise two weeks earlier.

Eek... a little crab suddenly popped out of his hole next to my beach chair.

Last night I met a tall, dark, and handsome Spaniard named Inigo. I wonder if he fences.

My parents are so adorable. They embarked together on a romantic walk down the beach. They met at Queens College and have been married 40 years.

I have been taking the utmost precautions against malaria and scurvy by drinking gin and tonics. The quinine works as malaria prophylaxis and the citrus from the limes will fend off scurvy.

December 29: Sunday

Today we are in St. Maarten. My favorite spot is Orient Beach, located on the French side of the island, but my parents prefer the Dutch side of the island, so we'll stay on the Dutch side today.

My parents are so freaking cute. They're curled up on the same beach chair together, sharing my dad's headphone. I took a picture.

Back on the ship. I love giant ocean waves and my sea legs are well established. All day ashore I felt as if the ground was moving.

7:35 pm: The television channels on the ship are in a variety of languages. One of the Muppet movies is on right now and it's being aired in French. My father is grumbling, but Momma and I refuse to change the channel.

December 30: Monday

7:39 am: I'm gathering my gear together to head out on my scuba diving excursion in Tortola. It's my first time diving without Casey. I'm a little nervous to be going without him but I must keep forging ahead.

6:04 pm: Our dive today was at the shipwreck of the RMS Rhone. For 35 minutes, I peacefully swam around the wreck at a depth of about 80 feet. The coral, of every color imaginable, waved in the slight current. A dolphin swam alongside our scuba guide for quite a while, as if catching up with an old friend. I've always loved turtles so the highlight of my dive was spotting a group of them lazily floating near the wreck. Within the wreck there were countless lobsters and fish in every crevice. Diving provides a peaceful isolation that I have yet to find above water. The only sounds are my rhythmic breathing and the flutter of bubbles when I exhale.

At the sail-away party while leaving port the following conversation took place:

Momma: "So, are you making any resolutions this year?"

Me: "Nope."

Momma: "Not even one?"

Me: "None at all."

Momma: "Are you sure?"

Me: "Yes. No resolutions."

Momma: "Not even one about no longer hanging out with a certain person who should no longer be in your life?"

Me: "Nope."

She rolled her eyes and walked away.

December 31: Tuesday

I met Magnus' long-lost twin yesterday. Of course, I want to be best friends with him. While hanging out with my new group of friends, a game of darts was started at the English Pub on the ship. The twin and I ended up on the same team and the game quickly intensified. For some reason, we ended up talking more shit to each other than to the other team.

It is a perfect day out by the terrace pool. The calypso steel drum band is playing Jimmy Buffett while I sip on a margarita. Whenever it gets too hot, I jump into the pool to cool off. My sore muscles are unwinding from all the nonsense of earlier this year.

January 1: Wednesday

Happy New Year!

Since it is now January 1, my 30th birthday is exactly four weeks away. I am back at the pool bar, sipping on a warm latte as we slowly make our way back north. The sun is out, but there is a hint of a cool breeze laced into the warm air current. We've already crossed the Tropic of Cancer so we are officially out of Caribbean waters.

About 30 minutes prior to midnight last night, while walking around and drinking a glass of Veuve Clicquot Demi-Sec, I decided that since I am single for the first time in forever, I do not want to start off my new year being kissed by anyone. When the clock struck 12, I went around toasting all the new friends I made on the ship and carefully avoided any handsome men.

1:45 pm: The captain has informed us that we are 680 miles from New York. I'm still sitting outside on the terrace pool deck but it's starting to get quite chilly. Time to relocate indoors. Farewell tropical weather. Besides, Momma and I are going to high tea shortly.

My parents spoil me to no end. I have been informed that I have a massage scheduled for five o'clock today. After everything that my family has gone through, all my parents want is for my sister Olivia and I to be happy and our lives filled with joy. They shower us with love and affection, and I appreciate everything they do for me. However, we would trade all the money we have and every single earthly possession to have Isaac and Leia back in our lives.

January 2: Thursday

9:49 am: There is a massive snowstorm blowing across the Midwest that is going to hit New York later today and continue into tomorrow. We are sailing straight into a blizzard.

Every afternoon, Momma and I attend a craft group on the ship. Momma is knitting sweaters for her grandsons while I work on my book. The other ladies are doing crafts such as needlepoint, jewelry making, and crochet. The lady who runs the group is Irish and has the most wonderful expressions. My favorite so far was when she regaled us with a story that involved her waking up early in the morning. She called it waking up at 'daft o'clock.' I might start using that.

2:45 pm: There is concern about limited visibility upon reaching Brooklyn. To avoid docking during the snowstorm, the captain of the ship has decided to book it to New York and get us safely docked tonight. We'll still disembark tomorrow morning. As we sail towards the storm, the waves are picking up and the ship is now noticeably rocking.

Shortly after writing that entry, I was rocked into a deep and peaceful nap on my lounge chair.

10:59 pm: Cruise ships have the best tiramisu.

January 3: Friday

11:10 am: Due to the inclement weather our scheduled time to disembark the ship became delayed by several hours. I'm chilling with my parents in one of the lounges. Since we're not trying to catch a flight, we're part of the last group to disembark. I love this ship so much. I am in no rush to leave the safe and happy confines of this vessel and return to the real world. I did way less editing than I had planned, but oh well.

8:15 pm: Now that I'm back in the States (and once again with cell phone reception), I've resumed texting with the pilot. He offered to call so we can chat for the first time. Hmm…

10:20 pm: Wow he's a got a deep voice! Surprising. Very chatty, too. According to his photos, he is tall and skinny and has light brown hair. I'm intrigued.

January 4: Saturday

9:20 am: Last night I laid down in bed and upon closing my eyes I felt as if I still rocked on gentle ocean waves. I wish I could make that feeling appear whenever I want.

2:30 pm: I can't believe I'm already on my flight heading back to my little Midwest city. Vacations and time away from the hospital always flies by.

January 5: Sunday

11:36 am: My last day of vacation will be filled with relaxing, laundry, cleaning, football, and a manicure. Not a bad little Sunday. I spent yesterday evening catching up with the girls, celebrating a belated New Year's Eve, and trading stories from our time away from rotations.

I love the Midwest (sometimes). The television at the nail salon stayed tuned to the NFL playoff game, and while grocery shopping there were score updates announced over the PA system.

6:59 pm: I have a feeling that even with a solid background in psychology, I am completely unprepared for the six weeks of psychiatry that lie ahead.

Inpatient Psychiatry

Song: Miike Snow. "Silvia." *Miike Snow*. Columbia Records. 2010.
Drink: Bombay Sapphire martini, slightly dirty, with three olives

January 6: Monday

7:00 am: At orientation for my psychiatry rotation. Our rotation supervisor is Dr. Freud. We're going around the room introducing ourselves to him.

10:00 am: After orientation I traveled over to the inpatient geriatric psychiatry ward at a nearby psychiatric hospital. I located my attending physician for the next three weeks. Before I even finished introducing myself, he interjected, "Hi, I'm Dr. Psych. Don't shake the patients' hands. They masturbate a lot and never wash their hands afterwards. And some patients have raging STDs (sexually transmitted diseases). Just don't shake their hands. Really, don't touch them at all. What was your name again?"

Welcome to psych.

The ward I'm on is designated for elderly patients. Younger psychotic patients are more prone to outbursts while older patients tend to quietly shuffle down the halls and be pleasantly demented.

My first patient is the lovely Mrs. Havisham. Her combination of schizophrenia and dementia results in fascinating conversation. Shortly after I met her she adamantly demanded that I read Shakespeare's *Two Gentlemen of Verona,* since Silvia is the name of one of the main characters.

4:30 pm: Casey won't go away. He's like an addiction. He keeps calling and texting and asking me to hang out. Help! In an active attempt to turn my attention elsewhere, the pilot and I chatted on the phone for over an hour. He will be flying through the city on Saturday and we made plans to grab drinks. I will finally get to associate a face with that deep voice.

January 7: Tuesday

8:15 am: "Let sleeping manics lie." Words of wisdom from my attending Dr. Psych.

Dr. Psych is wonderful with his patients. His tone of voice is always calm. His explanations and concerns are straightforward yet not condescending (in stark contrast to Neuroland's Dr. Sloth).

I have witnessed some providers using a patronizing voice with mentally ill people and it makes me feel uncomfortable. Patients should not be spoken to like children. They deserve the same respect and consideration that any other adult does.

It is distressing to see mental illness warp someone's brain and steal their personality, leaving them a mere a shell of who they once were.

9:20 am: My skin is crawling. The staff needs to perform a rape exam on a demented elderly lady. This poor woman.

11:01 am: While in a room talking to a patient this morning, I spied a group of three elderly psych patients shuffling along down the hallway. Their gait is halting, their hands gnarled with arthritis, and age has made their backs crooked with osteoporosis. Years of mental illness and harsh medications have distorted their gaunt faces, while giving their complexions a sallow hue. The three of them, each draped in multiple mismatched and poorly kept robes, paused at the doorway. I thought for a split second how they resembled a pack of zombies, creeping along and looking for prey. My mind couldn't help but imagine one of them suddenly having a burst of energy and lunging forward to grab my head in an attempt to eat my tasty and well-educated brain. After a moment's pause, one of them grunted and they continued their slow, ambling trek up the psych ward hallway.

167

4:58 pm: I take my graduation photo today. I can't believe it. Where is the time going?

January 8: Wednesday

9:03 am: Wednesdays are the lecture day for the psych rotation. We're sitting in class and instead of jumping right into our lesson, which in theory started at 8:30 am, we are once again introducing ourselves. Except that we all know each other, so technically we're just introducing ourselves to the lecturer – quite unlike the surgeon Dr. Mastermind, who had memorized our faces and names before the first surgery lecture way back when.

A rambling and uninspiring professor concluded his lecture by announcing, "The greatest gift I have ever given medical students…" and I had to stop listening because I started gagging.

2:24 pm: Afternoon lectures are held at a small, nearby hospital. The hospital specializes in addiction medicine and features a busy drug rehab unit. Each of our afternoon lectures center around a different aspect of addiction medicine.

2:45 pm: The lecturer has not been speaking but rather yelling at our class about drug addictions for the past 45 minutes. I'm not sure why, but at one point a student smiled at something and the professor immediately exploded, "Why are you smiling? Don't smile! This is serious!" I'm biting my lip to keep from laughing right now. He's so comically serious.

4:14 pm: A young soldier shared his heartbreaking story of being injured while deployed and subsequently developing PTSD and anxiety. His physically and mentally painful rehabilitation process was littered with narcotic pain medication and highly addictive anti-anxiety medications, which spiraled into an opioid pill addiction, then heroin addiction, then divorce, homelessness, and eventually jail.

January 9: Thursday

11:12 am: My only clinic today is from one to three pm, which is a free clinic designed for patients who would otherwise be unable to get psychiatric care. It is difficult for

168

many of these patients to make their appointments because of lack of transportation, and I've been forewarned that many don't show up.

I've had too much free time this week. I often only work half-days on this rotation. Free time gives my mind space to wander.

I've been reflecting on the young soldier opening up about his PTSD yesterday. For as long as I can remember, I've never been a great sleeper. Shortly after my sister Leia died, I began having nightmares. I would relive seeing my siblings (Leia and Isaac) in the hospital, dying, and an overwhelming feeling of helplessness and panic would always be the undercurrent of the dream. After the 9/11 attacks, my nightmares worsened. I began vividly dreaming of being inside a collapsing building, being shot by terrorists, or seeing horrifically gruesome and mutilated bodies and people around me. At its worst, there were nights I feared sleeping.

Throughout my college years the nightmares lessened. That is, until Hurricane Katrina slammed the Gulf Coast a few days before my senior year at Tulane started. Driving down from NY for the semester, my car was assaulted with increasingly strong rain and wind. As I neared New Orleans my roommate called to tell me that Tulane was being evacuated. I turned around my car and drove back north, opting to wait out the storm in Atlanta.

Over the next five days I watched on television as the levees broke, devastating my home and much of my beloved New Orleans. A new wave of nightmares began. On returning to my New Orleans home in January 2006, I found that the relentless floodwaters had destroyed not only my furniture and books but had also left the entire first floor covered in mold, making my house dangerous and uninhabitable.

A typical PTSD nightmare is reliving the same scene over and over again. My nightmares are a mix of my siblings or other family members dying either by illness or terrorists, blood and gore, fear, helplessness, and mass destruction.

They still flare during stressful periods. Like right now. Thanks, Casey.

Off to clinic.

1:00 pm: No show.

2:00 pm: No show.

2:20 pm: The benefit of no shows is that my resident and I get to chat and discuss all things psych. Her name is Dr. NY and she's, not surprisingly, from New York.

3:02 pm: Our first patient is here. He shared that he has been trying to ignore his current manic episode but after staying up all night painting, he realized that he needed to get help. Dr. NY is calm, reassuring, and straightforward while talking with him. She provided a choice of medication options to help reign in his symptoms.

3:24 pm: Dr. NY and I discussed the importance of a good fit of a therapist with their patient. A patient may believe that therapy is not for them because they were working with someone who wasn't right for their personality.

I'm heading off to dinner and drinks with Dr. Red from my family medicine rotation.

January 10: Friday

8:11 am: Dr. Psych is a morning person and he arrives at the psych ward at 6 am. If I were to pre-round on my patients I would have to arrive at 5:30 am. Not happening. This isn't surgery. Fortunately, he realizes that 6 am is daft o'clock, so he doesn't require me to be at the hospital until eight most days. In addition to not pre-rounding, he has also already written notes on most of the people by eight, so there's really not much for me to do. Dr. Psych also doesn't believe in working past 11. Basically, I round with him, update the social workers, and then leave.

Even though my patient-care duties are nil, I still chat with Mrs. Havisham every morning because she enjoys the company and is endearing.

9:03 am: Dr. Psych explained to a patient that we would treat his mental illness with medication, the same as his other docs use medication to treat his diabetes and high

170

blood pressure. Some people, my classmates included, struggle with the concept that mental illness is an organic disease process, similar to any other disease.

Dinner with Dr. Red and her friends last night was so fun!

10:03 am: Never turn your back on the ocean. Ditto for patients in the psych ward. I suddenly heard fast footsteps behind me and turned to see a patient running towards Dr. Psych and myself. The patient had a panic-stricken look on her face and wanted to make sure that we hadn't forgotten to see her.

Another elderly patient believes she is in a hotel and has lost her tour group.

Overheard at the nursing station this morning: "The Duchess is doing better today; she only kicked the nurse twice this morning."

The Duchess has a profoundly sad background. She is severely demented, lives in a state of constant fear and paranoia, and wholeheartedly believes that the staff is trying to kill her. A look of wide-eyed terror is permanently etched onto her face. She screams all day long and tries to fight the staff any time they enter her room. Her brain is irreversibly damaged and there are no known medications that can help her. Out of curiosity, would you rather be dead or live in that state of mind for the rest of your days?

I'm so impressed with the staff on this unit. They treat the patients with care and dignity, even when the patients are being challenging.

A male and a female patient were caught snuggling this morning. As far as the staff knows, they were not doing anything inappropriate. Both patients were notably calmer than their usual baseline status. Per Dr. Psych, people with certain mental illnesses often have difficulty making human connections, so the staff is hesitant to chastise them, even though it means they are breaking rules and sneaking into each other's rooms.

While talking to the social worker, I saw one patient gently pushing another patient's wheelchair. Many instances

171

of human connection and bonding are visible on this locked ward.

5:01 pm: Time to kick off my nightshift in the psychiatric emergency department. I'm curious what kind of crazy events will transpire during my shift. It's not that I want to work in psychiatry, but as long as I have to be here, I at least want some good stories.

6:43 pm: The resident working tonight does not like answering pages. She dislikes it so much that within 30 minutes of me showing up she asked me if I would be okay taking the pager and answering all the calls for her. I immediately replied "yes!" The only page I've gotten so far was a nurse on another floor asking if she can give extra doses of anxiety meds to a patient who is demanding it, to which I answered "no."

Casey is texting that he wants to hang out tonight. As I'm stuck working, I am forced to deny his request. I guess being locked inside a psych ward is one way to get me to stay away from him. Maybe I should work more often?

7:20 pm: So far, it's pretty quiet. The resident with whom I'm working seems like a complete moron when it comes to patient care. She cannot for the life of her figure out how to input medication orders into the computer. The resident and the nurse have spent the past 20 minutes trying to figure it out. I would offer to help with this basic task, but watching them is the most entertaining thing going on right now.

Oh, the only other entertaining person is Angry Santa. No, he is not a patient. He is a mental health care worker with a big belly, full white beard, and red plaid shirt. He is talking to himself at his computer. Occasionally I hear him exclaim, "Oh my God" and "You've got to be kidding me!" Um… the people who go into psych seem to be a bit off themselves.

I expected more crazy stories from the ED psych ward.

7:50 pm: After two more pages about the patient demanding medication, my resident caved and told the nurse

172

to, "Just give it to them." The resident then turned to me and justified her actions by explaining, "I know it's wrong to give the patient that med, but then they'll stop paging us." Why don't you just tell the nurse to stop paging us? This is way less fun of a Friday night than I'd hoped for.

8:35 pm: The resident told me that she'll let me go at nine o'clock. Thank God. This is the most boring/frustrating Friday night. I'm scheduled to be here until midnight, so I really appreciate her letting me go. At least now I'll get to meet up with my friends and celebrate one of my classmate's birthdays. I won't let Casey know that they've released me early from the psych ward.

January 11: Saturday

1:01 pm: The pilot gets into town today. I should already be getting into a shower but I'm off to a slow start. After escaping the psych ward last night I met up with a group of classmates. There were a ton of people hanging out and partying, and eventually we all went downtown. All in all, a fun night but we stayed out way too late and now I'm dragging.

2:30 pm: Finally, off to a shower, then to an airport hotel to pick up the pilot. Today already wins for being the most random date ever. Once again, Casey texted about hanging out. I'm not even disappointed that I already have plans with the pilot. I know that I need to stop hanging out with Casey, but we're so bad at not being together. I'll get myself into a bad situation if we don't stop. I'll get hurt. Again.

January 12: Sunday

9:59 am: I drove to an airport hotel last night and saw a guy with light brown hair standing outside. This must be the pilot. He strolled over to my car and got into my passenger seat. He looked a little older than I had imagined but with a bright smile and golden eyes. Off we went to a bar where we watched the Saints game and chatted. Shortly after arriving at the bar we joked about how it was the most random date ever. Conversation flowed throughout the night, we laughed, flirted, and had a surprisingly fun time. I

173

dropped him off at his hotel around 11:30 pm because he had to be up early today for work. After kissing goodnight, we both agreed that we'd like to hang out again the next time he flies through.

January 13: Monday

3:42 pm: I spent the past hour talking with a young war veteran (younger than me), who is completing an inpatient rehab program for substance abuse and addiction. Similar to the other young veteran from last week, this soldier survived injuries sustained during combat and became addicted to pain pills while in recovery. As his tolerance increased and PTSD sank in, he turned to stronger medications and then to cheaper ways to get high.

Also akin to the soldier from a couple of days ago, this young man became addicted to heroin. I've learned on this rotation that his story is not unique; it is happening to young, wounded veterans throughout our nation. What are we doing to the young war heroes of this country? It's horrific.

I asked him the questions I needed to ask for class, but afterwards we just chatted for a while. We talked about his descent into using drugs and how it spiraled out of control, how he lost his wife, lost custody of his child, lost his business and all his money, as well as his home and basically all of his possessions. On finishing up, I thanked him and wished him the best with his recovery.

January 14: Tuesday

Mrs. Havisham kicked off our conversation this morning by telling me that her leg hurts. She is frail and unsteady on her feet so I immediately worried that she had fallen during the night and failed to inform the staff. She remained reticent to reveal the cause of her injury, going off on tangents about force fields. After a full exam of her leg, focusing on her knee, I did not find anything worrisome. Chatting with her longer, she eventually admitted that her leg hurt because she was covertly shot with a laser gun by "those people" about a month ago. Oh. Ok.

174

9:20 am: I worked two hours today. From 7 am until 9 am. Dr. Psych is a great teacher but I'm not sure how much I'm getting out of being there so few hours. What to do with the rest of my day? Party plan! I am hosting a big 30th birthday celebration at the end of the month so I need to start ordering decorations and figuring out my outfit.

5:15 pm: Casey keeps texting me to hang out. I agreed he could come over. I don't know.

January 15: Wednesday

7:20 am: I think I'm going to end things with Casey. Again. The only word I can use to describe how I felt last night is indifferent. I realized shortly after he arrived that I probably would have been just as content watching Netflix by myself.

11:01 am: A dichotomy seems to exist between psychiatrists; some maintain a solid fund of basic medical knowledge, some don't. For example, during my shift at the psychiatric emergency department, the resident clearly lacked basic medical knowledge. On the contrary, Dr. Psych is impressively adept at addressing his patients' physiological as well as psychological ailments.

4:44 pm: The pilot offered to fly in tonight. I like that he can show up whenever he wants to, give me his undivided attention, and then leave. This has potential.

Heading off to dinner with The Boss and some other people from the hospital. After dinner, I'll swing by the airport and pick up the pilot.

January 16: Thursday

1:45 pm: The more time I spend with Dr. NY, the more I like her. Today she shared about how she hates prescribing medication without doing counseling at the same time. I can already tell I want to be friends with her the way that I am now friends with Dr. Red.

2:20 pm: The sooner I finish work the sooner I can head back to my apartment, where I left the pilot watching TV. I'm waiting for the two o'clock patient at Dr. NY's clinic to show up. I'm fairly certain at this point they're not going to show up, but I'll wait around until 2:30 pm before I officially bounce.

6:30 pm: I spent the morning with the pilot, worked for a whopping two hours, and then came home. We had an early dinner before I dropped him off at the airport. His next scheduled visit is on the 27th, which is the eve of me turning 30. He's the polar opposite of Casey: super chatty, kind of goofy, and totally obsessed with airplanes. I like this pilot.

January 17: Friday

Mrs. Havisham is so darling, but it's sad to know that she will never get better. Her dementia is progressive and is confounding the delusions she harbors. Today she suggested that we go shopping after she finishes talking to the caterers about her meeting with a group of electrical engineers.

Another patient explained to me, while cautiously looking around the room, "It is one of those days, you know, when you feel people watching you…" Fortunately, I don't know that feeling.

When I have a million things to do, a million and one things will get done. When I have ten things to do, about six and a half will get done. Unless I have to manage my time, I totally waste it. Even though I only work a couple of hours each day, I am behind on my writing, haven't painted since returning from the cruise, and my apartment needs to be cleaned. I still study every day, but am otherwise unproductive.

January 18: Saturday

Many patients I've encountered this rotation are sad, scared, frustrated, and in pain. Their overlapping psychological and physical ailments create complex medical situations. The psychiatrists caring for this difficult population are commendable. As much as I am enjoying this rotation, I know that leaving my job as a psychologist and going to medical school was the right decision for me. It's too draining; I couldn't do this every day for the rest of my working life.

2:52 pm: I have tickets to see *Book of Mormon* tonight. So excited! I will study a bit and get ready for an early dinner before the show.

January 19: Sunday

I did it. Casey texted to hang out and I called him and declared, "No, no more."

To keep me distracted, I'm heading out with Magnus and a bunch of other people from class to go watch Sunday Night Football.

January 20: Monday

10:48 am: Martin Luther King Day. Our country still has so far to go in terms of racial (and gender) equality.

11:00 am: I actually have the holiday off today. I wish I could share more about my patients, but I've got nothing. I enjoy work when I'm at the hospital, but I'm barely there. I have too much free time.

Magnus's girlfriend abruptly broke up with him last night. He seems devastated, and it doesn't sound like she really explained her reasoning behind the split. I feel his pain. Side note, no, I don't plan on going down that road again. We're better just being friends.

4:05 pm: Birthday party decorations are going up momentarily.

January 21: Tuesday

9:15 am: Mrs. Havisham told me today that she used to be a firefighter. She's previously related that she was a mental health worker, an electrical engineer, and a laser specialist. I love working with her. I hope I am providing some comfort and companionship for her each morning, as I'm not sure there is anything I can do for her medically. Perhaps just having our morning chats keeps her from getting too lonely. I have yet to see, or hear about, any family members visiting her.

Noon: One week until the big day.

4:15 pm: The Olympics are fast approaching. I keep seeing reports on the news about suspicious activity being investigated in and around Sochi. The anxious part of me worries about terrorist attacks during any major event – the

Super Bowl, the Oscars, large political gatherings, etc. Pretty much anytime there is a large collection of high-profile people. I firmly tell myself that I have no control over such bad people and horrific attacks, but I can't help but think that Sochi is a giant target. I will do my best to enjoy the opening ceremonies and not stress too much.

January 22: Wednesday

I have one lecture today. One. From 11 to 12 o'clock. At least it's interesting. We're learning about personality disorders, which I find fascinating. The most frustrating thing about working with these patients is that, by definition, they don't know that they have a personality disorder. From the patient's point of view, it's everyone else that has a problem.

Dr. Freud implored during his lectures today, "Be a surrogate frontal lobe for your patients."

9:23 pm: Other than studying for boards, the rest of today was a waste of time. I'm so bored.

January 23: Thursday

12:54 pm: Back at Dr. NY's clinic. Patient One cancelled but Dr. NY and I are discussing his current plan of care anyway. She informed me that One has PTSD, which causes him to have anxiety, nightmares, and depression. She added that she focuses on controlling his anxiety and she flippantly remarked, "The nightmares aren't a big deal."

I'm a professional and I'm at work, so I'm not about to contradict her, but I felt a little pang of anger and sadness to hear her so casually disregard his nightmares. Maybe Patient One's nightmares aren't that bad, but PTSD nightmares are not normal nightmares. She doesn't understand what it's like when you're afraid to go to sleep for fear of what torture your brain will subject you to while you're unconscious. She doesn't know the exhaustion that builds when you spend entire nights tossing and turning, unable to fall asleep. Mine aren't even that bad or frequent compared to most people's. I wonder if Patient One thinks Dr. NY is disregarding that part of his PTSD.

While waiting for Patient Two to arrive, Dr. NY opened up to me about her patients, her career goals, and her personal life. Other than the nightmare comment, I really like her. She comes across as so genuinely concerned about the care and well-being of her patients.

1:31 pm: Patient Two is giving me a weird vibe and he's only been here a minute.

1:34 pm: Two is talking about his nightmares, specifically one where his family members are getting injured and he's helpless and can't intervene even though he's desperately trying to help.

Umm… Two is now sharing a fantasy of his where he mutilates another person and keeps their body as a trophy. At least he's acknowledging that this is a disturbing fantasy.

1:41 pm: The clock is ticking really loudly in the room. Two is making me feel on edge, like I want to locate all the doors, so I know how to escape if he loses his cool and his temper explodes. He doesn't seem safe to be out in society.

1:52 pm: Dr. NY is convincing Patient Two that he needs to have further evaluation at an inpatient psychiatric facility because he doesn't seem safe to her. He certainly wasn't happy about it, but he agreed with her that he needs some extra supervision and care right now. It is distressing to see a grown man crumble under the weight of his mental illness, but Dr. NY (and I) feel that he is high risk for suicide or harm to others. Waiting for the ambulance to arrive to collect him was undoubtedly the longest eight minutes of this year so far.

2:49 pm: To wrap up the day we had a quick visit with Patient Three. Three informed us matter-of-factly that she woke up sad, then she felt happy for a bit, but became frustrated at work later in the day. I wasn't picking up on any red flags at this visit. On the contrary, I felt that Three was trying to play us. Three's day may very well have been a bad one, but it was a day that I, and probably you, have had many times. It's called "Welcome to being an adult." You can't be happy all the time and that's not a bad thing. Dr. NY must have not been worried either because she explained to Three that they would not be given any additional anxiety medication. Dr. NY didn't roll her eyes when Three left, but I had the feeling that she wanted to.

10:02 pm: I baked and decorated a boatload of cupcakes for my party. I had to get all my prep done tonight because the pilot and I have a date tomorrow night. The cupcakes are peppermint mocha with a Swiss meringue buttercream frosting and chocolate ganache drizzle. Major yum. My kitchen looks and smells like a cupcakery. The party decor is all elegant turquoise and silver, and I've requested that everyone dress up in fancy, cocktail party attire.

January 24: Friday

8:12 am: Last day working with geriatric psychiatric patients. I need to have a more full work schedule; I've been so unproductive these past few weeks. Mrs. Havisham was discharged to a nursing home, so I don't even have anyone to round on.

8:31 am: One of our patients insists, strongly, that we call her Mrs. Martha Washington. She refuses to answer to anything else. Period.

8:51 am: There is now an arsonist and a psychotic preacher on the floor. Why are the patients getting more interesting on my last day?

While standing in the hallway waiting for Dr. Psych, The Duchess (the lady with the irreversible brain damage and dementia) walked up to me, gripped my arm above the elbow, and stared at me as tears rolled out of her wide eyes, looking absolutely petrified. I tried soothing her by calmly repeating, "It's ok, you're safe here. We're taking care of you" and stuff like that. She began dragging me down the hallway, still sobbing. I wasn't expecting her to be so strong so she succeeded in pulling me off balance and before I realized it, she was leading me down the hallway.

I wasn't particularly concerned by the strange situation but I felt pity for her. I kept trying to soothe her while she forcefully directed me down the hall. Dr. Psych had his back towards me as I got pulled farther and farther away. I managed to rotate The Duchess, so we ended up walking back towards Dr. Psych, at which point one of her nurses stepped in. As the nurse pried The Duchess off my arm, Dr. Psych finished whatever he was doing and looked up, completely oblivious to my recent trek up and down the ward.

Well, it's time to bid farewell to the psych hospital's geriatric ward. I enjoy working with older people, but I kind of wish I had been placed on one of the other inpatient floors. Most patients I encountered were pleasantly demented and spent their days quietly zombie-shuffling the halls. The stories I heard from my peers on other floors were way more chaotic, explosive, and overall entertaining. I must admit, I hoped for a little more excitement. From a grading standpoint, I don't know how Dr. Psych will assess my clinical skills. It's hard to impress someone when you don't do anything.

The pilot is flying in tonight. I informed him I rented his favorite movie, *Jurassic Park*, because I've never seen it. He responded, "U just melted my heart..." He's cute and all but I have a sneaking suspicion that he's a relationship person and things won't end well for him. Who goes on Tinder looking for a relationship?

January 25: Saturday

11:44 am: My 30th birthday party is today! My actual birthday is January 28. I dropped the pilot off at the airport this morning after a fun date last night. I cooked dinner and we watched *Jurassic Park*. Overall a low key, relaxing night in. A bouquet from him featuring orange lilies in a giant martini glass is now part of my party decor. He's sweet and affectionate in a usually non-overwhelming way. Right now, I'm cleaning up the apartment a bit. I have a hair appointment at three o'clock for a color and blow out, and then party, party, party tonight.

January 26: Sunday

10:00 am: Last night was simply perfect. Nearly 50 friends showed up to celebrate, eat cupcakes, and party.

181

Everyone arrived decked out in beautiful cocktail party attire, truly making the party feel like a special occasion. I felt loved, joyful. What else can anyone ask for? I wore a sparkling, short, bright blue sequined backless dress from the website Rent the Runway, along with a pair of killer black heels. Several friends inquired about whether I'd be throwing a spring party to round out my fall Halloween party and winter birthday party schedule. I hadn't really thought about it, but throwing parties makes me really happy, so I guess sure, why not?

The only awkward part of the night involved running into K Canoe at the bar we were partying at after my house party ended. He gave me a pretty nasty look. I did not end things appropriately back in the fall, I totally ghosted him and stopped answering his texts and phone calls. Oops.

11:55 pm: I know I should go to bed, but I keep writing and editing.

I'm heading back to The General Hospital tomorrow. I haven't worked there since I finished on thoracic surgery way back in October. I miss being there; it's such a great hospital. My schedule will be a normal, full workday, which I need. I sleep better when I'm exhausted. Needless to say, I haven't slept well the past few weeks. Ok, it's 12:16 am, I am finally off to bed.

Psychiatry Consults

Song: Broken Bells. "The High Road." *Broken Bells.*
Columbia Records. 2009.
Drink: Mulled wine

January 27: Monday

7:45 am: Sitting at a table across from the Starbucks inside The General Hospital before heading down to meet with my team. As part of the psychiatry consult team, we are called to evaluate patients who appear to have a psychiatric concern. The range of consults may involve patients with a new cancer diagnoses who are depressed, to suicidal patients recovering from self-inflicted wounds, to patients with addictions to various substances.

After assessing the patient we will then make recommendations to their primary medical team as to whether or not they would benefit from anti-depressants, anti-psychotics, or any other psych meds. The first morning at any new site is always a little disorienting.

Off I go...

10:16 am: I already like this better than being on the geriatric psychiatry ward. My new attending, Dr. Jung, has a penchant for analytical psychology.

I went off to see my first patient, a young woman named Alice who has multiple (potentially fatal) medical problems, all stemming from her IV drug use. From what I could gather, her life went from being on track and relatively uneventful to spiraling out of control and dangerously close to death within a couple of months.

Alice and I chatted for a long time and she asked if I could be her pseudo-therapist for the next few weeks. Since The General Hospital doesn't have psychologists on staff, I ran the idea by Dr. Jung and she approved of me chatting with Alice each day. In addition to offering Alice counseling, I made one suggestion to her team regarding her medical care. She is on narcotics for pain control, yet she is a

183

recovering heroin addict. That makes no sense to me. I humbly suggested (and by humbly, I mean repeatedly asked until Dr. Jung caved and added the rec into her note) that she be switched to methadone and a non-opioid pain medication. Methadone is used to prevent withdrawal symptoms in recovering opiate users. Dr. Jung informed me that there stood almost no chance of the primary medical team making the switch, but I felt strongly about the matter. If nothing else, I will fight to prevent my patients from being subject to the horrendous opioid epidemic raging in this country.

12:50 pm: If you stab yourself several times please do not be insulted when we question your mental status.

It's awkward when you walk into a patient's room and they're peeing into a little urinal and you're like, "I can wait to come in and talk to you" and they reply casually, "No, please, come right in." You can hear the stream of urination taking place and then poof! They produce a freshly filled disposable urinal and reach out their arm to hand it to you so you can dispose of it in the bathroom for them. Thanks.

On afternoon rounds. A sampling of answers to the question, "What day is it today?"

Patient One: "Monday-ish?"

Patient Two: "Tuesday/Monday."

Patient Three: "No."

Patient Four: "It's Thursday."

Patient Five: "January?"

Patient Six: "Friday."

Dr. Jung: "No ma'am, it's Monday."

Patient Six: "No... It's Friday."

Dr. Jung: "No, really, it's Monday. That's a statement, not a question anymore."

To determine whether or not a patient is delirious, one can utilize 'the junk sign.' If you walk into a patient's room and their junk is on display for all the world to see and the patient doesn't notice or mind, then they are probably delirious. A psych resident went so far as to claim that the junk sign is pathognomonic for delirium, since even psychotic patients should know whether or not their pants are on.

4:14 pm: A patient is adamant that he has a centipede, or possibly a caterpillar, crawling around in his brain.

Another patient informed me in no uncertain terms that $1+1=4$.

A resident explained that the mnemonic BMDC is short hand for, 'bitch made dude crazy.' Succinct and descriptive. I like it!

January 28: Tuesday

6:32 am: I never would have guessed that I'd ring in my 30th birthday at an airport hotel in the Midwest with a pilot from New Jersey. My birthday present from him? In bag number one there were fresh everything bagels flown in directly from NY. Thrilled, I'm thinking, "Man, he knows me well, this is the best present ever!" In bag number two I assumed there would be cream cheese. Nope. Bag number two contained a little blue box, cradling a Tiffany's necklace. He should have stopped at the bagels. It's been like two weeks. Now I'm thinking, "Oh shit, no, we're not on the same page." My initial instinct was to run. I am concerned that he's pushing for a relationship. Why can't I relax and just enjoy being with a really sweet guy trying to date me? Ugh... I'm getting itchy again. Though why should I try and force myself to want to date someone? I finally just got rid of Casey again. I'd rather be single than be with another person who is wrong for me.

9:11 am: I am content to be back at The General Hospital and working with the inpatient crowd. Not that I particularly enjoy psychiatry, but I prefer this level of acuity to any outpatient setting.

I met Alice's mother while pre-rounding. She looked like a stereotypical suburban mom whose prim and proper daughter fell in with the wrong crowd and is now a recovering heroin and crack cocaine-addicted prostitute.

2:34 pm: Patients lie constantly. Not always on purpose, but still, you never know if what the patients tell you will be anywhere close to what they tell your resident or attending.

Triskaidekaphobia: a legit phobia of the number 13.

A patient believes they broke multiple bones while participating in an ice luge race at the Sochi Winter Olympics (which are still two weeks away). I wish we didn't have to tell them that it's really because they drove themselves into a tree while high on all sorts of drugs. We're still not sure whether the crash was a suicide attempt or an accidental drug-related injury.

6:24 pm: On a typical day, the psychiatry consult team will see three, maybe four consults. Today we had 14. Fourteen! Fortunately, the team released me at six o'clock. The two residents complained that they would likely be at work until 11 pm. No offense to psychiatry, but there's no way in hell I'll be working until 11 pm on my birthday. It's too depressing here. Lots of heroin overdoses and suicide attempts.

7:07 pm: Happy birthday to me! I'm curled up on my couch in my most comfortable pajamas eating Chinese food and watching E! News. I hope it's a wonderful year. I loved throwing a huge party at my place and going out all Saturday night, and I had a great time with the pilot last night, but tonight is just for me. As extroverted as I can be, sometimes I crave alone time. Time to reflect, time to journal, time to relax, and talk to no one. Including my readers.

January 29: Wednesday

8:48 am: I should be in class right now. But, after running late this morning and rushing to my 8 am class, I found out the class had been canceled... by a 5:30 am email! The secretary then condescendingly informed me that I should always check my emails before class. Really? I'm pretty sure that the last thing I'm going to do when I'm running late is to stop and peruse my morning pile of emails. Ugh. At least now I can sit peacefully with my bagel and coffee.

Dr. Freud started off our lecture by having us read a *NY Times* article entitled, "Reinventing the Third-Year Medical Student" by Pauline W. Chen.[6] We then had a discussion about the 'emotional erosion' that occurs among us third year medical students. He concluded the class by giving us the following assignment: write a paragraph about a patient encounter that was meaningful to you. Well that's easy, I've written more than half a book consisting almost entirely of such stories.

Final session of afternoon addiction lectures.

3:00 pm: The lecture is about professionals, such as doctors and lawyers, getting addicted to drugs and alcohol. Apparently 10-15% of physicians have substance abuse disorders, with the highest rates of substance abuse seen in emergency physicians and psychiatrists. On the plus side, physicians have higher-than-average rates of successful long-term recovery due to better resources, better follow up care, and a greater incentive to seek treatment as compared to the general public.

January 30: Thursday

8:17 am: Last night I dreamt that Alice had improved and would leave the hospital. This morning I found out that her health is rapidly declining, she has multiple organs failing, and is likely entering hospice. Alice and her family are not yet aware of this development.

I hung out with the pilot last night though I didn't spend the night. We went to a movie and then back to his hotel. He was being oppressively affectionate, so I told him I wasn't feeling well (which was true) and I had to leave. In my defense, I woke up with a raging cold. Sick again.

9:10 am: I spent the morning with Alice. Her lab results keep trending in the wrong direction. I did notice in her notes that her medical team switched her to methadone and non-narcotic pain medications. I'm going to take credit for that one.

12:18 pm: I'm feeling weak and missing Casey. I texted this to all my girlfriends and hopefully someone is around tonight to keep me from calling him. I really, really don't want to keep venturing down that road again and again and again.

12:25 pm: Thank goodness, Piper immediately texted back that she'll keep an eye on me tonight until the moment of weakness passes. Phew! He's like a fucking addiction. You'd think that with all my education this month on addiction medicine I'd have learned how to kick him. Part of me can't decide whether or not I miss him, or I just miss the relationship and the role he played in my life. Probably both. Either way it's over. Move on.

12:55 pm: Dr. NY is clearly frustrated today. One of her patients is blatantly ignoring all of her advice, believes that he knows everything, and at the same time is basically asking for a magic pill to make him feel better. I agree completely with Dr. NY that this patient is really irritating. How can you help someone who feigns wanting assistance and then sabotages all of your efforts? It feels as if he is taking advantage of her time and her kind nature.

Piper and I went for dinner and she kept an eye on me. She's rotating through obstetrics this month and got reamed yesterday for something ridiculous. She is by far the sweetest and the smartest of my friends; definitely the least likely person to trigger the wrath of her superiors. After telling me the details of the situation she made the offhand comment that if she'd gotten yelled at like that during first year of medical school she would've cried, but now she's like, "Yeah, whatever." Even the sweetest among us is souring.

January 31: Friday

11:29 am: I just wrapped up with a fake patient in the simulation center. The patient cried during the encounter. I wonder if the fake patients in Los Angeles are more believable given all the Hollywood actors roaming about. At least she didn't call me emotionally sterile. I guess that means my emotional state is improving? Either that or I'm getting better at pretending.

4:32 pm: The pilot texted and inquired if I left on Wednesday night because I worried that he was coming on too quick. Well, at least he's perceptive.

February 1: Saturday

Where did today go?

February 2: Sunday

I finished typing up my psychiatry paper about the substance abuse interview I did with the young heroin-addicted Veteran back in mid-January. As I emailed the paper in, I saw the devastating breaking news that the actor Philip Seymour Hoffman was found dead in his apartment, needle in arm, of an apparent drug overdose.

9:59 pm: Most anticlimactic Super Bowl ever. Ever.

February 3: Monday

One of my classmate's siblings killed himself last week and she is back at work today. She was only excused from rotations for three days, and those days included traveling halfway across the country for the funeral. Cruel.

The first patient on rounds is hitting on my classmate, the one whose brother had killed himself. The patient is ignoring the rest of the team, and my classmate is smiling and playing along to appease the patient. She can't grieve, she can't process the event, and she can't be with her family. She is expected to be a fully focused 100% student doctor.

One of our patients is describing his anxiety as the sensation of a bee buzzing around inside his head. Another patient is overwhelmed by the incessant voices that are constantly telling him to kill himself.

In another room, we arrived to find a patient crying. They are depressed after finding their partner hanging in their home and having to help cut them down.

Jesus Christ, the savior of humankind, is also on our service right now.

If you're wondering what heroin withdrawal looks like, please watch the movie *Trainspotting*. You may want to cover your eyes during the scary baby scene.

My favorite way for patients to start sentences is, "Please don't think I'm crazy, but…"

February 4: Tuesday

10:32 am: I'm sitting in the psychiatry resident's lounge with the other medical students. There is absolutely nothing going on. I've seen my four patients already and the attending won't be here to round until 1 pm. Awesome. Sitting around for hours waiting for something to happen. Maybe we'll start getting consults.

11:28 am: I spent a lot of time with Alice this morning. She seems to have turned a small corner. We talked about how she's progressing and how she's been feeling. She informed me that her ex-boyfriend snuck onto the hospital floor over the weekend. At Alice's request, I talked to her primary medical team and managed to get him banned from the hospital. I have a nagging suspicion that he's trying to sneak heroin to her or is trying to assess how long before he can start pimping her out again.

When getting ready to leave her room I let her know that I don't come in on Wednesdays because I have class. She looked at me sadly and whispered "Oh." Pause. "Can you come in after your class?" I replied "Yes."

February 5: Wednesday

8:44 am: Sitting in class. It took me a solid 20 minutes to clear off the five inches of snow and quarter inch of ice off my car. With the recent polar vortex there have been many days with dangerously icy roads. I receive all the emergency alerts broadcast by the university affiliated with my med school. The alerts arrive by both text and email to ensure the highest likelihood that the students will receive proper warning that the university has been closed or will have a delayed opening. There's always a little disclaimer at the bottom of these messages, though. It reads, "The following units never close under any circumstances: College of Medicine, The General Hospital…" I don't know why they even bother sending these emails through the med school listserv. It's like a spiteful little teaser telling us, "Hey, look! Everyone else gets a snow day but NOT you!"

11:53 am: Home. The 11 o'clock prof didn't show up. I guess he decided he wanted a snow day. I feel bad for not visiting Alice, but the roads are horrendous and it's difficult to get over to the hospital. Plus, I'm bundled up in layers of snow gear, not exactly my usual professional dress expected of a med student working at The General Hospital. Is it normal to feel guilty? I'll check in with her tomorrow.

12:11 pm: The pilot hopped a flight from his home base to here 'cause his other flights today were cancelled due to weather. If he had asked, I probably would have told him not to visit because I don't like driving out to the airport when the roads are shit. I also have work to get done for school.

February 6: Thursday

At any given time about half of the patients on our census are suicidal. Many (most?) are also recovering heroin addicts.

Dr. Jung is caring and gentle when breaking bad news to patients and family members about their prognoses.

Three patients on our census witnessed the deaths of loved ones years ago. None of them sought help or counseling at the time of the event. The theme with these three is that they all turned to alcohol in order to suppress their feelings. Now, years later, instead of just being depressed, they're alcoholics who are also depressed. Each of them went through treatment to become sober, and all are now suicidal as they try to process the pain and loss that they didn't face years ago.

Clinic: The 1 pm, 2 pm, and 2:30 pm patients cancelled. Once the 1:30 patient has been seen I can go home.

Dr. NY helps her patients by normalizing their experiences and letting them know that they are not alone. She explains that everyone has peaks and valleys in their moods.

4:00 pm: The pilot and I went to the aquarium yesterday. The massive tanks were brimming with sharks, penguins, alligators, snakes, and tons of fish. Turns out there are lots of fish in the sea. He's adorable and dorky but something is missing, and he's moving too fast.

10:17 pm: I was hungry but now I'm not. I'm actually kind of nauseous. Casey just left. He came over to pick up the holiday gift he had tried to give me but I didn't accept. On arriving, he mentioned how happy I seem now. He told me he noticed it months ago and thought to himself, "There she is, the Silvia I once knew. Where had she gone?" We talked. I explained that carrying the weight of trying to figure out why someone doesn't want to commit to you is draining. Exhausting. Painful. It ate away at the relationship. I told him things that I've already written here in earlier chapters, including that I spent a tremendous amount of time thinking there was something wrong with me and that he never seemed quite as interested in me as I was in him. He replied that's just how he is; I shouldn't have questioned how he felt. Somehow this is still my fault?

We talked about how stressful the first two years of med school were for me and how I had to study all the time to maintain average grades. The pressure of med school ate at me, eroding away the carefree and mellow side of me, and the longer he went without proposing, the more our relationship spiraled away from the fun and loving place it once had been. I told him that if he had proposed two years earlier, maybe I wouldn't have been so stressed with school and everything. He revealed that he had thought the same thing.

He went on, uninvited, to tell me he feels guilty and confused when he sees me so happy now. I couldn't adequately describe to him how it feels to spend two years thinking you're not good enough for someone. Since we split, I've told myself numerous times that if he actually wanted to be with me, he would have known. Or tried harder. Or tried differently once he saw that I was drowning and unhappy. If his response to me being stressed out is to shut down emotionally, then the relationship would not have worked anyway. The painful part of all this is that I have a strong suspicion he is wondering about what it would be like

192

to be with me now that I'm happy and back to being my usual self again.

There is a Shel Silverstein poem called "Whatif" and I'm fighting those whatifs so hard right now.[7]

What if he misses me?

What if he is regretting not proposing two years ago?

What if he realizes he does want to be with me?

What if he is now regretting our breakup?

What if...

What if...

What if it's too late for him?

What if I've moved on?

What if I've realized I'm happier without him?

What if he tried to get me back?

The closing line of the poem sums up my brain at the moment. "Everything seems well, and then/ the nighttime Whatifs strike again!"

February 7: Friday

9:13 am: I'm the only medical student here today. The other third years are away at funerals and the fourth year is off doing fourth year things. I shouldn't be alone with my thoughts right now.

10:02 am: One of our patients wants to stop her cancer treatment and be allowed to go home and die. We were consulted, ostensibly, for medication recommendations, though I think the medical team is hoping that we will convince her to continue treatment. Patients have complete autonomy, but physicians do not take it well when people voluntarily choose a course that will ultimately hasten their death.

11:23 am: A severely injured post-suicide attempt patient is now awake, but she does not remember jumping. She denies knowing how she ended up in hospital. The medicine team punted and told our psych team that the news would be better handled if it came from us. So, we broke the news. At the patient's request, I then spoke with her parents about what happened because she was too ashamed to tell them herself. Telling a parent that their child is in the hospital because they tried to kill themselves tops the list of worst conversations I have had this year.

Noon: I can't move on from Casey. I'm increasingly certain that he is now rethinking our relationship. Which he may not be. I have no actual proof. How can one backslide so far after one conversation? But what if (those fucking whatifs) we're supposed to be together? I had thought he was it for me. I had planned a life with him. Now what? Probably just setting myself up to get hurt again. Badly. Possibly worse than before. What do I do now?

There is a patient with a lifelong history of psychiatric illness, but he is now acting psychotic in a different way than his usual M.O. His head imaging came back and it turns out that he has a brain tumor. We know this, but the patient doesn't. The psych team is punting that discussion and letting the medical team break that news.

5:35 pm: You don't wake up in the morning knowing it's going to be the longest day ever.

A family member of a patient demanded a meeting with the care teams. Health care providers from psychiatry, critical care, palliative care, nursing, social work, and the ethics committee all came together. For the first 20 minutes of the meeting, the family member reamed us all for not believing in the miracles of Jesus. The next 20 minutes were a tirade about how we are all awful people for suggesting that the 100ish-year-old brain-dead family member receive only comfort care, and no aggressive interventions such as brain surgery. Any attempts to redirect or have a productive discussion were immediately cut off by her screaming, "I'm not in denial!" and, "You doctors are cutting me off and won't let me talk just to make sure you're outta here by 5 pm!" And I'm sitting there thinking, "Seriously, a sincere fuck you at the five o'clock comment."

The patient's young grandchild (great-grandchild?) was in the room, witnessing this horrific verbal abuse being indiscriminately handed out. The kid began crying, and really, I kind of wanted to cry also, so I immediately hopped up and offered to take him outside.

We sat in the waiting room and chatted about school and sports. I segued into asking him about his grandmother and if he had questions. He asked me why she had a tube in her mouth. I explained it is to help her breathe and so that her doctors and nurses can make sure she is getting enough air. I explained that his grandmother's nurses, doctors, and his family were all watching her closely. He questioned if she was in pain. I told him that she is being given pain medicine to make sure she is comfortable. It felt important to let him know that it's ok to be sad, as he seemed to be an overlooked member of the family.

While I managed to make some of that debacle into a positive experience by focusing on helping the child, I can't help but be shook by the way the family member verbally abused the team. What recourse is there? Sit there and take it? Wait until it becomes physical abuse before calling security? I wonder if each doc and nurse secretly was waiting for someone else to interrupt and end the meeting. There's so much more to this problem, I just don't have the brain capacity to think about it anymore.

February 8: Saturday

7:59 am: I'm starting my second shift in the psychiatric emergency department, though this will only be a half-day. Happily, Dr. NY is the resident here today and she's updating me on the patients we've seen in her outpatient clinic.

All my ranting and raving is mostly contained within these pages and never gets expressed at work. The rest of my frustration comes out either while hanging out with my friends if I'm feeling social, or while painting or at the gym if I'm feeling introverted. Depends on the day.

Patient One is here with the main complaint that he is hungry. The intake nurse queried, "And you feel the psychiatric hospital is an appropriate place to get your needs met?"

Dr. NY asked another patient if he felt suicidal. His response? "I will be if you try and discharge me out into the cold."

A third patient is here asking for pain medication. Dr. NY answered, "No sir, you tried to overdose on your pain medication last night, we're not giving you any more."

Sometime around mid-morning we confiscated a 'rock in a sock' from a homeless man, which the patient had been using to defend himself on the streets of the city. I learned that this is a common homemade (street made?) weapon among homeless individuals. He is not allowed to keep it while hospitalized. He'll get it back when he is discharged.

Our next patient is on government-approved disability. He stated that after getting his check each month, he immediately spends it on marijuana and heroin. I've heard versions of this story countless times in the past few weeks.

A patient on another floor was becoming dangerously agitated so they called staff from around the hospital for 'a show of force.' A show of force is when a large number of people convene to help convince a patient to voluntarily take sedating or antipsychotic medications. This tends to be an effective yet minimally restrictive way to help patients make good choices. Additionally, if the patient escalates and becomes violent then there are many people present to assist in physically restraining the patient. This patient did not voluntarily make a 'good' choice. He ended up needing to be physically restrained, injected with meds against his will, and then locked in a padded room. I've seen this a couple of times and it always makes me uncomfortable.

11:50 am: I can't stop thinking about Casey. For better or worse, I must know what he's thinking, or I won't be able to move on. I need final confirmation that it's over.

Noon: Done for the day.

February 9: Sunday
Mental flat line.

196

February 10: Monday

Another heroin overdose.

Initially, I thought the following story too specific to share. However, in the past two weeks, variations of this story have occurred half a dozen times, suggesting that it is actually a disturbingly common occurrence. A man is involved with or is witnessing an argument, and in order to stop said argument, he stabs himself. Six times in the past two weeks! In a million years, I don't think I would ever decide that stabbing myself is a reasonable way to stop an argument, but it turns out this happens with some regularity. None of them were suicide attempts per se, and half of the guys didn't even have any history of mental illness at all. Rather, they all had an enormous amount of frustration, coupled with poorly controlled impulses, and easy access to kitchenware. BMDC.

I think I've mentioned this before, but if you have recently tried to kill yourself do not get annoyed when we ask you about your current level of suicidal ideation each morning on rounds.

Dr. Jung gives wonderful mini-lectures to the med students in between seeing consults. Today she is talking about the desire of Americans for a quick fix for every little life disturbance. She is explaining, "As physicians, we tend to throw pills at everything. Generally, less is more."

7:17 pm: So about yesterday. I invited Casey for lunch and afterwards we sat down for a little chat. I started the conversation by telling him I'm having trouble moving on until I know for certain that we will not be getting back together. All he had to do was tell me that we were over for good. I had mentally prepared myself for that response. However, his response back to me started with, "Well, actually..."

So now we're back on the stupid merry-go-round. Because that shithead is rethinking our entire relationship. ALL HE HAD TO DO WAS CONFIRM THAT IT WAS OVER. My main concern is that if we start dating again, then I will once again drift back into being the stressed and insecure person that I had morphed into during the past year or so of our relationship. Why am I even considering this? Maybe me walking away after seven years is the fire he needs to actually realize that we should be together.

February 11: Tuesday

8:38 am: I am dragging this morning. I stayed up way too late chatting on the phone with my mom and watching Netflix.

The consult room has no windows and I'm feeling antsy and claustrophobic today.

10:04 am: I'm over the whole psychiatry rotation thing. So many of our patients are here for problems related to heroin dependence and suicide attempts. It's too depressing.

Another patient just told me, "Each month, as soon as I get my disability check, I buy as much as alcohol, crack, and marijuana that I can."

A patient is here for what is either a suicide attempt by hanging or autoerotic asphyxiation gone wrong. Oddly, the patient seems not to remember which scenario is correct.

There is a blurring between genius and madness. I spent nearly 45 minutes with a PTSD patient, who spends their time painting and journaling.

More and more patients with suicide attempts and heroin overdoses are appearing on our census. Psychiatry is obviously not my field, and psychiatrists are not my people.

9:34 pm: I ended things with the pilot. It would have been unfair to string him along while I wait to see what happens with Casey. And he was too lovey-dovey for me anyway. I'm not a snuggles-and-flowers kind of woman, which is why I sought him out on Tinder, not on a website like IWantToGetMarried.com (I don't even know if that's a thing.) I failed at Tinder.

February 12: Wednesday

7:23 am: Last day of psychiatry lectures.

8:33 am: I am always skeptical when a professor starts off a lecture by stating it's going to be 'interactive.'

8:36 am: I have already lost interest in this lecture.

9:42 am: This next lecture is about different types of psychotherapy. Had I stayed in psychology I would have become a Jungian psychoanalyst. I'm a big believer in individuation (the process of becoming who one is meant to be), the collective unconscious, and not surprisingly, I'm also quite interested in dreams and the role they play in one's life.

9:48 am: I dislike when professors rely on videos to make a point. It makes me think they are not confident enough to teach us themselves. This professor felt the need to utilize a YouTube video where the speaker simply gave a definition of psychotherapy. Kind of unnecessary. I'm feeling extremely judgy and opinionated today.

10:14 am: This lecture is terrible. For some reason she is telling us about babies puking. Yeah, your guess is as good as mine on this one. I feel bad, but it's kind of entertaining to look around the lecture room and see everyone playing on their iPads and phones, messing with their hair, or whispering with each other. Magnus is sitting behind me and we're texting while he catches up on the daily news on his iPad. He has informed me he'd like to put an ice pick in his eye right now.

10:26 am: The lecturer is rambling on and made some comment about slaying dragons. If you figure out a way to segue from baby puke to dragons, please let me know.

10:28 am: Time for another video. You know it's bad when I'm bored in lecture because I have a genuine interest in how one's mental health influences their physical health. Many (most?) of my classmates haven't given a shit during this entire rotation. At a poignant moment in the video the therapist asserts, "You appear like a cork, bobbing around in the sea of life." Glancing around the class, I see that everyone is holding back laughter at her analogy. I don't think hilarity is the response the lecturer hoped to evoke.

10:35 am: Hooray another video!

10:36 am: Did you know that many people in the Midwest do not understand sarcasm? I swear. As a New

Yorker, it's made for some awkward conversations. I've had a fair number of Midwesterners look at me strangely when I use sarcasm. For example, K Canoe did not 'get' sarcasm, which incidentally led to Piper going off on a fantastic rant about him one night, explaining why K Canoe and I could never be in a relationship.

We're in the midst of our last lecture, which is more of a wrap-up session, with Dr. Freud. He is talking to us about our responsibilities as students and throws out the comment, "You [medical students] have a net, you're not going to kill anyone." The comment caught my attention because it wasn't a figurative or metaphorical use of the word 'kill.' He used the word in the most literal way possible, referring to the fact that when we are no longer safety-netted students, we will likely, literally (however unintentionally), make a mistake that results in us ending a life. It's disturbing to think about potentially killing someone.

12:52 pm: Talking to my mom, she is terrified about the position I'm in with Casey. She agrees that she would have done the same thing, though. We were joking around, and in her best *Laurel and Hardy* impersonation informed me, "That's a fine mess you've got yourself into."

9:16 pm: Please don't hit on me at the gym.

10:13 pm: I'm loving the Olympics. I love seeing the athletes and their families celebrate triumphs. Mostly I love knowing that every evening all around the world there are people like me tuning in to root for their country. There's a sense of worldwide camaraderie. It makes me think there is some hope for the countries of this world being able to get along with each other.

Also, there's a funny article online at *Us Weekly* about one of the Olympic skiers joking about how excellent Tinder has been in Sochi.[8]

February 13: Thursday

Last day of being on the psychiatry consult team. I hope this day doesn't drag on forever.

8:09 am: I went looking for Alice and couldn't locate her this morning. My immediate concern was that she died and nobody had bothered to tell me.

Many years ago, when I worked as a psychologist, I became close with a young woman named Crystal. She had cancer, and I was her therapist from the time of her diagnosis through her last treatment. I bonded with her family, her husband, and her baby boy. Her positive outlook on life never wavered. I saw her on a Friday afternoon, shortly after her final round of chemo finished, and we cheered the momentous milestone. I returned to work on Monday and found out she had died. Her medical team told me she had developed a raging infection and died suddenly on Sunday night. I sat with her family on Monday morning and told her baby how much her mother loved him. I went home and cried for days. Shortly thereafter I quit my job.

Fortunately, Alice hadn't died. She had been discharged to a long-term rehab facility to continue her recovery. I'm really upset that I didn't get a chance to say goodbye. If you're wondering how I came up with her name, don't ask me. *Go ask Alice.*

Casey and I have been texting.

There is a retired physician on our service, referred to as a 'terror' by the emergency department. Of course, the team offered me up as sacrifice to go see him. He tried to kick me out of his room the moment I entered. While slowly walking toward the door I turned and asked, "Are you sure you wouldn't like to talk for just a few minutes?"

"Well, I suppose until my breakfast tray comes in…"

Before long, the floodgates opened and wow, what a deluge. He opened up and provided me with unfiltered insight into his life. Any time I thought the conversation neared closing and I stood to leave, he would start down a new topic. I would immediately sit again, fascinated to be the person chosen to share in this doctor's most secret thoughts, regrets, and wishes. Simultaneously thrilled and humbled that he opened up to me, I stayed in his room for quite some time. I imagine that most of his thoughts and feelings about life up until this point have remained between him and God.

10:21 am: The resident, followed by the attending, tried to see the retired physician, but both were promptly dismissed from his room.

As I packed up my bags, I chatted with Dr. Jung about the rotation. She gave me excellent clinical reviews, and specifically noted in her evaluation that I need to be more confident in making diagnoses and coming up with plans for my patients because most of the time I'm spot on.

After covering the mandatory stuff, she told me to let her know if I ever want to catch up and grab coffee. She then asked me what I was up to for Valentine's Day. I told her I ended things with the pilot. She looked at me with a critical eye and then casually commented, "There's someone else, isn't there?" I confided to her that my ex still roamed around my thoughts. In turn, she divulged that she's incapable of turning off her habit of psychoanalyzing people.

Off to my last afternoon clinic with Dr. NY. It's so cold and depressing in this polar vortex that many patients still aren't showing up for appointments.

10:32 pm: When Casey and I hung out last weekend he called me "hon" at one point to get my attention. I don't remember when exactly he started calling me honey (or hon), but he has done it for years. I always found it sweet but never gave much thought as to how or why he came up with that particular moniker for me. It wasn't until we spent our first Christmas together at his parent's house that I figured it out: honey is the term of endearment his father uses when talking to his mother.

February 14: Friday

12:17 pm: Happy (?) Valentine's Day.

Sitting post-final exam and having lunch. The rotation finals are always harder than I imagine they will be. In this case, the exam required a lot of general medical knowledge outside of psychiatry, as well as having to know the details of the stages of physical and mental development of children. I happen to know very little about children.

Oh well. It's over.

3:29 pm: Since I fired my flying Valentine, I am not sure how I will spend my weekend. Most of my friends are attached and already have plans for this V-day. I suppose I could round up my other single friends for a movie and wine night. That's what single women do, right? I haven't been without a valentine, specifically without Casey, since undergrad. Our tradition always involved cooking an elaborate meal and dessert together.

4:42 pm: Oh, speak of the devil. He is inviting me over for Valentine's Day. I guess since I'm on a psychiatry rotation, this is the most appropriate time to do something crazy. What's the craziest thing I could possibly do? Consider taking Casey back.

Off I go to his apartment for Valentine's Day.

Radiology

Song: Two Door Cinema Club. "What You Know."
Tourist History. Kitsuné Records. 2011.
Drink: Bulleit Rye Old Fashioned

February 16: Sunday

11:02 am: I've finally returned to my apartment from Casey's place. I went over Friday night for dinner and never quite left. Kind of like the weekend before when he came over for lunch on Saturday and didn't leave until late Sunday night. Still, nothing has been figured out. He is leaving on a nearly-two-week vacation and promised to think things through. We cooked dinner together Friday night, and I spent yesterday being a typical med student with a free day – we slept in, watched a marathon of *Sherlock*, went to the mall, and basically did nothing productive. No writing, no editing, no reading, no studying; nothing. It felt wonderful.

11:04 am: Third year medical students get to choose two electives. Electives are rotations outside of the required core rotations and can be anything from oncology to dermatology to sports medicine to palliative care and many more. I went with radiology for my first elective, which will start tomorrow. Radiology seemed to be a logical choice because no matter what one's specialty, imaging is usually a part of it. And radiology is a specialty in and of itself- the art and science of interpreting imaging. Two whole weeks of x-rays, magnetic resonance imaging (MRIs), ultrasounds, and computed tomography (CT) scans galore. The artist in me is completely psyched about spending two whole weeks staring at and interpreting pictures. Perhaps I will become a radiologist.

7:15 pm: My non-medical goal for the radiology rotation is to finish the fountain painting for my cousin Violet and her new hubby David.

9:59 pm: I wish Zooey still lived here with me. We chatted for a while tonight; I miss talking to her so much. We had such a blast together. My current roommate is sweet but pretty much keeps to herself and stays in the guest room.

February 17: Monday

7:35 am: We still haven't received an email or any instructions about when and where we're supposed to meet for our radiology orientation. A bunch of us are going to wait at the radiology conference area and see who, if anyone, shows up.

8:01 am: Rumor has it that orientation probably starts at 8:30 am. Magnus and I are heading off to get breakfast and coffee.

8:39 am: Still waiting to start. I'm not saying that people routinely forget about the medical students, but I've definitely noticed a trend this year.

12:30 pm: So, no one showed up to orient us at 8:30, but a professor appeared around 9 am and started lecturing to us about how to identify all the different tubes and lines that can appear on imaging studies. We just went with it. Around noon, the radiology rotation supervisor let us know that we have lectures from 8 am to 10 am each morning, and then we are distributed among the various reading rooms.

10:48 pm: It has taken all of my willpower not to check the final scores from the Olympic ice dancing event that took place earlier today. The final American couple, Davis and White, is about to skate.

10:58 pm: Gold!!

February 18: Tuesday

8:03 am: Today in morning radiology lectures we're learning about the basics of computed tomography scans, aka CT scans, or CAT (computerized axial tomography) scans.

12:38 pm: Having lunch with Magnus, who is still recovering from his own recent break-up. I feel his pain. At least Casey is on vacation and away from me for a while.

4:03 pm: My short afternoon was spent in the ultrasound reading room. I saw many a gallbladder, some bursting with stones, some benign, as well as an ill-appearing appendix. On other screens in the dark reading room I noted ultrasound images of hearts, babies of various sizes, and even an eyeball. Is there any body part you can't ultrasound? According to the resident, pretty much anything can be ultrasounded, but the image quality degrades when the ultrasound waves travel through adipose tissue (aka fat).

10:25 pm: Wahoo! After months of going to the gym I finally have new muscles developing. Growing up and throughout college I worked out nearly every day. Although I used to be pretty ripped, I had become frail and scrawny throughout my twenties. I'm a former uber-competitive epee fencer, going all the way to competing at the Junior Olympics. Fencing, like painting, provided a therapeutic outlet for me. A solid workout helped me sleep at night. Who doesn't feel better after getting out all their aggression by legally and safely stabbing someone while people cheer you on?

When I started working out again this past fall I had a rough time getting into a routine. I had to learn how to do something other than a fencing-based workout. I got sidetracked every time I got sick, and I spent nearly a month on the DL around New Years after a knee injury from running too much. When I miss a week or two, or several weeks, in a row I try not to let it ruin the work I've put in thus far. Anyway, I am finally starting to put muscle back on. It feels great!

As an aside, in my ideal life, I'll figure out a way to fence again. Fencing is not a sport that ends when one finishes college. It's a lifelong pursuit that can be enjoyed by people of all ages. One day. Oops, it's 1:15 am and it's way past my bedtime.

February 19: Wednesday

7:54 am: The weather rapidly warmed and the city is a giant, wet mess of dirty slush and puddles.

8:02 am: "You never want to be an interesting case," is how our lecturer began the morning. Interesting cases typically occur when the patient has an unusual illness or injury. This results in all the docs in the room looking at the image and simultaneously exclaiming "ooh" and "aah." We were then given the assignment of finding an interesting radiology case to present on Friday morning.

10:08 am: Sitting in a quiet, dark reading room, examining CT scans that are rolling in. The CT scans are from patients all over the hospital, including the emergency department, surgery, the medicine floors, and the ICUs. The only noises are the gentle hum of the computers and quiet chatter as residents speak into high tech microphones that transcribe their words.

Multiple CT trauma scans are flooding the list of images to be read stat (now!). Judging by the sudden influx of scans, the emergency department must be hopping. I have a strange longing to be in the emergency department right now, not looking at screen images, remote from the action.

Before looking at the new ED scans, the resident and I finish up evaluating the scan of a man shot through the neck and rendered a quadriplegic a couple of months ago. Looks like he has pneumonia.

More and more stat CT scans are popping in from the ED. Trauma after trauma. The resident noted how busy the trauma bay must be. Perhaps a multiple car pile-up occurred? A gang fight? An explosion? What type of catastrophe occurred at 10:15 am on a Wednesday to fill up the ED? It's too calm in here. I'm itching to get out of here to go see what's going on in the trauma bay. Clearly, I do not belong in a specialty where you don't see patients. I keep posing my theories about all the traumas to the rads resident, but he seems entirely uninterested in the backstory surrounding these images.

2:35 pm: Radiology will be my last light-duty rotation for the next four months, so I am getting my life in order. I spent much of the afternoon spring-cleaning my apartment and tomorrow I'm heading to the dentist for the first time in longer than I would like to admit.

3:57 pm: Every May there is a national emergency medicine conference. Emergency physicians and residents from around the country gather and share the latest EM research. The conference is organized and run by a collection of EM bigwigs from around the country, including The Boss. Each year, the program committee selects a handful of medical students out of nearly a hundred applicants to assist with running the conference. About two months ago I sent in my application to be one of these medical student ambassadors on the program committee. Two minutes ago, I received a congratulatory letter stating that I have been chosen! Off to Dallas, Texas for the EM conference in May. I'll have to email The Boss and let her know. She'll be so excited!

6:55 pm: I don't think I mentioned it earlier, but my parents are visiting this weekend. They haven't been here in nearly two years and I'm excited to see them.

February 20: Thursday

7:30 am: Woke up antsy.

11:04 am: My morning is being spent in the neuroradiology reading room. Images of brains are illuminated on the computers that are dotted around the perimeter of the room. As there are no sources of light aside from the computer screens, the brains appear to be floating eerily in the darkened room.

The resident is totally geeking out about brain images and is thinking about doing a neuroradiology fellowship. Looking at the blobs of white and grey, he is teasing out small variations from what a normal brain should look like. At least that is what he is telling me, I still only see blobs of grey and white. I can see why a radiology residency takes so many years; reading blips is definitely an acquired skill. The resident is explaining his systematic approach by assessing the shape, size, location, and overall geometry of the image. The goal is to be concise, accurate, and not waver. He cautions, "Don't get too caught up in the first thing that pops out at you. Be systematic; make sure to identify *all* abnormalities." Makes sense.

There is a fuzzy little blip on one slice of a CT scan, which is possibly a cancerous lesion. The resident asked me, "Can you hallucinate that there's something there?"

For me, looking at CTs and MRIs is like looking at clouds. Amorphous shapes begin to resemble familiar objects such as an animal or a ship or something like that. Today I saw a fire breathing dragon, a poisonous mushroom, and little puppy among the CT slices.

2:18 pm: Waiting at the dentist office.

3:10 pm: No cavities. Go me.

February 21: Friday

9:45 am: All morning long the third year and fourth year students are presenting interesting radiology cases to the group. Some of the case presentations were: an atypical presentation of multiple sclerosis; unique arterial anatomy leading to a rare type of stroke; an unusually large brain aneurysm that is basically a ticking time bomb; an incidental lung nodule found during a work up for an unrelated illness; and a wide of variety of spinal and extremity (limb) trauma. I presented a case of internal decapitation, which is essentially when your spinal cord gets severed from your body (as if you were decapitated) but your head is actually still firmly attached to your body. Bodies are weird.

1:40 pm: Ugh. Soooo sad. Stupid fog grounded all flights leaving New York, so my parents can't make it in. I'm so disappointed.

February 22: Saturday

Most boring day ever. All my friends are working or studying for their big upcoming final exams. Radiology doesn't have a big final exam since it is an elective, so I'm just hanging out.

February 23: Sunday

8:14 pm: I painted all day long, while a marathon of *Archer* played in the background. My wedding present of The Bethesda Fountain for Violet and David is nearly finished. Yes, I know it's been forever since their wedding but the fountain is seriously complicated. In order to personalize the painting, I added two little figures sitting on the edge of the fountain, holding hands. I did some Facebook stalking and based on a photo from that night, I painted the figures wearing the outfits that they had been wearing when he popped the question. It's all about the details. I need to find the right frame then put it (carefully) in the mail.

9:53 pm: The closing ceremonies for Sochi are about over and they featured a scene advertising the 2018 Winter Olympics. By winter 2018, I'll be 34 years old and hopefully a third-year resident, though who knows where I'll be living. Perhaps by then I'll be married, even pregnant. Probably not pregnant, though married might be nice.

February 24: Monday

7:04 am: This cold, depression-inducing polar vortex weather makes it so hard to want to get out of bed in the morning.

8:58 am: I'm spending my day at The Kiddie Hospital, learning all about pediatric radiology. Kids bones are not fully developed and their scans are phenomenally confusing to interpret.

My main assignment is in the fluoroscopy reading room. Fluoroscopy involves mixing radioactive chemicals into liquids of different densities, making the fluid visible on radiography and other imaging. Patients then ingest the dye, or have it injected into them, and subsequently have imaging done. This is usually to evaluate the digestive tract, the urinary tract, or the reproductive organs.

The dye glows in the images and allows physicians to assess potential problems such as leaks or obstructions. I routinely saw similar studies done in post-esophagectomy patients, back when I rotated through thoracic surgery. It's one thing to watch adults undergo these studies; it's another to see it done to children. Watching babies and children drink radioactive dye and have imaging (replete with cancer-inducing ionizing radiation) done in order to visualize their insides is strange but sadly necessary. At this point, there's no other way to better assess for certain medical problems. I imagine that the waste from these studies is how the Ninja Turtles and other radioactive superheroes were created.

210

12:43 pm: During lunch, one of my classmates shared that his wife was diagnosed with a slowly-progressive autoimmune disease with no known cure. Of course, he is one of the friendliest, kindest, and hardworking students in our class. How do you comfort someone who is well aware of the painful and disfiguring disease that is now afflicting his previously healthy wife? Everything has changed for them. They are thinking about starting a family soon, before her disease progresses. They must consider the cost of her medications, and physical therapy, as well as plan for her future disability. When you work in medicine, you know too much.

They have been dealing with this news for months. I see this student nearly every day, and am pretty friendly with him, but I had no idea of his personal struggle. Just like the rest of us, he had to continue to study and attend class while planning for residency. He showed up to rotations every day with a smile and never let on that anything had changed in his life. I wonder whether or not this will affect his choice of medical specialty. Is he contemplating avoiding an overly demanding specialty, such as surgery, which would keep him working a hundred hours a week and away from his wife while she is still fully mobile? I wasn't sure how to appropriately respond to this news. I'm glad he opened up to us and hopefully he found some relief in sharing his burden.

3:12 pm: All afternoon we played around with the ultrasound machines. There are many different probe sizes and shapes, depending on whether you want to look at larger organs or at smaller body parts like blood vessels or eyeballs. Some probes are tiny. New ones are designed to plug directly into iPhones, turning phones into portable ultrasound machines. That's so cool! Having a portable and non-invasive way to assess patients is pretty incredible and applications are far reaching, including disaster medicine and international medicine. I also learned about the utility of ultrasound during trauma examinations, such as looking for broken bones, internal bleeding, and collapsed lungs.

As part of our afternoon we have to present an interesting case from the morning. I presented the case of a young man with a straddle injury and subsequent development of a urethral stricture (ouch). Essentially, this means that a guy fell onto his crotch and now he can't pee. Shortly after a student started presenting, she developed a nosebleed. Granted, it wasn't a gusher but still, a nosebleed nonetheless. Another medical student handed her some tissues and she kept right on presenting her patient. She didn't skip a beat. This is merely speculation, but I'm guessing that in normal professions, the speaker would have stepped out to the restroom to clean herself up. Not medicine.

4-ish pm: Our options for our fourth-year schedules were emailed to us. I can't believe that it's already time to plan for fourth year! We have only two required rotations; one in internal medicine and another in the specialty in which we'll be doing residency. The other nine months will be filled entirely with electives and time off for interviewing.

February 25: Tuesday

8:04 am: I arrived at my assigned site, the abdominal reading room, at 7:56 am to start at 8 am. The friendly rads resident, four minutes away from finishing her overnight shift, asked me what field I wanted to go into. When I replied "emergency medicine," she gave me a quick overview of the traumas that came in overnight.

The most interesting (and least sad) image involved a CT scan of a patient who survived being karate chopped but ended up with a busted spleen. He went to the OR and thus far is alive. Some of the other trauma patients did not fare so well. The resident then showed me the head imaging of a guy who came in after a bad car accident. His head appeared to be busted in, and the resident knew that the patient died shortly after arriving to the hospital. She didn't know any information about the circumstances of the accident or the details of the patient. She didn't know if he was with anyone, what his other injuries were, what interventions were done in the ED, or if his family had arrived in time to be with him before he died. After kindly giving me this rundown, she concluded, "Now my shift is over so I'm going home. The day team will be here any minute." With that, she strolled into the hallway, leaving me alone in the darkened room with only the hum of computers and my own thoughts.

So here I am. It's now ten minutes after 8 o'clock and no one is here yet. I would like to leave because I feel super awkward sitting here by myself. I have a feeling that all of the residents are off in a conference or somewhere else and probably won't show up till nine. Our rotation supervisor is really sweet, but she is super scatterbrained and probably didn't consider the residents' schedule when she did the medical student room assignments.

It's so strange and isolated in these dark reading rooms. Where are the patients?

8:16 am: A resident arrived! I've definitely mentioned before how awkward it is to approach a physician as they walk in the door in the morning and be like, "Hi! Guess what? I'm going to be following you all morning and you have no say in the matter."

10:43 am: The attending physician walked in, ignored me for a bit, and eventually asked what field of medicine I planned to pursue. Upon revealing my intention to enter emergency medicine, he immediately launched into a ten-minute tirade about how EM is awful and I should not enter it for residency. His opinion was based on burn out rates, and an unhappy wife whom who he believes would have been happier in another field. I nodded my head and occasionally murmured, "ok" and, "I see" but inside I squirmed, bordering on getting angry.

It's one thing to poke fun at other specialties and stereotypes of physicians a field attracts. Some of the typical stereotypes are that internal medicine folks are super nerdy, surgeons are cocky assholes, emergency medicine docs are adrenaline junkies, orthopods are macho gym rats, ob-gyn docs are bitchy sorority girls, pediatricians are sugary sweet, and pathologists are weird loners. It's another thing entirely

213

to tell a medical student that they shouldn't pursue their field of interest because it is a horrific choice and will ruin their life. As a final note, while I appreciated (not really) their unsolicited advice, it's kind of hard to listen to a physician who has never met me before and doesn't actually see patients in person.

On a brighter note, the majority of my morning was spent working with a great resident, and not the cranky attending. He taught me how to approach abdominal CT scans in greater detail than was covered in lectures and made it interesting.

I still can't help but look at images and see cloud shapes. Today, I saw a Georgia O'Keeffe-like cow skull, a Thanksgiving turkey, a human-ish face, a bat, and a Pac-Man ghost. In reality, I saw a horseshoe kidney (fused kindey), a small bowel obstruction (gut blockage), a 35-pound tumor (yes, 35 pounds), an obstructing gallstone, a splenic laceration, "suspicious injuries," cirrhosis, and an abdomen filled with cancerous metastases (tumors everywhere). I'm enjoying the variety of cases that pop up on the computers here, but as interesting and unique as some of those findings were, I'd be way happier speaking to patients in person. I'm certain that the person is way more interesting than their medical condition.

I could never spend my life sitting in a dark room staring at a computer screen.

11:00 am: It's not that radiologists care any less about their patients, but there's generally no doctor/patient relationship. Radiologists don't see their patients' faces, shake their hands, hear their voices, meet their loved ones, talk to them, or comfort them.

There is a resident or attending physician at every desk, and each of them is holding their personal microphone and babbling away into the computer about what they are seeing on the image in front of them. As an outsider, this seems to be a subdued, lonely profession. On the flip side, they all seem really happy.

214

11:28 am: I'm so antsy. I'm terrible at sitting still and being quiet.

The pilot is still texting me. Why couldn't I fall for the sweet, affectionate, smart, and successful pilot? Why am I hung up on the emotionally-stunted surgeon?

2:15 pm: Violet and David's painting of the Bethesda Fountain is off in the mail. They should have it by Friday.

9:15 pm: The weather sucks but Rihanna, Kesha, Katy Perry, and Lil' Kim keep me motivated during my increasingly intense workouts.

February 26: Wednesday

Last day of my radiology rotation.

8:32 am: A radiologist joked that he can determine how sick a patient is by evaluating their tube-to-orifice ratio. If all of a patient's orifices have tubes in them, such as a breathing tube, central line, nasogatric tube, Foley, arterial line ("tubes" in trachea, vein, stomach, bladder and artery), then they are likely in critical condition.

Spending my afternoon in the musculoskeletal reading room. The resident today enjoys devising backstories for his patients, based on their imaging. One x-ray showed a femur fracture due to a gunshot wound, with many bullet fragments noted. Due to the pattern of soft tissue damage and the trajectory of the bullet, the radiologist determined that the patient likely accidentally shot himself while putting his gun in his pocket. He imagined the patient being some punk, with no business having a gun, who thought he was being cool by putting it in his pants' pocket, loaded and unlocked.

Another patient had distal fractures of the radius and ulna, (broken bones near the wrist). The radiologist imagined this patient to be an independent and industrious older woman who likely slipped while shoveling snow, falling squarely on her outstretched arm. While we had fun creating these backstories, we'll never know if they are even close to the truth.

Pop quiz: Which fracture is the hardest to see?

Answer: The second one. The lesson being, don't stop looking for injuries after finding the first fracture.

2:09 pm: Casey returns today, I think.

10:24 pm: During the past six or so years (pretty much since I decided to go down the med school route), my brain has become hardwired to study and work all the time. So much so that I am now nearly incapable of just watching TV. I've never really been one to sit and watch TV all day anyway, but now, if I'm ever in the mood to do nothing I feel as if I'm being a slacker. Like right now, for example: I watched barely an hour of TV and immediately then stressed, "Why wasn't I studying? Or reading a book? Or editing this book? Or planning my next painting/trip/meal/shopping/trip/gym workout," on and on and on. I guess I've always been like that, but it's worse now that I'm in med school. It is hard to relax when there's always something I could be doing for school.

10:59 pm: I've been more antsy than usual this week.

11:00 pm: Fine. I admit it. I'm thinking about Casey and waiting for him to get back from vacation, so we can figure out what, if anything, is going on between us.

February 27: Thursday

10:28 am: Lots of studying today. Well, not really. A little bit of studying. My exam tomorrow is not a national final exam like during other rotations. Rather, this one is a short departmental exam on which students tend to do well. I will quickly review the lectures and chapter outlines, most of which overlap with each other, and then be done.

11:07 am: Reviewing some cringe worthy radiographs (x-rays) from various trauma lectures. Ever seen a finger dislocated 90°?

Viewing all these images and reviewing the underlying pathophysiology (disease state) has been incredibly helpful as review for medicine and surgery though this is certainly not the career for me. I need to see my patients. I need to talk with them and interact. I need to be part of a team and certainly can't be in a field where most of

216

my day is spent sitting at a desk. Radiologists are definitely not my people.

February 28: Friday

8:44 am: I could be studying but Magnus and I are gossiping.

10:45 am: Radiology test is over. Easy peasy. Today is the end of the second block of med school rotations, so everyone will be out tonight. We are officially two thirds done with third year. The partying tonight should be epic.

11:15 am: I spent last night with Casey. We had the most frustrating conversation ever. He revealed that he took the breakup really hard and supposedly couldn't bring himself to date anyone else, or even hit on anyone else, for the past seven months. He is now thinking that I may, in fact, be "the one." It would have been great if he stopped speaking right then and there and we got back together, but no! The asshat kept going. He droned on that he'd never had another girlfriend and he "needs" to date other people.

Any reasonable, logical person would run like hell. Here he is, my ex asking me to wait around while he tries dating other women 'just to make sure.' It's really embarrassing to share that I even considered his proposition. I'm logical, straightforward, self-respecting, and realistic in every aspect of my life, except with him. When he looks at me, my brain and heart refuse to cooperate within the normal confines of reason and sanity.

I would love to tell him to fuck off and that he's not worth my time. I want to demand that he decide right here, right now, whether or not we're getting back together. I want to yell at him that I've been waiting seven years (now technically seven years and seven months) for him, and fuck no, I'm not waiting anymore. Run, Silvia! Run! Instead, I told him I would think about what he said and get back to him.

When it comes to relationships, my momma's favorite quote is, "Love isn't blind, it's stupid." Stupid is a phenomenal way to sum up my willingness to put up with him.

11:40 am: Passed my radiology rotation with honors. I have yet to receive my grade from psychiatry.

3:40 pm: Off to the airport to pick up the parents who rescheduled their previously-cancelled trip for this weekend.

After a scrumptious dinner at my favorite little Italian restaurant with the parents and Daria and Jane, I'll be heading off to celebrate this slew of rotations being over.

March 1: Saturday

Last night, my friends introduced me to a drink called the gin bucket, jazzed up with the addition of glow sticks. Apparently, it is a big Midwest thing. Basically, a bucket is filled with gin and mixers (traditionally, Fresca) and then consumed by the group exclusively and strictly via a turkey baster. My head is a little foggy and my parents are laughing at me while I nurse my coffee.

Violet and David called to tell me they received their wedding present painting. I feel a sense of pride and happiness that I could commemorate the beginning of their lives together.

Dinner with the parents, Piper, and Sophia tonight at a local steakhouse. For all its faults, the Midwest has the most fantastic beef.

After dad went to bed, momma and I topped off our night by watching *Brave* and gossiping about my year so far.

March 2: Sunday

5:23 am: A shadow passed by my bedroom window. There's a tall, lanky man outside my apartment, peering in. He's taunting, "I can see you. I can see you. Just let me in. I see you!" I desperately crawled from my bed to the floor, towards the living room, in order to hide. I woke up in bed with my heart racing so fast that I nearly lost my breath.

I couldn't close my eyes again for a good hour or so after waking. Pure torture. To help understand my nightmares, I try to identify the emotions underlying the events in the dreams. In this one, I felt exposed and vulnerable, with an overwhelming fear for my safety and wellbeing.

6:36 pm: I love watching the red carpet during the Oscars. I almost like it more than the actual ceremony.

11:48 pm: Casey finally left. For good. Again.

We talked about our relationship for nearly two hours throughout the night and we basically determined that he is an idiot who cannot commit. And that the problem is squarely with him, and not me. I don't know why it is so hard for him to figure his shit out. Even after this talk, he lingered at my apartment for nearly an hour, stubbornly rooted to my couch, watching the Oscars, his head resting in my lap. I've done everything possible so the only thing left to do was send him on his way. I pity whatever women fall for his shit in the future.

Maybe it will turn out like a med school version of *Legally Blonde*. If he comes to his senses and returns to tell me that I am "the one" for him, perhaps I will simply channel my inner Elle Woods and respond, "I've been waiting for a long time for you to say that. But if I'm going to be a partner in a law firm *[attending at a kickass hospital]* by the time I'm 30 *[well, 35]*, I need a boyfriend who's not such a complete bonehead." Then I'll flip my gorgeous locks and walk away towards my awesome new life without him.

Intersession III

Song: alt-J. "Something Good." *An Awesome Wave.*
Infectious Records. 2012.
Drink: Red eye coffee

March 3: Monday

8:03 am: Once again in a large lecture hall, flanked by Sophia, Piper, and Maggie, among other friends and classmates. I'm in my third and final block of third year medical school rotations. This intersession week will prep me for my two months of pediatrics and six weeks of obstetrics and gynecology. Tucked in between those rotations I have my two-week elective in emergency medicine.

I have decided that the worst thing about being in medicine is not the hours, the endless studying, the life or death decisions, or anything else. Rather, it is the lack of snow days. I will never again get a day off for weather because hospitals never close. Snow? Sleet? Alien invasion? Zombie Apocalypse? Doesn't matter. Go to work.

9:40 am: The Dean of Something Financial is talking to us about the cost of applying to residency during fourth year. Every student must interview in person at every potential residency location. This means flying all over the country, pay for hotels, car rental, meals and more. The average fourth year medical student will shell out $6,000 during interview season. This is in addition to the next part of our board exams, which costs about $1,800.

1:29 pm: The entire afternoon contains cheery talks about child and elder physical and sexual abuse.

3:15 pm: Now I'm in a women's reproductive health ethics lecture. The professor is posing questions about a hypothetical brain-dead pregnant lady, whose medical wishes clearly state that she never wants to be on life-support. Keep her alive against her wishes to let the fetus develop? Honor her medical wishes and let her die, and the

220

baby along with her? What if the fetus is at six weeks? What about 24 weeks, which is at the cusp of viability? What about at 39 weeks, which is full term?

7:43 pm: It's so strange. The past couple of months have been calm and quiet on the school front between low-key rotations, fourth year seemingly far away, and a lack of worrying about Step 2 of next fall's board exams. Today, everything seemed to explode. All of a sudden we have only till this Friday to plan and submit our fourth-year rotation requests. Planning your schedule assumes that you have decided which specialty to enter. Our schedules need to include time for away rotations at other hospitals, studying for board exams, and interviews for residency.

I'm banking on my interest in emergency medicine not changing, though it is a little stressful to commit to a specialty before actually rotating in it. If I hate it, I have no idea what field I would go into. Vascular surgery? I doubt my grades would be competitive enough. Maybe I'll love pediatrics or ob-gyn. Stranger things certainly have happened. Magnus and Callie have their sights set on EM as well. Thinking about the emergency department and those within it, I sought out Callie and once again inquired if Maverick was single. She again laughed and rolled her eyes at me while offering to do some digging and find out.

March 4: Tuesday

7:40 am: Another 10° F outside. Will this winter ever end? California is sounding more and more tempting.

9:10 am: I'm in a lecture about vaccines. The speaker is talking about rabies, which immediately makes me think about one of my favorite Chuck Palahniuk novels *Rant*, and the main character Buster Casey.

10:17 am: Does a baby have weird ear bumps? Check their kidneys. Who knew?

11:43 am: I'm greatly enjoying the ob lectures. Ob may seem to be all vaginas, but it is a surgical subspecialty, and this is reflected in their high yield and efficient lectures.

4:58 pm: While I truly appreciate the selfless gesture of donating one's body to science, I still get creeped out around dead bodies. Even after dissecting bodies almost weekly for two straight years, I still never got used to being in gross anatomy lab.

March 5: Wednesday

10:39 am: We're in the simulation center all morning doing pelvic exams on volunteer patients. Yes, people get paid to have a hundred medical students in a row examine their cervix. Being a 30-year-old female, I've heard the phrase "scoot down" many times. I'm quite familiar with stirrups, speculums, and other equipment that belongs in a medieval torture chamber. That being said, there are a lot of young, unmarried, childless men in our class who probably have never seen, or ever really thought about, the components of a female pelvic exam. Surprise! All men should be forced to have the experience of sitting with their legs hoisted up in stirrups.

Medical students have the opportunity to use the strangest simulation equipment. One of the display models is a female pelvic bone mounted on a wooden board. In order to demonstrate how a full-term baby begins to pass through the pelvic canal, a plastic baby head is attached to a metal, moveable arm next to the pelvis. The baby head can be maneuvered to pass through the pelvic canal. Seriously bizarre looking.

Upon entering the room where we would be practicing breast exams, I immediately recognized the instructor but couldn't quite place her. After a few moments, I realized she happened to be the standardized patient with whom I worked back on my family medicine rotation. She was the one who called me "emotionally sterile." I wonder if she thought I was emotionally sterile today while doing a breast exam on a plastic, fake breast on a half torso because I didn't talk to it (yes, other students did talk to it).

10:16 pm: Lent began. I know this mainly because I know Mardi Gras occurred yesterday but also because the gym was really crowded tonight. Just like the first few weeks of the year, people made lent resolutions to go to the gym more often. It'll pass, and I'll once again have the gym in my apartment complex all to myself.

March 6: Thursday

8:10 am: The professor is discussing how we regress under stress. So true. My past seven months, much?

We still don't have our schedules for the next two months. I don't even know if I'm starting on outpatient or inpatient pediatrics. God forbid we know when we have our one or two free weekends so that we can try to make plans and have a life outside of work.

11:17 am: My morning started with a review of fetal development and birth, followed by an informative and entertaining lecture on breastfeeding, and now one on pediatric nutrition.

2:20 pm: Our afternoon session is a hands-on workshop about contraception. Different types of condoms (both male and female), long-term implantables, such as Nexplanon and intrauterine devices (IUDs), NuvaRings, sponges ("Is he sponge-worthy?"), diaphragms, and assorted varieties of birth control pills were passed about the room. For practice using these devices, we have a variety of plastic pelvic models on which we can place diaphragms, IUDs, and NuvaRings.

For the NuvaRing, our ob professor explained that a life hack to placing a NuvaRing is to load it in an empty tampon applicator to help guide the ring into place against the cervix. The females in the class all recognized the brilliance of utilizing the applicator. The men, however, displayed a mixture of fascination, confusion, and fear regarding the tampons themselves. A basic misunderstanding among the male students, due to using the applicator for the NuvaRing, is that a female needs to load the tampon into an applicator in the first place and that the applicator itself was reusable. Eww... Many guys in our class were observed trying to force a deployed tampon into a tampon applicator.

4:29 pm: OMG I have been in class since 8 am this day is sooooo long.

Dinner tonight with the usual suspects, including Piper, Sophia, and Jane, followed by a party at Maggie's house. Most of our dinner conversation centered on our schedules for next year. It's depressing to think about all of us being scattered away from each other and across the country next summer.

March 7: Friday

9:05 am: The pediatricians and ob-gyns have given great lectures all week. Until today.

9:28 am: Translational genomics. Ok. Seriously way over my head. I haven't the foggiest idea what the lecturer is going on about.

1:00 pm: Ethics all afternoon, from 1-5 pm. It's gorgeously sunny outside! I hope they let us out early.

1:40 pm: Shockingly, afternoon lectures were abruptly cancelled, and we were firmly instructed to go enjoy the weather. Well this is a wonderful surprise. Off I go to celebrate the start of this weekend's beer festival, Bockfest.

March 8: Saturday

1:30 pm: A goat and the reigning Sausage Queen from last year's Bockfest led the parade, which kicked off the beer festival yesterday evening. This city has some seriously bizarre traditions.

March 9: Sunday

1:15 pm: Off on an indiscriminate lunch date with a guy from a dating website.

3:45 pm: Post-date. Nope. He does not qualify for round two.

I read through some of my old journals from late college and early graduate school today. My conclusion is that I think too much.

10:31 pm: In the past week, I've submitted my schedule requests for fourth year, I've booked Step 2 for the end of July, and I've applied to do EM rotations in two different coastal cities. My plot to escape the Midwest is in motion. Next year seems under control at the moment, while on the other hand, I have no idea about my schedule for the next two months. The only information I have is to show up tomorrow morning at 8 am at The Kiddie Hospital for orientation. I'm psyched to once again be in a hospital, caring for patients. As physically and mentally torturous as medicine and surgery both were, I preferred them to the low-key, hands-off rotations that were psych, neuro, and radiology. I don't think I've really examined a patient since family medicine back in November. I'm going to have to start going to bed earlier again. Back to the grind.

Outpatient Pediatrics

Song: MGMT. "Kids." *Oracular Spectacular*.
Columbia Records. 2008.
Drink: Hot Chocolate with whipped cream and
sprinkles

March 10: Monday

7:37 am: The Kiddie Hospital is exceptionally well-funded. This is relevant to me specifically because it translates into having free food whenever I'm here, starting with the breakfast spread they have sitting out for us at the moment.

Unlike surgery orientation, which was 20 minutes, this orientation lasts from 8 am until 3 pm.

9:28 am: Finally received my schedule. Outpatient pediatrics first. I'll be bouncing between various outpatient clinics and I have a few pediatric emergency department shifts sprinkled throughout. Ok. Good to know.

The attending physicians (who all arrived on time!) welcomed us warmly. One gets the feeling that when they chimed, "We're happy to have you here," they really mean it. They seem genuinely pleased to have us experience a rotation here at the world-renowned Kiddie Hospital.

Child Life is a department in many children's hospitals. Their role is to help keep children (and their caregivers) calm and relaxed during their hospital stay, especially during stressful events such as procedures and imaging. A charming and engaging woman from Child Life is speaking to us about the program and all its benefits. I can imagine that kids love being around her and her bright persona. At one point, she passed around her most frequently employed toys. An array of brightly colored gizmos appeared from her magic satchel. She's a modern-day Mary Poppins. Some toys have lights and sparkles, while others play soothing music. Then she reaches into her bag of tricks and pulls out a smooth, slightly curved, rod shaped toy with

226

a big knobby head at the tip that lights up. This is undeniably the most phallic-looking toy I have ever seen. I knew I couldn't be the only student thinking this, so I glanced around the room and caught Magnus's eye. He smirked and nodded his head inappropriately.

11:10 am: Each student ceremoniously received a little bottle of bubbles to carry in our white coats. Peds is gonna be fun. Hopefully.

9:48 pm: My favorite spy, *Archer,* brings up an excellent question: Is there a word to describe a situation that is both literal and figurative?

March 11: Tuesday

7:59 am: Trekked an hour out to a kiddie clinic located in Bumblefuck that serves a wide variety of patients. When I called yesterday to confirm my start date and time, they told me the first patient was scheduled for 8:15 am. So far, I am the only one here.

8:15 am: Turns out we start around 9 o'clock on Tuesdays. Not sure who I spoke with yesterday.

9:40 am: I know nothing about children. They're small and they squirm and they giggle at random times.

10:46 am: I know less than nothing about pediatric dermatology. Rashes. Eww... Do not touch. Ever.

10:55 am: I just got sneezed on. A big, squishy, wet sneeze. Right in the face.

11:07 am: The kiddos are adorable and sweet and all, but after two hours and seven minutes, I can definitively say that I do not want to be a pediatrician.

Well-child checks are appointments to make sure a baby or child is growing appropriately, meeting developmental milestones, and getting vaccines on time. Those are fun.

Children come in for all sorts of reasons, but whatever the reason, they all have colds. Every. Single. One.

All my mini-patients this morning warmed up to me quickly, and even during my awkward, fumbling peds exam, none of them started crying.

The attending physicians are warm, knowledgeable, and excited to teach. So, even though I don't want to be in peds, I imagine I'll learn a lot and be content to work with these excellent docs every day.

8:45 pm: I'm watching *Glee*. The clips of the male lead Finn (Corey Monteith's character) interspersed in this episode were so touching. Another beloved and great talent lost to the ongoing heroin epidemic.

March 12: Wednesday

7:45 am: Off to my first shift in the pediatric emergency department.

5:30 pm: What a great shift. I didn't even mind today that the patients were miniature-sized humans and not of the full-sized adult variety. I did the initial history and physical on each of my patients, presented my differential (diagnostic thoughts) and plan to the attending, put in all of my own orders (which I couldn't sign, but hey, I placed them all), made calls, updated patients and families on all test results and explained abnormal findings, and then wrapped up each visit by doing either the admission or discharge paperwork. None of this was groundbreaking. I basically did exactly what will be expected of me in the future, when I'm a real doctor.

A young patient with knee pain appeared to have one diagnosis based on their history, but during my physical exam I became suspicious that the patient actually had something else going on. If I was right, the patient would need surgery ASAP. I presented my case to the attending and we got an x-ray to confirm my diagnosis. The attending let me call the surgery consult and share my concerns with the patient and their family. The attending really succeeded in making me feel as if I was my patient's primary doctor, not just the med student. The last physician to really do that was Dr. Red on family medicine. It's been so long. Oh, how I have missed this!

The attending had my patients and the general chaos of the ED squarely under control, so she sent me and the other medical student to the noontime pediatrics conference.

This afforded us the opportunity to do two important things: sit and eat. I ran into Dr. Spengler during noon conference and we chatted pleasantly for a few minutes. He's still attractive and endearing. It's not that I miss him, but I do have a soft spot for him since he happened to be my first first-date and first kiss after oh so many years. Of course, he has no idea about any of that.

As I packed up to leave for the night, I saw my patient heading off to the operating room.

6:13 pm: Yesterday reached nearly 70° F, and now it's snowing. WTF.

8:10 pm: I amped up my gym playlist on my orange mini iPod by mixing in a bunch of old and new Shakira songs.

11:07 pm: I should go to bed but I'm about to dive back into Ernest Cline's book *Ready Player One*. I'm so caught up in the story that I probably won't go to sleep until I finish it.

March 13: Thursday

7:41 am: An entire day working at the adolescent medicine clinic. Yippee! Sarcasm.

10:35 am: Lots of sexually transmitted illness (STI). Lots of them. Everywhere. First time STIs. Repeat customers with repeat STIs all over the place. Seriously teens, use condoms. Birth control pills are not enough, use condoms! Every single time fucking.

During lunch, I asked one of my classmates how he liked pediatrics. He responded thoughtfully, "I like working with people who like to work with children." Yep. That about sums it up for me as well.

3:12 pm: Sadly, there is a small cohort of child gang members who come here for their medical care. Not teenagers (well, yes, there are teen gang members, too), but these are children.

4:52 pm: My workday is about over. If someone twisted my arm and threatened my life and forced me to work in pediatrics, I would choose to work only with small kids, between the ages of three and five years old, as they are still cute and giggly.

4:54 pm: The 4:15 pm patient just showed up. Noooo. Please send me home?

4:55 pm: Thank you peds resident. She leaned over when the attending wasn't looking and whispered, "Get outta here." I ran for it.

Between one day in the pediatric emergency department and one day working in the adolescent clinic, I've learned that children in this city know how to locate, buy, and use guns but not condoms. The consequences are devastating all around.

On leaving the clinic I called my mom and joked that if I never have children, it will be because of this rotation. I've tried to tell her before that I'm indifferent about having kids and she'll be like, "No, you're not." She refuses to believe that I may not have kids. She informed me that I'll leave no legacy. I tried to point out that I'm going to be a doctor saving lives. I also pointed out to her that not only am I kind of preoccupied with the whole med school and residency thing, but that I'm very single. I finally told her she had to stop bothering me about kids.

March 14: Friday

9:19 am: You know what I did this morning? Drove an hour to the clinic in Bumblefuck and upon arriving there found a sign stating, "Closed for training until 1:15 pm." While I am thrilled to have the morning off from seeing the ankle biters (Magnus's term, not mine), I'm kind of annoyed at the complete lack of respect for my time. Yes, I know I'm just a med student and the places at which I rotate own me and my time, but a little consideration? The clinic has all of my information, it wouldn't have been that hard to send me an email or a text. Anyway, I'm at my school. I figure I'll get some paperwork done and study.

10:46 am: It's just gonna be one of those days, I guess. The forms for my away rotation next year are a mess because my state school doesn't provide the amount of liability insurance that some of the coastal institutions require for visiting students. My grades from radiology and psych are still not uploaded. I was berated for not remembering the details in one of the 50 emails I got about my transcripts. I tried to be productive and study, but not one minute after settling into my desk the fire alarms went off, forcing me out of the building. I got hangry at this point, so I thought it best to have a snack and immediately dropped food on my pants. The annoying events are accumulating exponentially and souring my mood today.

12:13 pm: This might sound ridiculous to some people, but I went and got my nails done and seriously, I feel so much better. I wasn't quite Elle Woods in *Legally Blonde* distraught when I walked into the salon but I still needed some calming. I had planned on going tomorrow anyway. The usual young lady that does my nails expressed her surprise at seeing me during a workday. She got my fingers with the old Cabernet colored polish soaking right away. I left with Peach Blossom gel on my nails, ready to face my afternoon back at the Bumblefuck clinic.

When I returned to Bumblefuck, the attending physician apologized profusely to me for not letting me know about the clinic closure this morning. She clearly felt badly and she rocks as a physician, so I couldn't stay annoyed. Being annoyed is not a productive mental state anyway. I spent the rest of my afternoon contentedly working with different residents and helping with well-baby and well-child visits.

While I removed sutures from a child, the kid's parent listened to an iPod. This continued from the waiting room to the exam room, including when being asked questions about the health of their child, and even when I explained the instructions for follow up care. The whole time. Must have been an awesome playlist.

1:36 pm: There is a measles outbreak in the Northeast with a particularly concerning nidus in New York City. Whooping cough has spread across the country. There are increasing reports of mumps and rubella too. These statistics always sadden me and make me think of my favorite author, Roald Dahl, and how his eldest daughter died from measles. The reason we have vaccines is because the bugs we're vaccinated against can kill you.

Off to dinner with some of the surgery residents for my friend Jenna's birthday.

March 15: Saturday

A relaxing night in with Sophia and Piper. We discussed our schedules for next year and residency, as well as gossiped about the men in our lives. They're awesome, I love hanging out with them. Just good-hearted loyal people, destined to be wonderful doctors.

March 16: Sunday

6:14 pm: I'm spending Monday, Tuesday, and Wednesday morning this week working in the neonatal unit at a magical hospital called Babyland. To prep, I spent the entire day learning all about baby development, baby poop, and baby vomit. Babies can come in all different colors. They shouldn't, but sometimes they do. There is the common spectrum of pale pink to dark brown, but also blue, yellow, grey, red, spotted, splotchy, stained, mottled, and even pink but with blue hands and feet (which surprisingly, is usually ok). Who knew?

I've been emailing with a handsome rocket scientist.

March 17: Monday

8:49 am: The neonatologist I'm assigned to work with at Babyland is a legit baby whisperer. His name is Dr. Baby Whisperer, or Dr. BW, for short. He emphasizes the importance of observation, and voiced his concern that as medical imaging improves, a physician's physical exam skills decline. While talking about observational skills, he flew off on an incredibly entertaining tangent about Dr. Joseph Bell, the Scottish surgeon who became the inspiration for Sherlock Holmes. He then laughed at me for taking five full minutes to undress a one-day-old newborn, because of my concern that I would somehow break the tiny human. Dr. BW assured me that I would not.

10:07 am: Between see patients, Dr. BW regaled me with insightful stories from his lifetime of working with newborns.

11:18 am: Oh, I'm heartbroken. The heroin epidemic has crept into Babyland as well. There's a ward exclusively for babies born to heroin-addicted mothers. The tiniest and most helpless victims in the heroin epidemic.

Noon: Off to Bumblefuck clinic.

1:28 pm: There is a constant baseline background of crying. Every single child has some combination of a rash, diarrhea or constipation, and a cold.

1:35 pm: Another rash.

1:54 pm: Chief complaint: "Poo problems."

2:10 pm: More poo.

2:21 pm: More crying in the background.

2:43 pm: OMG even more poo.

3:01 pm: The screaming in the background is getting louder.

3:05 pm: Now there is a kid shrieking at the top of their lungs.

3:20 pm: Pediatricians have hearts of gold and patience for miles and miles.

4:08 pm: If I never have kids it's because of my pediatrics rotation. My day's highlight featured getting a heartfelt "thank you" from an overwhelmed parent to whom I provided some supportive social services.

To top off my day, I saw parents driving away from the clinic with their kids in the back of the car, windows rolled up, and both parents smoking. Strong work guys. You should be fired from being parents. Is it child endangerment if it happens slowly and chronically? Or, does it have to be sudden and dramatic like a beating?

7:20 pm: Today kicks off Match Week, leading up to Match Day on Friday. Match Day is med school's denouement, the day that fourth years finally find out where they'll do their residencies. Early in fourth year medical students apply to residency programs in their intended medical specialty, with the hope of being invited for an interview. They then trek all over the country, interviewing at different hospitals, learning about different programs, and seeing if those hospitals would be a good fit for their personality, educational needs, and learning styles. At the end of interview season, the students rank their potential residency sites, from most desirable to least desirable.

At the same time, the hospitals rank which interviewees they liked the best on their own rank list. The student and program rank lists are fed into a magic computer that matches the two lists together based on rank compatibility. Hence the name of the process: The Match. Students and programs alike hope to match to their top ranked spot. Needless to say, a med student matching to their first ranked spot will likely be ecstatic, while a student matching to their least favorite place might be devastated.

On Match Day, at noon, every fourth-year med student in the entire country is handed a sealed envelope. Inside the envelope is the name of the residency program where they've matched. And, oh wait, it gets better: The Match is a binding job contract. Med students must go wherever they are assigned. There's no turning back. So, you better rank your programs carefully.

9:15 pm: While I'm still on outpatient with some free time I've decided to up the ante on my workouts. I've started doing Jillian Michael's conditioning workout videos. The intensity level is insane. I'm hooked.

10:28 pm: Archer has another gem this week. "Why would you worry about that before you need to? Why clog your brain with a bunch of hypothetical-maybe-what-if bullshit?" He should have spewed this line a few months ago. I could've used the advice.

March 18: Tuesday

9:36 am: Another morning in Babyland with the neonatologist Dr. BW. He taught me to do detailed exams on tiny newborn boys and girls. I even changed my first diaper after one of the boys felt it necessary to pee on me and mark me as his territory. Kind of gross but I guess diaper changing is a life skill one should acquire. While deftly swaddling a newborn, he shared tips and tricks for working with newborns.

10:19 am: This one-on-one teaching is pretty phenomenal. I'm learning a ton from Dr. BW and he's entertaining. He is clearly a medical history buff as he keeps spewing fun historical facts and fascinatingly nerdy tidbits about physicians and nurses of old. If I had to guess, I think he has a crush on Florence Nightingale.

10:42 am: Another one of our babies has a positive drug screen, and I immediately began to judge the parents. Dr. BW shared his wise and well-weathered opinion that it is not our place to judge. He explained that we should respect the privilege that we as doctors have to take care of the sick. We should care for our patients, protect them, and give them resources. All those things, but not judge. Hmm...

Noon: With the guidance and input of Dr. BW, I'm now getting somewhat competent at newborn exams. Ok, time to finalize my schedule for next year.

1:42 pm: Back in Bumblefuck clinic. I really should come up with a better name for the clinic but it's just so damn far away.

One of the senior residents spent a while pondering aloud how I skittered across the career landscape from the "thoughtful and interesting field of psychology" to wanting to be a "cowboy," aka an ER doc.

5:15 pm: I'm sitting in the deli downstairs from my apartment waiting for my carryout order. I've come down here about once a week for the past few years for either lunch or dinner, more so this year, as I'm often too tired to cook after standing and running around all day. After placing my order, the guy behind the counter kindly asked his usual question, "Would you like a cup of water while you wait?" I replied "No, thank you," to which he responded, "Ok, let me guess, you're going to sit down and..." He then mimicked typing on a keyboard. I laughed and confirmed that, yes, I am going to sit down and start typing. A lot of this book has been edited while waiting for deli sandwiches.

5:35 pm: I was offered, and immediately accepted, a position to be a visiting fourth year medical student at one of my top choice residency programs. Early next fall I'll get the chance to spend a month rotating through their emergency department. It's a bit of a gamble because it's like being on a month-long interview but The Boss felt confident that I'd rock it.

March 19: Wednesday

7:48 am: Last morning in Babyland.

I did several head-to-toe newborn examines today with minimal guidance, as well as some other special tests, and overall feel quite comfortable and confident in my new abilities to do a full newborn assessment. Other skills I acquired included how to change a diaper, and how to undress and then re-dress a tiny, squirming baby.

1:30 pm: I have the afternoon off so I've been studying at my med school.

7:58 pm: Eww… While studying I learned about a rare disease called aplasia cutis congenita. It's the congenital absence of skin. Born without skin! Can you imagine? No skin at all! It sounds like an *X-Files* episode. Yet another reason to dislike peds.

10:03 pm: One of my friends posted on Facebook "First time doing CPR today. First time losing a patient. Not an easy day." They say you never forget losing your first patient.

Mine occurred during first year. I was shadowing The Boss in the ED when a patient coded in one of the trauma bays. As I learned in *House of God*, when someone codes, the first pulse you should take is your own. So, I checked my pulse, took a deep breath, then grabbed a pair of gloves, and walked to the trauma bay to help do chest compressions.

I clearly remember what the patient looked like, with his dark hair and slightly stocky frame. I remember being able to feel one of his heart monitor leads under my right hand as I did compressions. I saw frothy, bloody fluid rhythmically rise and fall in his breathing tube, his eyes bulging slightly, with each compression. The family watched as we worked on him and I could hear the emergency physician explaining how we were doing everything.

My arms were so tired after my two minutes that they were shaking. It's a strange kind of workout. You're doing an exercise where if you stop, someone dies.

March 20: Thursday

7:50 am: Another fun day working with adolescents. I'm mentally steeling myself for what's to come today.

10:01 am: Guess what can happen if you don't get the flu shot? You can get the flu.

Best quote so far today is from one of the nurses yelling, in response to family members fighting and being escorted out of the clinic, "This is not the Jerry Springer show!"

There are children here with multiple sexual partners and multiple STIs who are still going through puberty. Some of them don't even understand basic principles of consent, let alone the mental and emotional aspects of having sex.

12:34 pm: While at lunch with Magnus and some other classmates, Magnus shared a touching story of father-son bonding. The father and son were standing outside The Kiddie Hospital. The bald kid – not more than 12 or 13 years old – was standing in his little hospital gown, hooked up to an IV pole. The bonding moment occurred when both father and son lit up cigarettes and enjoyed a smoke together. How sweet.

1:35 pm: A nurse informed me of the location of the panic button in response to the family being escorted out earlier by security. You know, just in case. One of the peds attendings then reminded me that no matter what, peds will always be safer than working in an emergency department. Whatever.

I learned a bit about caring for and styling African-American hair from one the residents and an entertaining mother-daughter duo.

The pediatricians are always kind and complementary when they speak of their colleagues and other healthcare professionals.

10:35 pm: Being able to build my own schedule for next year refreshed and renewed my motivation to power through the rest of this year.

I've spent years and years doing things I don't want to do in order to get to where I eventually want to be. Four years of undergrad, a year doing research, and three years of med school so far. Endless studying, weekends working, crunching data, writing reports, and always being the lowest on the totem pole.

Every single class I have taken since premed has been the exact same as all of my classmates. We have no say in what we study. I know the basics are necessary; it comes with the territory of being a doctor. But it's tiring. Out of the past eight years of my life, I get a meager two weeks of EM. I think that's part of the reason why third year gets to be so difficult. I feel ready to go explore my own interest, and the end is in sight, but I'm not there yet. I still have 12 more weeks locked into required rotations.

But now, my schedule is my own making. Every month in fourth year is a rotation I picked, and I even get to choose when I take vacation next year. What a novel idea.

I scheduled four EM rotations at various hospitals, including one at a pediatric hospital. My medical school education will be rounded out by several other electives. I will do an EKG reading rotation, as many patients in the ED require EKGs.

Anesthesia is on my list, so I can learn how to intubate patients, which is another procedure commonly done in the ED. I will once again take radiology, because there is so much imaging done in the ED (and let's be honest, the hours are great). Finally, I signed up for a global health elective, so I can spend a month abroad next spring. I've always wanted to be involved with global health, even when I worked in psychology. I love traveling more than anything and I see myself being deployed to natural and man-made disasters around the world once I'm an emergency medicine doc.

March 21: Friday

Happy Match Day!

8:22 am: Have I mentioned that there are police officers stationed at Bumblefuck? These are not clinic security guards, they are legit cops. Going to the pediatrician should not be a dangerous outing.

So many patients with trouble breathing and asthma exacerbations today. Yes, it is springtime, but most patient charts, if not all, have documented that there is at least one smoker in the house. This is not a coincidence.

8:47 am: I've learned that I'm a fan of children aged three to five years old. They're adorable and hilarious. I'm fascinated by their unusual and oddly deep insight into everyday events. I also like well-baby checks when the patient is anywhere from nine months to about one year old.

During lunch I ran over to The College of Medicine to see some of the Match Day festivities. It's insane over there. I could hear music blasting and bursts of cheering coming from the auditorium. There were a few fourth years aimlessly wandering in the hallway, most often displaying a look I can only describe as shell-shocked relief coupled with overwhelming happiness. I can't believe that will be my friends and me in 365 days. I wished I could've stayed longer but I had to get back to the clinic.

There were more medical school graduates than residency positions this year. Over 400 fourth year medical students did not match this year. Going through medical school and NOT being able to start residency? Going through all this for nothing? I can't imagine what I would do with myself.

The weather changed this week from wintry to spring-like, bringing an onslaught of kiddies with colds to the clinic. One resident left an exam room and ran to the sink, scrubbing his hands while exclaiming, "That kid is like, pure snot."

After seeing a baby being poorly parented by two heroin users, I thought to myself, I wish I could take this kid home with me because I could give them such a better life. Under my care they would be loved, cared for, supervised, educated, and given opportunities. Currently, the baby is on the cusp of entering the foster care system, and will likely end up bouncing around in the system until they are eventually funneled through the school-to-prison pipeline.

I brought this up to one of the residents and she admitted that she occasionally feels that way too. Our job is to make sure the proper authorities are contacted, and to not let my concerns about the potential poor outcomes of some patients linger in my head. I agree with Dr. BW that we shouldn't judge these parents, but the trajectory of this child's life is so poor.

7:23 pm: Dinner with Sophia and Piper and then off to celebrate Match Day with the fourth years.

March 22: Saturday

12:41 pm: Sophia, Piper, and I had a spectacularly nerdy debate during dinner about whether *The Lord of the Rings* is in the genre of science fiction or fantasy. I then headed to a house party, where many of my classmates were celebrating Match Day and playing drinking games. While playing the drinking game Boom! I notice a tall and unfamiliar guy playing at the opposite end of the table. I sought more information.

Me: "Who's that?"

Friend: "Our classmate's little brother."

Me: "How old is he?"

Friend: "He's single."

Me: (nods head) "Thanks."

From the house party we went to a bar to dance, drink, and celebrate with the newly-matched fourth years.

Many, many, many drinks later.

Me: "So, really, how old is his little brother?"

Friend: "Twenty-four or 25, I think. Does it matter?"

Me: "Thanks and yeah, I had to check. I almost hooked up with an 18-year-old over December break."

240

I've woken up in stranger places though this morning was pretty unusual.

I'd like to retire the phrase 'one-night stand' and start using the term 'tiramisu' instead. One-night stand often has negative connotations associated with it. I don't agree, but whatever, society is weird about women enjoying random sexual encounters. A tiramisu, historically, is an Italian dessert that has a bit of espresso in it. Between the sugar and caffeine, the delectable delight is designed to provide the consumer with a little energy and good mojo. The literal translation of tiramisu is Italian for 'pick me up.' Tirare (to pull), mi (me), su (up).

As I will use the term, and as you should, too, from this point on, the word describes a sexual encounter that is a short-lived indulgence designed to lift one's spirit and mood. It is enjoyable, brief, and requires no commitment. However, indulging in daily tiramisu might lead to obesity or a (shudder) boyfriend. Be careful!

9:00 pm: I've been extraordinarily unproductive today. Staying in tonight and taking it easy so I can get a lot of studying done tomorrow. My all-time favorite movie, *The Goonies*, just started.

Mama Fratelli sums up my peds rotation perfectly: kids suck.

March 23: Sunday

Getting studying done seemed like a good idea so I packed up my stuff and went to Starbucks. Not 15 minutes after sitting down, a couple of fourth years walked in and joined me at my table. After working for a bit we discussed The Match and whether they were happy with their matches. One expressed pure joy, the second felt "ehh, ok," and the third admitted to devastation. They warned me how increasingly competitive The Match is, and not to rank programs if I would be really upset about actually having to go to them. There was some lamenting, some discussion of what they would do differently, and how they're now preparing for moves to different cities all over the country.

241

Eventually our chat turned to how sad they all are to be leaving each other and scattering across the country. These women celebrated together during the good times, leaned on each other during the rough days, and watched each other grow and evolve from clueless, idealistic first years to being ready to take on intern year as newly-minted physicians. I can't imagine how hard it will be to say goodbye to every one of my friends, especially Piper and Sophia.

5:05 pm: Tubes of paint are once again covering my kitchen table as I started a surprise painting for The Boss. The painting will be of her beloved dogs, based on a photo of them sitting in a field of flowers.

March 24: Monday

7:37 am: It sucks to wake up and realize it's only Monday. Off to Bumblefuck.

9:35 am: A cute little kid ran to me for comfort after the attending examined them.

9:46 am: A toddler is getting weighed but judging from the way they are shrieking you'd think they're being tortured. I can't imagine the sounds that they will emit when it's time for them to get their shots. Poor little munchkin. Earplugs anyone?

The attending with whom I've worked with for the past two weeks referred to me as Christina in the patient room. Um… Do I correct her?

So many parents are playing on their phones or answering calls during their children's appointments. Their priorities are so jacked up.

One of my patients had chief complaints of X and Y listed on the census. I read their chart, learned about the patient's recent issues and doctor visits, saw the patient, and then searched for an attending so I could present the patient. The only doc available was an attending with whom I had not worked before.

I started my presentation, "So and so is a child with a prior medical history of blah, blah, blah…"

She interrupted me a moment later and demanded, "Well what about problem Z? That's why they're here. Didn't you read the chart?"

Oh. Well, I had, but that problem wasn't listed as why they were here. A sucky way to start off with an attending. That would have been bad enough, but then in the room with the patient, the attending began by saying to the patient, "The medical student *wrongly* thought you were here for X and Y, but you're really here for Z." She referred to me in such a disparaging tone. My stomach dropped and I could feel my face flush in embarrassment. I seriously considered leaving the room.

While I admit I should have caught the third diagnosis (because I somehow should have known that the two chief complaints were wrong?), she didn't have to embarrass me and make me look incompetent in front of the family. I guess I'm lucky that it's March 24 and this is the first time something like this has happened? It's not like the information I gathered was useless, she needed updates on problems X and Y anyway. Maybe the attending could've remarked, "The med student already covered X and Y, but I'd really like to focus on problem Z..." I don't know. Hopefully I'll remember this encounter in the future and not embarrass my own med students one day.

12:57 pm: I'm not saying that I actively avoid tweens and teens, but if two patients show up at the same time, I'm going to opt for seeing the younger one.

I wanted to do my pediatrics rotation in the spring to avoid flu season. What I failed to appreciate is that this time of year is "gastro" season. For those unfamiliar with gastro, it's a combo of nausea, vomiting, diarrhea, and belly cramps. I've already seen two patients today with it. I can't seem to wash my hands enough today.

2:52 pm: It took some convincing, but I finally proved to the new attending that I'm not incompetent. She'd appeared reluctantly impressed when she realized that I'd read through all the patient charts. Then she was surprised by my efficiency ("Wow, you're really on top of things"). She was openly skeptical that I even did an exam on one of my patients ("That was quick. You did an exam, too?" she scoffed) until I was able to provide information that I could only know after having done a full physical assessment. It's remarkable how quickly and observably a physician's demeanor changes when they decide to like you.

4:29 pm: An itty-bitty adorable patient took my stethoscope, put it in her ears, and started listening to my heart while I talked to her attentive and involved parent. When I looked down, she proudly informed me, "I'm the doctor!" She is hands down my favorite patient so far this rotation.

March 25: Tuesday

I made a preliminary list of residency programs at which I'd like to apply. The list covers programs from coast-to-coast, as I have no idea where I want to move to.

2:06 pm: It's snowing again. I quit. All the warm weather residency programs just moved up on my list.

11:27 pm: My classmate's little brother from last weekend texted me. Aww, that's cute and unexpected.

March 26: Wednesday

7:58 am: I woke up during the night with a stomachache. I've been really nauseous for the past hour, though fortunately no other symptoms. I've only been able to have one bite of breakfast. My pediatric ED shift starts at nine o'clock. I'm debating whether or not I can get off the couch and go to work.

8:58 am: Sitting in the peds ED waiting for the attending. I took some tums and prophylactically loaded up on Imodium. My symptoms are most likely some random upset stomach from God knows what, but worst-case scenario is that it could be gastro, so I'd like to head off that particular symptom to prevent it from striking at work. I wish I had some prescription strength anti-nausea and anti-vomiting wonder drugs. My nausea is slightly better and I'm hoping some interesting cases will keep me distracted enough to forget that I can't really stand fully upright at the moment.

Some attendings allow their med students to evaluate any and all new patients, no matter how complicated, to see what they're capable of. Other attendings insist that you start with simple cases and only advance to more difficult patients after proving that you've mastered the basics. I prefer to be thrown in and test my skills, but the attending today wants us to start with the basics.

The attending escorted us from our assigned unit in the emergency department to what is basically the urgent care area: coughs, colds, runny noses, and rashes. Gah. He followed this up by informing us that he expects a formal presentation with all the details for each patient we see. Well, this is a disappointing turn of events. I feel like I'm back on day one of third year.

6:15 pm: I finally have enough energy to write. I saw one and a half patients this morning. While seeing my second patient I had a sudden spell of lightheadedness and had to excuse myself from the room. My hearing dimmed and my vision tunneled so I knew I was about to pass out. I managed to make it into the bathroom next to the patient's room, lock the door behind me, and take off my white coat. This was done just in time to drop to my knees and lower myself to the floor safely, using my white coat as a pillow/cushion, before blacking out.

I awoke on the floor and stayed down until I broke out in a cold sweat and the lightheadedness passed. I know, I know, the floor of the hospital ED bathroom is disgusting. I had no other option, or I would've been face down in the hallway, causing all sorts of commotion. I swear I'll wash my white coat before seeing any other patients.

I crept out of the bathroom, located my attending and explained. I must have looked like shit, because he immediately brought me a sprite, a cold compress, called in a prescription for nausea meds, and told me to go home. He was really kind, though I felt super embarrassed. No one likes a sick med student working and spreading around their nastiness to the patients and the rest of the staff. I hadn't appreciated how sick I was or I wouldn't have gone to work in the first place.

This is the first time since starting my clinical rotations that I've been too sick to work. No amount or variety of medications could've kept me propped up and functional enough to finish my shift.

Once I got home, I crawled into bed and couldn't move for the next five hours. Almost immediately after getting under my covers I developed a migraine. I spent my afternoon in bed, in the fetal position, in pain, cursing the daytime for being so bright and loud, kind of wishing I was dead or at least comatose, alternating between burning up and cold sweats. As of 6:35 pm, thanks to a hefty combination of Zofran, Imodium, water, Excedrin migraine, and Advil, I finally feel somewhat better… for the moment. I still don't have enough energy to walk downstairs to the market to pick up any Gatorade, but I've managed to comfortably keep down some toast for the past 15 minutes so that's a good sign. I'm getting back into bed now. Kids suck.

March 27: Thursday

7:33 am: :(

2-ish: Meh.

6:00 pm: I don't feel anything. This is a great improvement over nausea and cramps, but it's strange. I'm not hungry, I'm not in pain, I'm just… I don't know, here. I haven't eaten a full meal since Tuesday so I'm pretty much just waiting for my appetite to return. I could've pushed it and gone back to work in the afternoon, but I opted to stay home and recoup a bit longer.

1:30 am: The worst thing about feeling better and sleeping for most of the past 48 hours is that I'm wide awake now and Casey is forcing his way into my thoughts. Even though I wouldn't take him back, it still stings every once in a while to think about everything that happened. Sometimes I wonder who else I could have met between age 22 and 30. It's ok; I'm allowed to have bad nights now and again.

March 28: Friday

8 am: It feels like spring outside; real spring, not just a half a day burst of warm air visiting here between cold fronts.

9:13 am: I'm back at work and feeling infinitely better. I have resumed my usual routine of avoiding tweens and teens.

12:38 am: The attending I've been working with since day one has been addressing me all morning by the correct name. Small victory.

I saw a young patient with gastro and cringed during the entire physical exam. I washed my hands an OCD level of times immediately following their visit.

Seeing a patient with two parents present and engaged in their child's health care makes me happy. Perhaps because I've rarely seen it in my three weeks here?

8:12 pm: It shouldn't be difficult to make plans for a Friday night but the problem with med students is that they're always working. Most of my friends are on call tonight or will be waking up to go to work somewhere in the ballpark of 5 am tomorrow morning. So here I am. I feel better, my hair looks nice, my makeup is half done, and I have a cute outfit in mind, but no one is around. On the flip side, a marathon weekend of *Harry Potter* recently started... I think I know which way my night is going.

9:30 pm: Getting cozy with Harry and Pinterest. Oh well. At least I'm not at work. Callie, who is on ob-gyn right now, and I are debating via text message whether peds is worse or ob is worse. I think we both have compelling arguments.

Off to delve a bit further in Hunter S. Thompson's *The Rum Diary*, then bed. Maybe. I'm falling in love with his gonzo journalism writing style. In the same vein, I record events as I interpret them and how I react to them. Passionately, angrily, blissfully, intensely. I'm incapable of recording events objectively. The events are as real as I remember them and are only presented from my point of view.

March 29: Saturday

Turns out a bunch of other med students this week were knocked out of work with a stomach bug too. Who is patient zero?

I'm venturing back out into the land of the living tonight and going out with some classmates.

March 30: Sunday

Beautiful sunny day.

11:30 am: I've been chatting with an online guy who lives in a neighboring city. We decided to meet up at a state park located between our respective cities and go for a hike today. Looking at the situation one way, a hike on an early spring day after being cooped up all winter sounds lovely. On the flip side, I'll be meeting a stranger known only through a few emails and going into deserted woods. Nothing could go wrong, right? As a precaution, I've let Jane know exactly where I'll be and around what time I should return.

3:00: Survived my date in the woods. The park was beautiful, full of trails and scenic overlooks. The park was a little muddy from all the rain yesterday but still fun. I'd love to go back once the trees grow in and explore the trails a bit more. The guy himself was quite a character, and I mean that in an "I want to be friends with him because he's very entertaining" but not in an "I want to sleep with him" kind of way. He's the most loquacious person I have ever met. If there had been a word-counter keeping track of our conversation, it would have been a million to maybe 15.

10:32 pm: I'm in the midst of the eighth Harry Potter movie. I may have watched parts or all of each of the movies this weekend.

March 31: Monday

7:02 am: Last week on outpatient pediatrics. Not that I'm counting down the days or anything…

8:48 am: A tiny patient sang the "Time for your check-up!" song from *Doc McStuffins* while I did my physical exam. In my three weeks on peds, I determined that children who watch *Doc McStuffins*, even the really little ones, are more comfortable at the doctor. They have a vague

248

idea of what's going on and they understand that the doctor is a helpful, not scary, person.

Caught a previously missed diagnosis. Score.

10:21 am: A completely verbal and super chatty 18-month-old informed me, "I like your shoes!" OMG she is too cute. She talked the entire visit. She is more verbal than some kids twice her age. According to her mom, she has been talking non-stop since birth.

The little girl patients and their siblings have had the most fabulous spring outfits today. All different combinations of pink, purple, sequins, tutus, animal prints, and headbands with ginormous flowers have been spotted.

1:31 pm: Not infrequently, we have teenage girls arrive together for their Depo shots. Instead of a gym buddy, these girls are Depo buddies. Whatever works.

3:54 pm: Some residents, most actually, on this rotation as well as others, have been great. But every once in a while, you run across a resident who is so clueless that you begin to wonder who ties their shoes for them in the morning. You can almost see the cogs in their head spinning and you can imagine steam coming out of their ears when they are thinking. One of those residents is here today.

Polydactyly is pretty neat. It is the medical term for having more than ten fingers or toes.

6:25 pm: I saw a ton of patients today and got excellent feedback about the patient load I successfully managed.

It's increasingly difficult to talk to my mother while on this rotation. I called her and started venting about the kiddos and joking about how I never ever want children and instead of being like, "Oh, that sucks, sorry you had a bad day" she started going off on a tirade about how children are the best thing ever and how could I say such a blasphemous thing. I believe she thinks children are the best thing ever. But, at the present time I happen to think they are the worst thing ever. This has happened several times now.

April 1: Tuesday

Happy April Fools' Day.

8:38 am: As a psychologist, I hated waking up and going to work. My alarm would blare and I would instantly start a countdown to the end of the workday. Today I reached that point on peds.

Children's ears are notoriously difficult to examine but I made a good call on an iffy case, so my attending started off the day happy with me. My skill at examining ears has improved tremendously. My tolerance for drowning out the shrieks of a child and willingness to forcefully hold them down while I exam their ears has increased tremendously, too.

I hate being in Bumblefuck longer than I need to be and I escape for lunch every day. While at a nearby lunch spot I ran into the ortho resident with whom I had an awkward half-date a few months ago. He came over to say hi and asked how I was enjoying my peds rotation. I responded that it's not for me and I hate it. His face contorted in surprise and horror while exclaiming, "Oh my God, why?" People seriously judge you for not liking pediatrics. Like I must be a terrible person for not enjoying working with the wondrous miracle that is children. I didn't feel the need to justify my answer so I went back to reviewing my peds textbook. He got the message and walked away.

One of the residents described a bad day as the combination of feeling sad, dumb, and tired. Spot on.

I got excellent feedback from my team. Not enjoying peds is no reason to slack. I still have a responsibility to my patients. My work ethic can be attributed to my dad. He taught me that work is work, and not every minute of every job will be enjoyable, but regardless of how you feel, it must get done. I have a job that is a privilege, and one that many would kill to have.

April 2: Wednesday

6:38 pm: OMG Worst day ever. Ever. Biggest waste of time. My day was spent in the pediatric emergency department with a classmate and an attending. Not even the real ED, as we were relegated to urgent care. Want to guess how many patients I saw during my eight hours of captivity there? One. Yep. One. Instead of letting us see patients, the attending spent the first two hours of my shift teaching the other medical student and me how to take a history and do a physical exam.

Today was such a ridiculous waste of time. She babbled on about microbiology, pharmacology, and such. The topics were so scattered and all over the place that it wasn't even helpful information. She babbled on and on about everything, *except* for dealing with pediatric emergencies and working in the ED. My classmate and I kept looking at each other and making faces like, "What the fuck is she talking about?" While she rambled, I sat with my pleasant-neutral face but vividly imagined myself banging my head against the closest wall. Repeatedly. I spent eight hours in urgent care and the highlight of my day revolved around diagnosing one snotty-nosed kid with a cold. At the end of the shift, my classmate and I wandered out dumbfounded.

April 3: Thursday

7:15 am: April showers galore.

7:57 am: Last day working at the adolescent clinic.

Noon: Just me and an attending this morning. I saw and wrote notes on seven of her patients. After each patient, the attending reviewed my notes and suggested some additional questions that I could have asked during each encounter. On top of that, we reviewed some common pediatric rashes. A combination of teaching/learning, seeing patients, and helpful feedback. Now that's a productive morning.

The Boss gathered her research crew and we all went out for dinner last night. Afterwards, our group strolled to get ice cream. On the stroll over, I casually suggested that she set me up with one of her residents. After some prodding, I admitted that specifically, she should set me up with Maverick. She thoroughly ignored my request.

April 4: Friday

7:51 am: I didn't get much sleep last night. I awoke from a torturous nightmare in which my skin became covered in a painful, head-to-toe rash. Several areas of my skin bubbled with pulsating clusters of pus and green ooze-filled bumps. Someone in my dream stabbed open one of the lesions on my right forearm, leaving a three-inch gaping gash in my skin that went down into my muscles, exposing bone. I tried to pinch the open skin together with my left hand while running to find someone to help me.

When I finally pulled myself to consciousness I had to get out of bed for a while. As I paced around my living room, I noticed the time was 3:45 am. I think it was nearly 6 am before I was able to get back to sleep. At least today is my last day at Bumblefuck clinic.

2:15 pm: The patient parking lot is full of glass as a couple of car windows were smashed in during lunch. I repeat, going to the pediatrician should not be a dangerous outing.

My Friday feedback was all positive. The attending highlighted my organization and efficiency, noting how those skills translated to me seeing a high patient volume.

April 5: Saturday

9:15 am: On this fine Saturday morning it's still too early to be productive so I'm indulging in one of my favorite homemade breakfast sandwiches, slowly working my way through a pot of chicory coffee. I'm also recovering from Piper's birthday festivities last night. Piper, Jane, Sophia, Maggie, some other friends, and I kicked off the evening at a downtown happy hour and dinner. This particular bar has one of my favorite appetizers, mini pork belly buns, which I passionately described to the table. Jane made fun of me for this, until she took a bite and then had to excuse herself for having a foodgasm at the table.

From dinner, we hung out and played a fiercely competitive round of The Hat Game at one of the guy's apartments. Drinking and merriment ensued at the bars downtown. Jane and I topped off the night by enjoying late night pizza. An excellent evening with my closest friends.

April 6: Sunday

11:08 am: This afternoon, as soon as it gets a bit warmer outside, I'm going to clear the dead and dried out branches from the pots of last year's patio garden. Hopefully, I'll soon be able to start planting the first round of veggies and herbs for my spring garden. I'm thinking this year's crop will have blueberries, tomatoes, jalapeño and banana peppers, as well as mint, basil, chives, and cilantro.

4:57 pm: After hours of digging out dead branches and leaves, my patio garden is now cleaned and prepped for planting. Surprisingly, one of my blueberry plants, my lilies, and my chives survived the winter. The blueberry bush is already flowering, and there are a few lily bulbs that are rooting right now. I couldn't salvage the chives, though, because weeds had infiltrated the pot. I couldn't believe anything survived the polar vortex. It was refreshing to get my hands dirty and get sweaty while playing in the soil.

Time for a shower and gearing up for my next rotation: inpatient pediatrics.

Inpatient Pediatrics

Song: Modest Mouse. "Float On." *Good News for People Who Love Bad News*. Epic Records. 2004.
Drink: Rhinegeist Bubbles Rosé Ale

April 7: Monday

7:48 am: I met my team at 7:15 am and was immediately instructed to go home and go to bed because I'm working nights this week. Again, would have been nice to know my schedule ahead of time.

11:48 am: Turns out that my work schedule today is 7:15 to 7:45 am this morning, 1-3:45 pm this afternoon, then 8 pm tonight until 10 am tomorrow morning, and then 12-1 pm tomorrow afternoon. Umm, this might be a silly question but when am I supposed to sleep? Welcome back to being on an inpatient medicine service.

Slept from 8 to10 this morning and I guess I can nap this afternoon from 4 to 6 or something. I've heard that I'm on the best team, paired with Allie, the best of the peds interns. Looks like I'll be surviving inpatient peds under the best of circumstances.

6:58 pm: Best part of being on nights? I get to wear scrubs to work.

9:22 pm: Admissions keep rolling in and Allie is overhead murmuring, "This is gonna be a bad night."

One of the residents on the other night team looks like a surfer. He's tall and built, with long-ish blond hair and a tan. What is he doing in the Midwest? How is he tan right now?

10:32 pm: During nighttime rounds a small child innocently queried his parents, "It's dark out, why aren't we going home?" He doesn't understand how sick he is and that he needs to be cared for in the hospital.

A young patient got gastro and became so dehydrated that he needed to be admitted to the hospital. I'm disturbed seeing this defenseless child connected to multiple

254

IVs and tubes. A stomach bug that knocked me out for two days nearly killed this patient.

11:40 pm: My team promised that there is food and coffee in our near future.

April 8: Tuesday

2:30 am: After a whole lot of chaos early in the night, the shift quieted down around 1 am. Once things were calm, we picked up food and went up to the resident lounge. This room is stocked with all the essentials one would want on an overnight shift. There is a large L-shaped couch, a coffee maker, and a flat screen television hooked up to Hulu and Netflix. I went to one arm of the L, intern Allie went to the other, and the senior resident took the middle part of the couch. We watched a movie while occasionally checking lab results and answering pages. Both residents took turns teaching me about common diseases, and we bonded over our love for the ridiculous TV show that is *Glee*. My team really is awesome.

3:47: We started stalking the list of patients down in the ED to prepare for which patients would most likely be added to our service. Rounds start at 7:30 am, so still a ways to go tonight.

4:20 am: Looks like I'll be getting my first patient soon. The kid most likely has pneumonia though it's too early to say for sure.

6:48 am: I got my first pediatric admission and did my first intake around 5:30 am. Attempting to complete an H&P at 5:30 in the morning is a remarkably more challenging experience compared to doing one in the middle of the day.

7:05 am: The sun is rising over the city. The night's most disturbing event? A child arrived to the ED, dead due to NAT... allegedly.

11:15 am: My eyeballs hurt. Off to another lecture.

1:32 pm: Sometimes I wonder why I chose such a difficult path. I am still so many exams and years of training away from where I want to be.

4:09 pm: I can't quite figure out when to eat and when to sleep.

9:10 pm: My schedule is too busy to date someone who is geographically undesirable. Unfortunately, several of the engaging, attractive men who've contacted me online are too far away to date. That being said, I now have a better idea of which nearby cities are hoarding all the attractive men. This may influence where I apply to residency.

10:14 pm: I hate to be blunt but if you have a goatee, a selfie, or God forbid a car selfie, I will not answer your email. Ditto if you tell me you're a "nice guy" who is "looking to take care of his woman." I'm not looking for a babysitter. I can take care of myself.

April 9: Wednesday

12:22 pm: Sitting in class learning about pediatric heart murmurs. There are a ton of murmurs, each with different patterns and frequencies. My favorite murmur? The 'mammary soufflé' murmur. That is not a typo, that's a real type of murmur. I love soufflé.

Words of wisdom from a peds attending: "When all else fails, rely on common sense."

Every time my alarm goes off I have no idea where I am, what day it is, or what shift I'm working.

8:01 pm: One minute into shift. First patient: NAT.

My team is lamenting the annual springtime spike in eating disorder patients as bathing suit season approaches.

9:20 pm: The next admit is a failed suicide attempt.

April 10: Thursday

12:43 am: Already have two admissions for the night.

2:14 am: No midnight snack yet. My stomach is growling. At least the cafeteria here is open 24 hours for when (and if!) we finally get a break.

2:45 am: Dinner!

2:57 am: Allie and I learned that our birthdays are one day apart. We've quickly bonded and decided that we're twins, though one born before midnight and one born after.

3:35 am: Hours to go. I'm dragging.

4:50 am: Hello coffee.

5:15 am: Our newest patient is the embodiment of little Peggy Ann McKay from the Shel Silverstein poem *Sick*. Everything hurts her. Ears, belly, knee, nose, head, toes; if you ask about it, it hurts. Every physical exam, vital sign, blood test, urinalysis, and imaging study under the sun has come back stone cold normal, and just as in poem, there is nothing wrong with the patient. Well, at least not physically. Our wonderful psychiatry team could possibly help her though.

9:29 am: Delicious bed! I'm out.

7:05 pm: Put on warm, fresh-out-of-the-dryer scrubs and poured myself a large mug of hot java. One more night shift left.

8:10 pm: Why hasn't my patient had their procedure yet? Allie ordered it this morning before we left.

8:24 pm: So, my patient needs a particular procedure done. After some digging, our team found out that a nurse cancelled the order. She apparently thought he didn't need it as he recently had a similar procedure done. The poor kid is stuck here another night because he cannot leave until it's done, and now no one is around to do it. I am floored that the nurse cancelled one of our orders without calling to clarify first. One of the senior residents is ranting about that particular nurse and yelling into the air, "If you went to doctor school, then you too could write and cancel doctors' orders!" She is referred to as a "special" nurse among the teams.

April 11: Friday

12:40 am: You want to send kids from the pediatric ICU to the floor, not the other way around.

3:03 am: Busy, busy, busy. This is my first time sitting this shift. Exhausting, yet infinitely preferable to seeing patients at any clinic.

4:30 am: One of my patients attempted to murder someone but failed and then attempted suicide.

Interesting discussing with Allie and the senior resident, about how female nurses treat female physicians differently than male physicians.

Lots of patients with bronchasthmonia; a diagnosis summarizing any combination of bronchitis, asthma, and pneumonia.

4:58 am: Allie shared that about three months into residency she suffered through a really bad night; so bad in fact, that she contemplated quitting medicine. There was too much stress, too much pressure, and the consequences of messing up were too high. It seems that most have no idea how hard doctors work or how difficult our training is.

5:38 am: The stench of tobacco is strong and long lasting. I routinely smell the reek of cigarettes leaching off the parents of kids being admitted with asthma exacerbations. News flash: You are killing your child.

7:09 am: Sunrise.

7:35 pm: My brain and my body are so confused by my schedule the past week. This weekend is supposed to be gorgeous, sunny, and 75° F. I'd love nothing more than to sleep in and spend some time outside tomorrow, but it doesn't matter what I want. I have a 6 am to 8 pm shift. What's that about Sunday? Nope, sorry. Working Sunday, too. I have next Saturday off though. Maybe it will be nice outside then? Next weekend is too depressingly far away to think about.

5:50 pm: Zooey randomly sends me funny videos. Today featured a clip of her singing along to the radio. I miss her bright smile.

9:32 pm: On a whim, I downloaded the pilot episode of *The Mindy Project*. I can't tell if it's amusing or horrifying about how much I relate to her character. The series starts off with 30-year-old Dr. Mindy Lahiri, devastated by her breakup with her long-time live-in surgeon boyfriend whom she thought was the love of her life, looking for love and in the meantime trying to become more mature and stop sleeping around with her friends and colleagues. The biggest difference? She is already an attending while

I'm still a lowly student. I think I need to keep watching so that I can find out what happens to me.

April 12: Saturday

6:00 am: Fourteen hours to go. Should be a good day though. Hopefully.

9:00 am: Or not. We started off rounds at 7:30 am being warned that the hospital is on lock down for a 'credible threat.' Oh. Umm... Ok. We heard that local police have beefed up security at all points of entry and egress, yet no one will give us any additional information. I guess we'll just go about our business as usual and hope nothing bad happens to us, the rest of the staff, or our patients.

9:39 am: My new patient is an adorable little one with bronchasthmonia. I practically held my own breath while watching the baby struggle to breathe.

10:51 am: The vast majority of nurses I've worked with this year are fabulous. They are on top of their teams, anticipate patient needs, problem solve well, and of course keep an eye on the med students. Which is why I hesitate to rant about Special Nurse, but her stupidity is so painful to witness.

We have manual blood pressure cuffs and electronic blood pressure cuffs. The manual ones tend to be more accurate. This speakerphone conversation between Special Nurse and an intern from another team recently took place.

Intern: "I'm concerned about a blood pressure reading. I need a manual blood pressure recheck."

Special Nurse: "I don't usually do that, so I don't know if we have a cuff for that."

Intern: "Ok..." *(Momentary confused silence at the inability to check a manual pressure.)* "Just check and call me back."

A few minutes later:

Special Nurse: "I couldn't check the blood pressure. We didn't have a cuff small enough for the kid's arm on the floor."

Intern: "How did you check the blood pressure electronically?"

Special Nurse: "On the kid's leg."

Intern: "So why don't you check a manual blood pressure on the leg then?"

Special Nurse: ...

Intern: "Ok, well, call me back after you check it."

Eventually, another nurse stepped in to help.

1:15 pm: I'm up in the resident's lounge and admiring the beautiful views. I've never seen the city from up here during daylight hours before.

2:47 pm: One of the floors is on lock down. We're not sure why and no one will tell us. When returning to our floor after lunch, we had to inform the police stationed at the elevator which floor we were going to, and they manually input the floor number for each passenger in the elevator. What if there's an active shooter? What if it's a bomb? What if it's like 9/11 and I need to evacuate the building before it's too late? My brain is starting to spiral into an anxious state.

7:45 pm: The hospital is still on lock down. Police are everywhere. At least we found out that the area of the hospital in which I work is not the targeted area for the threat. Which is great because these patients are not my children and I have no intention of dying for them.

8:20 pm: Post-sunset. From my brief glimpses out the window, it looked like a beautiful day.

9:15 pm: Finally, home. I'd love, in the following order: a bathroom, a hot shower, a large dinner, a bottle of wine, and to find a hot man in my bedroom. At least I can easily arrange for three out of five of those items. I barely sat all day so standing long enough to take a shower is highly unlikely to happen right now, and as far as I know there are no men in my apartment. But, I still checked.

April 13: Sunday

5:54 am: I stopped to pick up a cup of coffee on my way to the floor. While topping off my filled-to-the-brim java with milk, a woman (clearly a patient's mom) eyes me in my scrubs. She smiles and sweetly remarks, "Coffee should be free for you guys; you nurses work so hard!" Then, she spied my badge proclaiming STUDENT

DOCTOR in ginormous block letters. She reddened and quickly added, "Doctors too... They should get coffee too."

6:15 am: The Kiddie Hospital is still on lock down. Rumor has it that every car entering the visitor's parking lot is being stopped and inspected for weapons. Who the hell threatens a children's hospital?

9:45 am: A pale little baby is looking up at her mom with a face that reads, "I hurt, what's happening to me?" The baby is too young to speak, but her face says it all.

Police are stationed everywhere. Do we wait until after someone starts shooting or after the bomb goes off before evacuating? I wonder if any of the residents or attending physicians feel the same way I do.

2:35 pm: I'm also learning that decisions regarding medical care are often preferences, not necessarily right versus wrong choices.

After spending over 70 hours in the hospital this week and becoming phenomenally stir crazy, I finally get to see Piper and Sophia tonight. Given the glorious weather, we've chosen a place with outdoor seating for dinner.

April 14: Monday

9:55 am: I'm fairly certain that teenagers exist solely to torture their parents.

11:23 am: I received a covert invitation to grab coffee with all the interns after rounds. The other two medical students rotating with me were not invited.

For my own sanity, I'm ignoring the police roaming around.

12:45 pm: I'm sitting in the noon conference, surrounded by young resident physicians and medical students, being lectured to by an old and wise physician. He's sharing both knowledge and wisdom with us about abdominal pain in children. For example, knowledge is knowing to do a rectal exam on a patient with a certain type of suspected colon abnormality. Wisdom is knowing to step aside before pulling your finger out of the anus due to the high risk of explosive stool.

5:29 pm: I've been getting solid feedback on my presentations and props for my level of involvement regarding the care of my patients.

April 15: Tuesday

6:14 am: There are tons of one-day admissions. Many semi-sick kids are admitted for overnight observation and go home the next day. Since the patients are admitted and discharged so quickly, there is almost no chance to build any relationships with the patients or their families.

Kids stick really random objects in the unlikeliest places.

12:15 am: The Special Nurse freaked out and confused one of our patient's parents by making recommendations about their medical care that were entirely inappropriate. Allie made the first attempt at explaining to the parents why those actions weren't necessary. Special Nurse persisted, in front of the family, about how she is right. The senior resident and then the attending herself had to explain why Special Nurse was wrong and that our team would not be following that course of action.

2:42 pm: Special Nurse has spent the day angry, directing her rage towards the least threatening person on the team, which unfortunately is Allie, as she is the intern. Special Nurse is now questioning Allie's every order and paging her incessantly about stupid shit.

10:26 pm: One of the perks of being single is that I have no geographic restrictions when it comes to applying to residency. I'm considering cities throughout the country, and the only person I need to worry about is me. There are other perks as well. For instance, I used to watch *Glee* while Casey made fun of how ridiculous of a show it is. Now I watch *Glee* while having my own personal sing along. Waaaay better.

April 16: Wednesday

5:50 am: Being at work this early in the morning should be illegal.

8:05 am: Ran into Dr. Spengler at morning report.

Allie informed me that my patient's parents referred to me as Dr. Silvia. Score. We've developed a daily routine where I pre-round on most of Allie's patients, she helps me develop a plan for each of them, and then I present those patients on rounds as if they were my own.

A patient attempted suicide, survived, and went to an inpatient psych facility for further care. In response to that stressor, the patient's sibling then attempted suicide. Their poor mother. So many suicide attempts in the peds world!

Noon: Pediatrics morbidity and mortality is a whole new level of stress.

4:45 pm: Turns out I have minimal patience for people complaining to me about how busy they are and that they have no free time. This is especially true when they never work overnight or weekends, and when their mistakes at work don't end in people dying. Ditto if you have a job where you can sit down, eat, and take bathroom breaks at regular intervals.

There is a new *Daily Beast* article entitled, "How being a doctor became the most miserable profession."[9] The astonishingly high rates of burnout, suicide, and general misery continue to rise. The article is depressing, and now that I'm almost a year into rotations, I am starting to understand why it is true.

7:03 pm: I kind of have tentative plans with Dr. Spengler this week. We've chatted a few times at noon conference recently and made plans to go for coffee one day to catch up. While chatting with my mom I updated her on this new development. Her amusement came through with her response, "Well, now Casey is out of the picture and you've had some time being single, so Dr. Spengler will at least have a fighting chance this time, though the odds are still against him."

April 17: Thursday

7:15 am: I gave a nurse (not the "special" one) some straightforward orders and then afterwards informed Allie, who replied that she is impressed with my skills and let me know that my actions are, "Beyond the expectations of a third-year medical student, it is next level," which brought me a sense of pride. The other intern asked if Allie would share me with his team.

10:48 am: Allie and I chatted about how different all the medical students and residents are at this point in the year as compared to July. I told her about being on internal medicine in July, when the interns were hesitant to do anything, seemed reluctant to make decisions, and were terrified to let the medical students do anything because it was our first time out on the wards. Now, being on pediatrics in April, the interns are on top of everything, make decisions with authority and confidence, and are able to delegate appropriately to the medical students. She shared with me how much she's seen my classmates change, going from sharing bumbling presentations and having weak exam skills, to being able to independently manage basic patient care.

11:11 pm: I saw a one-in-a-million diagnosis.

2:50 pm: I unknowingly dressed in the appropriate uniform for a weekday afternoon of Starbucks studying: skinny jeans with Toms, a wide-striped slim fit tee, and sunglasses topping my head of long, straight hair. Acceptable variations include black leggings and ballet flats.

7:48 pm: Spengler and I started chitchatting via text about our schedules and other bullshit. Somehow coffee escalated into going for drinks at 8 pm this Saturday night. Then, this morning at conference, he casually mentioned that he's dating someone. Um… if you're dating someone, then why are you going for drinks with me on Saturday night?

April 18: Friday

6:02 am: Final 14-hour push until my first day off in nearly two weeks.

8:26 am: Ugh. Some parents told Allie and me one story, and then told our attending and the rest of the team a whole different set of issues on rounds.

9:55 am: This was a new experience: Allie, the attending, and I took turns examining a baby while he breastfed because we, mom included, figured the baby would cry if we interrupted his meal.

2:30 pm: My Friday feedback from Allie and the senior resident involved them telling me that I'm the best med student on our team, that I take initiative with patients and nurses, and that I contribute to the team because I help Allie with her daily intern "to do" list without being asked. In addition, they gave me practical advice and input on how to improve my patient presentations. I've been working my ass off and pushing myself to take an active role on the team, something I did not do on inpatient medicine way back in July. Receiving positive feedback that my efforts have been noticed makes me feel proud of my work and my development over the course of the year.

My newest patient is college-aged! Having a conversation with an adult patient is so refreshing.

Running around crazy busy for hours. Can't sit, eat, or pee.

6:50 pm: I'm free. Time to go out!

April 19: Saturday

11:59 am: First glorious day off since starting inpatient peds two weeks ago. My morning kicked off with a US Navy doc making me breakfast after we spent an entertaining night and morning together. Pretty solid way to start off a day.

Rewinding a bit: last night began with a house party and then grabbing a cab downtown to continue our revelry. As the cab arrived to the bar, I received a text from a friend warning me, "FYI Casey is at the bar." I was bound to run into him sooner or later. I first located my friends on the outdoor patio, and then spotted him sitting nearby, enjoying his new post-breakup habit of smoking cigarettes. I went over to say hello. We chatted pleasantly for about two minutes, then I said goodbye and hurried back to my friends. He didn't look good. He looked older, much skinnier, and more wrinkled. His face was more drawn. He looked sad. Oh well. Not my concern anymore.

Shortly after rejoining my friends, one of the guys in the group whom I had not yet met offered to buy me a drink. I replied that I'd walk with him to the bar, mainly to distance myself as much as possible from Casey. Turns out he is in the Navy and has been in this city for a couple of weeks rotating at a nearby Veterans Affairs hospital. We ended up chatting all night at the bar, which led to spending a fun night together. A veritable tiramisu. Really though, I'm just doing my part to support the troops of the good ol' US of A.

7:30 pm: Leaving shortly for my non-date with Spengler. Even though we're meeting up as friends, and tonight is supposed to be casual, I'm wearing a dress and heels, ostensibly because after our non-date I will be meeting up with my friends to go out for the night. All's fair, right?

10:30 pm: Back home. The conversation flowed, we talked about all sorts of stuff, and neither of us was in any rush as it took over two hours to drink two glasses of wine. I wonder if his girlfriend knew his whereabouts tonight. Nothing happened, but there was some flirting. At the end of our non-date, I informed him that I won't bring up going out again as home-wrecking is not my style. He expressed thanks and that he appreciated my sentiment. A few seconds later he added that he wants to hang out again. My friends and I are suspicious that this girlfriend of his is imaginary, as he doesn't seem like the kind of guy to do something behind someone's back.

April 20: Sunday

10:20 am: Casey and I were lying in bed and he proposed to me with a sparkling three-stone diamond ring. After a moment of confusion, I accepted the ring and excitedly began wondering the order in which I should share the news with my family and friends.

I woke up alone in my own bed. Stupid brain. For the record, I don't wish this to happen and I am spending less and less time thinking about him. I think my mind was just processing seeing him for the first time since I ended things. That, and my brain likes to fuck with me when I'm unconscious.

1:24 pm: Sometimes I get gloomy when I think about the fact that I will never have enough time in my life to read all the books in the world. My newly purchased collection includes Mindy Kaling's book (because I'm loving *The Mindy Project*), *A Walk in the Woods* by Bill Bryson, and *Fear and Loathing in Las Vegas,* to continue on my Hunter S. Thompson kick.

2:37 pm: Zooey sent me a video of her singing and dancing (which is not an unusual occurrence), and the video closes with her breaking into her sunny laughter, which is so adorable and heartwarming. Now I have the urge to hop on a plane to New Orleans to see her in person but maybe we can FaceTime later as a more reasonable alternative.

6:32 pm: I'm sitting on my little patio oasis, surrounded by colorful pots. It'll be wonderful once my herbs and flowers grow in so I'm not staring at containers full of dirt.

April 21: Monday

8:20 am: Back to the grind. At least the cops are gone. Whatever threat happened seems to have resolved itself.

It's heartbreaking to watch a small child in pain.

8:55 am: Falling asleep standing while on rounds is a new skill I've acquired.

9:20 am: A small kiddo waved enthusiastically and exclaimed, "Hello!" to each and every team member as we introduced ourselves on rounds. So freaking cute.

A three-year-old gave me one of the most evil eyes I have ever seen after I examined his ears.

10:32 am: A set of stressed out and tired parents, who have no medical background, are researching everything using Dr. Google.

As I noted earlier, I typically present most (if not all) of Allie's patients each day and have repeatedly been told that I'm the best student on our team. Today, I only had one patient to present on rounds. After rounds, the attending turned to me and loudly informed the team that I really need to speak more and to present at least one person on rounds each day. She thought I hadn't presented a single patient yet this entire rotation. Allie immediately jumped in to point out that I present every one of her patients during rounds, am proactive about patient care, and am generally on top everything. So frustrating! Once again, my efforts are going unnoticed. Why do I bother trying so hard?

3:19 pm: There's a class meeting today about applying for residency. The Dean of Whatever welcomed us and began talking about The Match. She then flippantly posed the question, "So, how many of you are couples matching?" She meant it as an innocent question, but couples matching is seen as akin to getting engaged. You're tying yourself and your residency to another person, and it's a conversation that some of the couples in our class have not yet had. Awkward sauce.

7:18 pm: Off to dinner with Magnus. Our schedules have conflicted while on peds so we haven't had the chance to catch up in a while.

Casey is texting me to hang out.

April 22: Tuesday

5:58 am: Casey. Sigh.

8:40 am: Spengler is texting me and keeping me entertained on rounds.

11:52 am: During rounds, some parents were waiting at their kid's door for our team. The parents immediately started on a tirade about their child's treatment plan. The parents were accusatory, rude, and frankly, they had no idea what they were talking about. They demanded that we run certain tests on their child and perform a couple of unnecessary and invasive procedures. Allie and I exchanged glances, mentally agreeing that these parents were nuts and wanted us to rule out diseases that the child couldn't possibly have. The parents were so unpleasant and idiotic that my left eyelid started twitching. They did not truly understand what they were asking from us and could not comprehend any attempts at explanation by my attending. Though, after the absurd feedback I received yesterday from my attending about not presenting patients, I secretly enjoyed watching her squirm a bit.

Oh, for fuck's sake. The parents are now namedropping who they know at the hospital and are threatening to sue if we don't cave to their litany of ridiculous demands. No one cares who you know. You're insane. This rotation is literally and figuratively making me twitchy. I'm so over this.

April 23: Wednesday

8:06 am: Sometimes it's difficult to tell whether a kid is simply funny looking or has an underlying genetic disease. The best way to tell? Look at the parents. Per an attending telling a story, "Yeah, the kid just didn't look right. We kept running tests and the results kept being normal. Then we looked more closely at the parents and decided, eh, the kid's alright. No weird genetic syndrome after all, just a funny looking mom and dad."

11:20 am: Allie refers to mono as the gateway STI.

April 24: Thursday

10:26 pm: I want to go to bed but I'm on the couch and my bedroom is so far away. I don't think I can make the trek across my apartment.

April 25: Friday

6:02 am: Usually there are three or four new patients admitted during an overnight shift. New patients take a while to present during rounds because their entire story and background has to be told to the group. Patients that have already been here usually just need an updated plan for the day. Unfortunately, we have 15 new patients. Blehh.

11:12 am: We have a new attending as of today and he looks like a walrus. During rounds he ripped apart one of the medical students in front of a patient and their mom. What an ass. Of course, I then became terrified to present my own patients to him. He's a mean walrus.

Noon: My team is still rounding and everyone is super cranky today. Fortunately, my senior told me to sneak off to noon conference so that I could get lunch.

Allie spoke with our previous attending and arranged for a new feedback session for me. The team went out of their way for me and informed the attending about me being a team player and all the shit I did the past few weeks. Turns out, the attending thought that Allie and I were the same person. Once the attending realized that it was actually me who did all those presentations, she was suddenly impressed. In an odd way, it turned into a compliment. It implied that my presentations and plans were good enough that she hadn't noticed that a third-year medical student, and not an intern, was talking to her. But still, it's ridiculous. After being bummed out and exhausted all week after my initial feedback session last Monday, this was an uplifting way to start the weekend.

April 26: Saturday

3:45 pm: Off to meet Spengler for coffee.

11:15 pm: Coffee turned into getting drinks, which naturally led into having dinner together, and finishing the night off with ice cream. He's easy to talk to, friendly, funny, and all good things, but he's got no sex appeal. I imagine he is the kind of guy that gets relegated to the friend zone a lot. I'm trying to keep an open mind, but I don't see this happening.

April 27: Sunday

6:03 am: Another bright and early day at The Kiddie Hospital. God, I hate this place.

9:10 am: I don't enjoy working with Dr. Mean Walrus. He's belittling to everyone.

Allie let me carry the pager today to help expand my role on the team. If nothing else, I'm learning to care for children.

As terrifying as it is to examine a physician, it is TEN TIMES WORSE to examine the child of TWO physicians. Completely nerve-wracking.

April 28: Monday

7:06 am: My patient is faking their belly pain. The kid winces and screams whenever I press on their belly with my hand. When I listen to their belly using my stethoscope and then covertly press on their belly while listening, ta da! No pain. I repeated this maneuver multiple times, as did the senior and my attending. Busted. The kid is going to be discharged today.

8:39 am: Crazy thunder and lightning storms so intense that the sky looks black. The rain will help my veggies grow.

There is a peds team dinner on Wednesday night. My invitation arrived, along with the request that I not mention it at work, as the other interns did not invite their own med students.

At the end of each day, Allie gives a short summary about every patient to the oncoming overnight team. Signing out patients to the next team is a role normally reserved for the residents, as transitions of care are ripe with error potential. Every piece of important information has to be conveyed. Under her supervision, Allie had me sign out all of our patients. I appreciate how much she's been teeing me up for when I get to be an intern.

April 29: Tuesday

The residents informed all the med students that we don't have to come in on Thursday so that we have an extra day to study for the notoriously grueling peds final. And really, no med student is paying attention to whatever is going on the day before an exam. All we're thinking about is studying.

Spengler and I are texting back and forth during conference. We're going to hang out again later.

April 30: Wednesday

5:58 am: I stayed up too late and am now dragging. At least today is my last day on peds and I can sleep in tomorrow. Hanging out with Spengler seemed more entertaining than studying for my peds final so we went out again last night.

While hanging out, we shared stories from various trips and favorite getaways. Our conversation took an unfortunate turn when we started discussing what we like to do while on vacation. He shared with me that he is not an adventurous person and would never go scuba diving with me or basically do anything else that I consider fun.

Well, what's the point then?

I'm looking for a partner in crime, not someone to keep my seat warm while I go out exploring the world by myself. I can't pretend to do this anymore. I knew it would never be anything, but I wanted to try dating one of 'the nice guys' because maybe it could have worked out. Sorry Spengler, you're out.

I presented to my team about cyclical vomiting, abdominal migraines, and cyclic neutropenia for my end-of-rotation talk.

Noon: The Mean Walrus has decreed that the med students on my team must come in tomorrow. Fuck. Why? What benefit is there in that?

1:12 pm: Now, due to the Mean Walrus being a dick, all the students on the other teams have to come in too, because the other residents don't want their med students getting in trouble. So, for the 50th time, tomorrow on rounds I will present a bunch of kids with bronchasthmonia. Hopefully we won't get too many patients overnight.

3:40 pm: My team felt badly that the Mean Walrus is being an ass so they sent me home early to get in some studying before our team dinner. If nothing else, I love my team! The peds residents have been my favorite residents to work with so far, coupled with my least favorite patient population.

8:19 pm: The team dinner at a local bar was so fun! None of the other med students were invited, which was nice, because they're really annoying. And now back to studying and bed soon. I'm running on fumes and due to the Mean Walrus, I can't sleep in tomorrow. Sigh.

May 1: Thursday

6:08 am: Fifteen new patients were admitted overnight. Fifteen! Dear God. We'll be rounding until my exam starts tomorrow. Once again, this is finally my last day of inpatient peds.

8:02 am: The Mean Walrus adamantly stated, "We must power through rounds today; we must be efficient and leave out extraneous information on patients." He emphasized that we must streamline our patient presentations due to the volume of new admits. Umm... why don't we do that on all days? Then rounds would be much shorter (like on surgery) but we'd get the same amount of work accomplished in much less time. I don't get it. These are not my people.

8:28 am: There are so many children here with medical problems related to their obesity; obstructive sleep apnea, diabetes, altered menstrual cycles, on and on.

8:47 am: More NAT and sexual abuse cases. Get me out of this hellhole.

8:50 am: Special Nurse interrupted rounds to share irrelevant information. She is now getting death stares from half the team.

9:20 am: Homicidal children are frightening. Especially the really sweet, innocent-looking ones.

9:40 am: God bless the intern. He is truly powering through these 15 new admits. The Mean Walrus is behaving himself and not giving the intern too much shit.

10:22 am: A mother's intuition that something is wrong with her child is usually correct.

10:45 am: I'm so impressed that the intern presented 15 new patients in under three hours. Now we just need to round on our established patients. My turn to present.

10:56 am: Will this day end?

Noon: Free! I seriously expected to be here all day. Time to study.

May 2: Friday

11:48 am: Holy fuck that was a difficult exam. I hope I passed so that I don't ever have to think about inpatient pediatrics again.

1:01 pm: The worst part of the rotation was undoubtedly that many patients' parents were consistently belittling and threatening my team. The power of Dr. Google has armed each family with information that is misunderstood, misinterpreted, or flat out wrong. The constant arguments from parents who think they know better than the medical team is exhausting, and quite frankly insulting. Older attendings bemoan the fact that physicians used to be respected, and now every day is a battle to provide even basic medical care such as giving vaccines.

I've come to hate this rotation. I hated waking up for work and grew to hate the families for whom I was supposed to be caring. I made it through, but I feel worn down. Exhausted. Beat. How can I provide adequate care when my patients and their families are fighting me every step of the way? I don't know how to shake this feeling of frustration and sadness.

My only consolation is that I start my EM rotation tomorrow. Unfortunately, I don't get the weekend off, as I have to jump right into my EM shifts tomorrow. My two-week elective has been condensed into eight days, so that I can fulfill my shift requirements before leaving for the annual EM conference. This rotation also includes five hours of didactics, two patient write-ups, and the department exam, all of which will be completed before I leave town. Just need to focus and get it done. Eventually I'll have a day off. Someday.

Off to brunch with Maggie and Piper, and there's rumor of a bonfire and s'mores later tonight at Sophia's house.

10:05 pm: Off to bed with a happy belly full of s'mores and an alarm set for 6 am. Maggie and Piper both told me straight up that Spengler was way too nice and well behaved for me. They told me that they would have been happy for me as long as I was happy, but that they were just waiting for me to get bored with him. Wow that was accurate. Ok but now, time for emergency medicine. My first shift in the ED starts 6:45 tomorrow morning.

Emergency Medicine

Song: MGMT. "Electric Feel." *Oracular Spectacular.*
Columbia Records. 2008.
Drink: Tempranillo, or other full-bodied, peppery red
wine

May 3: Saturday

6:28 am: First day! My trauma shears and EM pocket guides are loaded in my white coat while anything even remotely peds-related has been carefully extricated and incinerated in a biohazard bin. I'm excited and mildly nervous for this rotation.

6:42 am: Walking into the ED feels familiar, as if I am back on my home turf. I recognize half of the attendings and residents from my time spent shadowing The Boss.

7:40 am: My first shift is scheduled with the mildly sexist and blatantly med-student hating Dr. Richards, aka Dr. Dick. The Boss introduced me to him by stating, "Silvia's going into EM, she's one of us." He feigned an effort to be polite as The Boss had directly introduced me to him but I already knew his reputation, so I was unconcerned when he started ignoring me not a moment after The Boss walked away. The major perk to working with Dr. Dick is that I am now entirely free to roam about the ED and learn from any resident who is willing to teach me.

7:10 pm: The day flew by! I watched the following roll through the ED in a parade of illness and traumatic injuries: a severe chronic obstructive pulmonary disease exacerbation, a urinary tract infection causing near-deadly sepsis, a 30 foot fall resulting in spinal fractures and a collapsed lung, a stroke requiring stat clot-buster drugs (so called), and a patient with a gunshot wound to the forearm, which distorted one of his many intricate tattoos. The pace was nonstop; residents, nurses, and staff were constantly flitting in and out of patients' rooms. The ED buzzed with ceaseless movement and noise. I wondered, "Will I ever be able to do this?"

In the midst of the chaos, the residents involved me in patient care and seamlessly wove in teaching pearls about each of their patient's conditions. I chatted with many different patients, getting glimpses into their lives, and learning how they ended up in the ED.

Occasionally I'd check in with Dr. Dick and he'd be like, "Oh, you're still here."

I'd reply, "Yes, but I am keeping myself entertained,"

He would already be back to doing something else and distractedly nodding, "Hmm yea ok, that's good." I'd then leave and go check out whatever new crisis rolled in through the ambulance bay. You know what? He gave me a great evaluation at the end of the day, basically because I left him alone. I'm not sure that is the point of the rotation, but I had such an eventful and productive day.

Time to study. I can't mess up this exam and multiple-choice tests are not my strong suit. Having a poor grade from my EM rotation would traumatically injure my residency application.

May 4: Sunday

6:58 am: I'm assigned to work with one of the second-year residents today. I know him fairly well as he is dating one of my friends. His plan is to have me see patients, help with wound repairs, and do other small procedures. Sounds good to me.

7:05 am: Today is the big marathon in the city so we were forewarned that there might be a lot of sports injuries and overheated athletes today.

9:21 am: Sprawled across an ED gurney is an extremely drunk uncooperative guy who fell and hit his head, resulting in a huge hematoma (bruise) expanding across his forehead. An EM attending watched a resident fail at trying to convince the guy that he needs a CT scan of his head, because he may have a head bleed. The attending came up beside me and offered the following advice, "You can't reason with crazy or drunk."

10:55 am: A pain medication-seeking patient stormed out when we would not give him narcotics.

Noon: Casey is out of town for two months, doing a surgery rotation at a remote hospital. I didn't realize how much the constant annoyance about running into him at The General Hospital still stressed me out.

A runner arrived with a life-threatening temperature of 108.4° F! Ice dunk tank. Stat!

An ENT (ear, nose, and throat) resident is down in the ED, consulting on one of our patients who busted his face in an accident. In assessing the extent of the damage, and determining whether or not he should try to question the patient directly, the ENT resident inquired from the EM resident, "Does his face work?" I found that to be an entertaining way to pose his question.

I've been caring for a kind and chatty gent with a complicated medical history. While checking on him, I noticed that he had three legs, instead of the standard bipedal variety. Clearly outlined under the sheets were shapes created by his two hips and thighs, while a foot stuck out from the covers at a distinctly different angle from his other two legs. It took embarrassingly longer than a split second to realize that he possessed a prosthetic leg, which he had removed for his comfort.

1:29 pm: Already got blood on my white coat.

Overall positive feedback for the day about my history taking, exam skills, and procedural competence.

May 5: Monday

6:48 am: It's Cinco de Mayo and I'm spending my shift today working with Maverick. This will be a fun, albeit awkward, shift as I'm fairly certain I can't look at him without blushing. Hopefully that goes unnoticed. What is wrong with me? Somehow, I can easily hit on anyone at a bar, but this one, bouncing around the ED with his toned climbing forearms, he's killing me. It's gonna be a long day.

Where's The Boss when I need her to talk some sense into me?

9:02 am: I am being sternly reprimanded by a nurse for not asking an aggressive psychotic patient whether or not they have any weapons on them. Umm… while I absolutely agree that I should verify this information, shouldn't someone else have already assessed this? I'm like the fifth person to see this patient between the cops, the ambulance crew, the triage nurse, and the nurse assigned to his room.

There is a drunk guy sleeping in one of the hospital gurneys today. Seems like this is a daily occurrence.

10:21 am: I am so awkward today.

11:02 am: A charming little old lady patient informed me conspiratorially, "Having your nails manicured will help you get a man." Thanks for the tip. And good thing my nails are done – there happens to be a man standing about ten yards away that I'd like to get.

1:03 pm: I don't understand when ED residents sit or eat or pee. They're like machines.

1:54 pm: Two internal medicine residents are discussing medical wishes and resuscitation efforts with a nonagenarian who is being admitted to the hospital. The residents are explaining to her the options for invasive medical interventions, such as inserting a breathing tube or doing chest compressions, should her heart stop. One resident then added, "But don't worry, we don't expect it to."

The wrinkled patient looked up and replied, "That's too bad, I hope it would. I'm old. I'm ready to go."

The honesty and sincerity with which she replied stopped me in my tracks.

2:22 pm: The ED is the hospital's melting pot. Every complaint, every issue, no matter what it is, gets funneled through here. Even the peds patients pass through. I'm running into residents from so many prior services here, as all the different teams come down to see their newly-admitted patients.

5:05 pm: Maverick sent me home early to celebrate Cinco de Mayo. None of my friends are free to hang out yet, but it's still nice to leave early. Though really, I didn't mind spending the day working with him.

May 6: Tuesday

7:05 am: I'm assigned to work with an outgoing and chatty resident today, and The Boss is our attending physician. I love getting to see her and work with her in the department.

9:43 am: Acanthosis nigricans is an area of darkened velvety skin, usually found in the armpits or on the neck of diabetic patients. While examining an ostensibly healthy patient with a cough, I spotted the telltale skin finding. I asked him if he has diabetes. He replied "No," but I'm already thinking, "Oh yes you do, you just don't know it yet." A simple lab test and random blood sugar level later, sure enough, the poor guy has diabetes. I'm starting off the day strong by catching that diagnosis and earning props from the resident.

11:01 am: I not so subtly asked The Boss which of her residents are single and in reply she sternly informed me that her entire department is off limits to me. Hmph.

11:34 am: A healthy-appearing unsuspecting male came in with a headache. Turns out he has a ticking time bomb in his head in the form of a large aneurysm. Every time he moves, I (and every doctor in a two-mile vicinity) jump out of fear that it is going to burst.

Noon: The trauma bay is hopping today; injuries from falls, accidents, fights, and more.

3:34 pm: Um… so yeah, Maverick stopped by my workstation and got my number under the flimsy pretext of updating me about a patient. Interesting.

3:45 pm: The Boss, who witnessed this exchange, subsequently appeared to reiterate her ban on me getting involved with anyone in the ED until after I match next spring. She's concerned about me doing anything that could affect where I match for residency. I wanted to protest but she's right.

4:01 pm: There is a snarky drunk lady in one of the bays.

A lady with a massive head wound, down to bone, is in the trauma bay. Guess who gets to clean it out and suture it up?

After spending an extraordinary amount of time cleaning away the matted blood, the laceration turned out to be even larger than we all thought. The patient essentially split open the entire back of her head, like a coconut struck by a machete. The suture repair required closure of the deep layer of tissue that lies directly over the skull, called the galea. The galea is under a lot of tension and required a lot of patience to repair, as well as some creative suturing angles as I was working within the confines of the outer layer of the scalp laceration.

Slow and steady, with The Boss and Maverick occasionally checking on my progress, I closed the deep layer. I then turned my attention to the superficial laceration running from the crown of her head to the base of her skull. Typically, we use staples to close head lacerations, but some areas were so swollen and distorted that I ended up using sutures to approximate the macerated edges.

The coolest thing?

The patient sat there chatting with me the whole time. She felt no discomfort while I worked as I had injected a ton of anesthetic into the wound prior to starting. We spoke about her family and work and whatnot as I slowly and steadily put her back together. Like Frankenstein. Or a reverse Humpty Dumpty.

7:40 pm: The trauma bay is insane. There is non-stop action, people need help immediately, and more keep rolling in. Moaning and yelling hail from various patient beds. It does not smell good by any means, and there is blood leaking onto the floor from a stab wound. The residents move seamlessly between tasks, thriving on the pandemonium, adrenaline junkies in their element. A moment of clarity strikes. I feel with sudden certainty and unwavering conviction that I am going to be an emergency medicine physician. I'm not sure I've ever felt so certain of anything.

These are my people.

May 7: Wednesday

12:04 am: I am so wound up and excited from my shift that I can't sleep.

9:40 am: In the midst of five hours of lectures, then home to study and finish my case reports.

Maverick is texting me. Go away. Bad resident.

I can't believe that the EM final exam is the day after tomorrow already. So much work to do. My life this week has been a non-stop cycle of work, study, sleep.

May 8: Thursday

8:30 am: A patient's yelling and sobbing can be heard clear across the ED. I'm curious.

8:38 am: Turns out that the shouting and sobbing occurred in response to a patient being told that her fatigue and nausea stem from the fact that she is pregnant.

9:29 am: I'm helping perform the ultrasound to determine the gestational age of the above-mentioned patient's pregnancy. The ED resident easily located where the fetus had implanted in the uterus, inside a healthy-appearing little bubble called a yolk sac. While scanning the yolk sac to pinpoint the little flicker of a heartbeat, he noticed that there appeared to be an odd curvature on one side. By rotating the ultrasound probe, he obtained a better view of the odd shape, which turned out to be a *second* yolk sac. Future mom is going to have twins. Surprise!

I immediately thought of the joy and relief that my sister must have felt upon first laying eyes on her little one's heartbeats. However, my sister's children were born into a loving, stable, and well-educated family. The patient I'm looking at is young, single, visibly devastated, and just barely no longer a teenager.

11:21 am: I imagine that I will become skilled at removing the bodily fluids of others from my clothing.

A patient has two lacerations requiring closure; a large one on his head and a small one on his hand. The one on the head came together cleanly with a boatload of staples. I closed the one on the hand using sutures. Unlike suturing while on surgery, patients are awake and chatting while I work. There's something insanely gratifying about suturing or stapling someone back together. A patient will arrive looking like a hot mess, covered in blood, and I think, "Oh dear God, what happened to you?!" Then I clean them up and start putting the pieces back together. Once they are again whole, I get to admire my handiwork for a minute before they go home and I'm on my way to see another patient.

1:01 pm: Mom is texting me. She is telling me to listen to The Boss and behave myself.

3:50 pm: Attempts at self-decapitation are never a good idea. Fascinating to look at though.

7:19 pm: Crazy end of shift! New traumas rolled in every five minutes for nearly an hour! My main roles involved cutting off people's clothing and holding their neck steady during exams. I wished I could be more helpful. All in all, positive reviews and feedback from my shift today.

9:43 pm: My assigned readings, equivalent to nearly half of an EM textbook, are all completed, outlined, and memorized. I'm ready for my exam tomorrow.

May 9: Friday

8:00 am: Going into my EM final exam. Wish me luck.

11:35 am: I enjoyed taking the EM test in a private room because I could talk aloud to myself the whole time, which helped me reason through problems. I think I did well, so the pain of working and studying nonstop this week was well worth it (hopefully).

I have ten minutes to eat and get to the ED. Today is a noon to ten pm shift in the minor care area, and tomorrow I've got a stretch from seven am to seven pm. Minor care is for patients who have isolated issues and are less likely to be admitted to the hospital. Small lacerations, coughs and colds, general aches and pains.

12:48 pm: Out of curiosity, I asked a patient how he wrecked his arm. He nonchalantly informed me that the injury occurred while he was jumping off of a wall, as if this were an everyday occurrence. I declined to ask any follow up questions, such as why he was on said wall in the first place, why he jumped, or if he was being chased by the police or other concerning parties.

2:31 pm: I drained a gnarly abscess that burst with foul smelling pus. Ick.

6:38 pm: I reflexively pull back my hands when I examine a patient if it appears to be hurting them. The problem is, a thorough exam provides important information, so I need to learn to power through.

A patient arrived to the ED wearing a sombrero. After changing into his hospital gown, I peeked into his room and surprise to me, the patient still wore the sombrero. I later inquired and learned from his nurse that the sombrero was not removed during the entirety of his visit.

7:15 pm: My newest patient started off our interaction by informing me that she does not trust doctors because we are evil. She believes in the healing powers of crystals. She then informed me that her crystals have stopped working, so she needs to see a money-grubbing, know-it-all physician, who practices soulless western medicine. How do you respond to people like that? I don't care that she believes in crystals and shit, but to walk in here and insult my profession in as many ways as possible as quickly as possible while simultaneously asking for help? WTF.

What saddens me most is that she is not unique. Variations of her being have been presenting to the ED all day. People arrive here demanding tests and medications, being rude, and then ignoring us to take phone calls. I would never walk into someone's place of employment and treat the people working there the way that I see physicians and nurses being treated here. I have an idea as to where she can stick her crystals.

A patient arrived for evaluation after being involved in a high-speed car accident. He looked totally fine and did not appear to have any injuries. The resident examined him and reported that all looked well, though she suggested that we do a CT scan of his head because he seemed a little 'off.'

Upon entering his room with the attending, I spot a young guy lying down, with his hand resting behind his head, chilling on the hospital bed as if it were a lounge chair at the beach. In response to us asking how he's doing, he cocked his head to the side, gave us a sly smirk and replied, "I'm cool, man."

The attending started laughing and asked, "Dude, you smoke a little something tonight?"

The patient cracked up and snickered, "Oh yeah man..."

The resident had no idea that the patient was totally baked, thus explaining the mystery of why he seemed a little 'off' to her.

I love how unreservedly honest the attending is with the patients. I look forward to the day when I have enough experience and grey hairs to speak so bluntly to patients.

9:45 pm: A pain-medication seeking patient stormed out of the ED while yelling, "Thanks for nothing, you assholes." Alternatively, our self-medicated completely blitzed patient is quite pleased with our team and the care that we're providing to him. We're observing him for a bit just to make sure nothing changes.

10:34 pm: Home! I'm exhausted. I'm hyper aware of everything I do and say while in the ED, as this is a potential place for me to go for residency. It's like walking around with a spotlight following me. Every encounter with a resident or an attending feels like a mini interview. Any negative interactions, or pissing off the wrong person, can tank your chances for matching at a particular program.

May 10: Saturday

7:01 am: Sexual assault victims keep arriving to the ED. Some guy appears to have gone on a sexual rampage last night, as all of the victims are providing the same description of him. Seeing all these bruised and battered women strewn throughout the ED is horrifically distressing.

The residents, nurses, and police working with these traumatized women are truly the best. Their calming, gentle, and protective presence with these patients is evident. Thank you for your service to these women.

7:20 am: A homicidal psychotic patient is trying to escape. Police! Stop that man!

7:24 am: Yeah, so, busy morning so far.

9:23 am: People often think of hand washing when they think of someone with OCD. One of the rarer compulsions is peeling your skin off.

9:43 am: The resident asked a gloomy alcoholic patient, "Why are your knees bruised?"

The drunken patient resembled Eeyore from *Winnie The Pooh* as he looked down and sighed while replying, "The floor." Poor guy.

I love working with this particular attending, she rocks in all possible ways.

Benign neglect occurs when unstable, sick patients take our attention away from less sick patients. The less sick patients realize they are not really that ill, and then vacate the ED on their own accord.

What a whirlwind of patients. At shift's end my attending told me I'm the best med student she's had all year.

7:37 pm: Finally home. I've been so happy yet so stressed all week.

Maverick is still sending me random, friendly texts. I'm trying to not read anything into it.

May 11: Sunday

10:43 am: Happy Mother's Day.

10:44 am: I'm at my med school library typing up my case reports from the week. Once finished, I'm officially done with my EM rotation.

9:45 pm: Time to pack for the EM conference. I've arranged to room with three other med students from around the country. We've never met before but have been emailing back and forth over the past couple of weeks. Four female strangers sharing two beds and one bathroom for a week? Could be disastrous.

May 12: Monday

9:07 am: I'm flying to the conference on the airline for which the pilot works. I'll have to watch for him. I would find it mildly disconcerting if I heard his deep voice booming over the PA system from the flight deck.

Awaiting takeoff. My brain is spent from going straight from peds into nonstop work and studying for the EM exam. I'm spending the flight filling my mind with fluff by reading Mindy Kaling's book, *Is everyone hanging out without me, and other concerns*.

5:20 pm: Upon meeting the strangers with whom I'd be rooming, I felt an immediate connection with them. Any fears I had about rooming with complete strangers rapidly dissipated. We all welcomed each other with hugs and smiles and instantly knew that this week would be great.

9:41 pm: All the other medical student ambassadors and I met at the hotel bar earlier this evening to chat and get to know each other. I'm now hanging out in my room and trading outrageous patient stories with my three new roommates.

May 13: Tuesday

8:48 am: The first day of conference is pretty light and I don't have any responsibilities until 11:30 am. I (kind of) slept in, had a leisurely breakfast with my roommates/new friends, and I will be heading to the gym in ten minutes.

My job as a student volunteer is pretty sweet. Our group sits in on the program committee meetings each morning, and then we are distributed to each of the different lecture halls for the day. Our main job is to gather data about the attendance and utility of each lecture. As people arrive we hand out evaluations, so that the lecture attendees can rate the talk in terms of how interesting, useful, and engaging it is. The student ambassadors get to sit in on all the wonderful lectures, given by some of the most prominent people in the history of EM. Afterwards, we collect all of the evaluation forms and the data from each one is entered into a spreadsheet. The committee can then track how well attended and how well received a particular lecture has been. Lectures with high attendance and positive comments are invited back the following year. Lectures with poor turnout or negative reviews are axed.

11:42 am: The first lecture I'm attending is on the history of emergency medicine, which is impossible to do without mentioning The General Hospital.

I'm having so much fun already.

Off to dinner and drinks with The Boss, my former lab team, and some of the EM residents.

May 14: Wednesday

9:21 am: Already been to the gym and am now sitting in my first lecture.

11:54 am: One of my good friends is presenting today so I requested to be assigned to her lecture hall. Having worked with her in The Boss's lab, I know her research topic and her slides inside out. At the end of her presentation, I asked her a question that I knew she'd be able to address with one of her extra slides, making her look like a badass. The Boss smacked me afterwards for asking a "posed" question, but she was laughing while she did it.

2:31 pm: Ahh... my current session is about inferential statistics and is waaaay over my head.

3:51 pm: So yeah, Maverick has been texting me. And of course, I've been texting back. He arrives to the conference tomorrow evening.

May 15: Thursday

9:35 am: EM docs have notoriously short attention spans. Instead of forcing hour-long lectures onto people, someone (I think it may actually have been The Boss) came up with the brilliant and terrifying format of having a lecture where the slides automatically advance every 20 seconds, whether or not the speaker is ready. They have been dubbed "Lightning talks." Whoa. This is amazing. The talks move so fast! It's a race against the PowerPoint. EM docs are crazy. I can't wait to be one.

The past few lectures covered tourniquets, disinfecting the ED, and human trafficking. The audience's attention appears to be glued to the speakers during the lightning talks, quite unlike a few of the drier lectures I worked at yesterday.

2:10 pm: An hour break. I have a huge stack of evaluations with tons of data to enter into the spreadsheets. This is gonna take a while.

2:16 pm: Data entry is made much more palatable when being done at a pool. Gonna sit here and work while enjoying a bit of Texas sunshine.

4:51 pm: Done with work for the day. It's sinking in that I will soon be applying for residency. Is it worth it to start a relationship with anybody right now, knowing that I will likely be moving away for residency next year?

6:11 pm: Maverick is in town. We've been texting since he got my number last week. I've been warned to stay away. More than warned, I have been strictly *forbidden* from ED dabbling. But seriously… I mean.…

The Boss and I are heading off to dinner soon. While hanging out in her room earlier we chatted about our professional lives, our personal lives, and everything in between. I told her honestly that this moment, right now, is the happiest I have felt in my life since before I started medical school three years ago. It's pretty incredible. I'm in the right place, surrounded by the right people, heading in the right direction.

After dinner with The Boss, the plan is to meet up with other EM residents from my school… including Maverick.

May 16: Friday

7:45 am: A bunch of attendings, residents, and I ended up at a nightclub after dinner. At one point Maverick pulled me away from the group and we ended up dancing together on the crowded club floor and then grabbing a drink. After chatting for bit, we tried surreptitiously leaving the club together but ended up running straight into the group again while walking back to the hotel. Our night ended with a supremely awkward pretending-to-be-casual goodnight. He is off limits but I'm crushing so hard I feel like an effing teenager. What am I thinking? The Boss is going to kill me. Or him. Or both of us.

8:04 am: My morning is lecture-free so I can go to the medical student symposium.

10:12 am: These lectures are focused on issues related to medical students such as applying for residency, burnout, anxiety, and dealing with the stress that our future jobs will undoubtedly pile on us. While talking about stress, one lecturer noted, "Every day of our lives is the worst day of our patients' lives."

10:53 am: An EM doc is talking about cool cases he saw as an intern. OMG this is the coolest job.

11:02: Hmm... The lecturer is talking about choosing a residency based on where you want to settle down. I've lived all over the States. I have no idea where I want to settle down. I'm quite unsettled right now.

1:05 pm: Back to work, meeting and greeting folks at the door to each lecture, handing out and collecting evaluations.

1:35 pm: I'm at a thought-provoking international medicine talk that is focused on ethics. Some of the issues being touched upon include: being culturally sensitive to providing healthcare in a country that does not typically employ Western medicine, issues for female physicians in male-centric countries, and medical students/residents providing healthcare that is outside of their scope of practice while abroad. Fascinating.

Being surrounded by these physicians, I became overwhelmed with the realization that I am going to be a doctor. Soon. I almost got teary in the lecture hall.

2:11 pm: These talks are so inspiring. My current lecture is discussing the difficulties of obtaining grants for disaster preparedness. He is lamenting the reactionary approach to crises, as opposed to a proactive approach. The analogy he is using notes how it is cheaper to prevent diseases than to treat them, but just as with diseases everyone thinks, "It won't happen to me/my country."

2:15 pm: "It's hard to get people to behave in certain ways." Yeah, no shit Dr. Lecturer.

2:43 pm: My brain and my body are exhausted from the minimal sleep and feeling as if I'm in constant interview mode. I could (should?) finish my data entry but I'm fried. I need to recharge. I'm going to the pool... with Maverick. Shh...

7:01 pm: Casey is texting me. Why? Who the fuck knows. Whatever he wants, he's too late, so I'm ignoring him. On the other hand, now Maverick is making my life difficult. I don't know what he wants either, but I'm so drawn to him, his curly hair, and his happy, lighthearted demeanor. I keep reminding myself that I'm an adult and should behave responsibly.

May 17: Saturday

7:52 am: I'm in trouble. Last night at the department dinner, the Boss and I sat next to each other and she eyed Maverick suspiciously as he sat down at the table directly across from me. She is pretty damn intimidating, so I thought it was a bold move on his part. After dinner, Maverick and I slipped away from the group to grab a drink at the hotel bar.

We decided to hang out for a bit longer and check out the views from the top floor of the hotel. We leave the hotel lobby bar and step into the elevator. Not a moment after the elevator doors close, the first time we've ever been alone together, he turns to me, presses me up against the wall of the elevator, and kisses me for the entirety of the 38-floor elevator ride. As soon as the elevator halts and the doors slide open, he abruptly stops kissing me and strolls out of the elevator without so much as a glance back.

Once I regained motor function and started breathing again, I followed him out of the elevator. While strolling around the top floor of the hotel I tried to tell him that The Boss will kill him for messing around with me. He is apparently willing to risk his life. Entirely undeterred and unconcerned, he kept running his hands through my hair and pulling me closer to kiss me more. At one point he had me up against the outward slanting floor-to-ceiling windows overlooking downtown Dallas, which is an adrenaline inducing way to make out with someone. After being walked back to my room and sweetly kissed goodnight, I fell asleep repeatedly thinking, "Holy shit did that really just happen?"

My roommates, aka my new awesome friends, have been ripping on me nonstop for coming in so late last night/early this morning.

I had one very specific instruction from The Boss regarding this conference and my residency: Do not get involved with any of her EM residents. I am fairly incapable of lying and I have no poker face, so keeping this quiet will be an interesting challenge for me. Oh fuck. I'm gonna be in so much trouble.

9:01 am: Oh right, I'm still working and need to function like a competent, young professional today. Pull it together, Silvia. I need more coffee. A lot more.

9:10 am: The breadth of EM is truly astonishing, which I always knew, but I don't think I really appreciated until this conference. There are medical presentations on everything and anything including: toxicology, international medicine, cardiovascular disease, neurology, pediatrics, disaster medicine, deliveries and neonates, wilderness medicine, orthopedic trauma, antibiotics, ultrasound, hyperbaric medicine, intensive care, and pulmonary disease, and many more. Other sessions focused on legal issues, physician burnout, ethics, and resident wellness. Scattered throughout the conference were also workshops, small group discussions, leadership and mentoring forums, along with trivia games and team-based competitions.

The best part of it all?

People seem happy. These are not uptight, rigid, miserable people who spend every waking moment at work. When at work they bust their asses, but outside of work these are interesting people with all sorts of adventurous hobbies, wide interests, and a general love of the outdoors.

11:28 am: I'm riding out the rest of my last assigned session sitting outside of the conference room with the other students. I'm so sad to be parting from my new friends.

4:11 pm: At the airport, awaiting boarding to head back to my little Midwest blip on the map. The Boss and I are sitting together at the gate; she knows something is up between Maverick and I, but she's letting me pretend for the moment that she doesn't suspect anything.

5:58 pm: Sitting on the plane. I'm nearly at a loss for words as the whirlwind of the past two weeks replays in my head. Finding my place in medicine and finding my people. Solidifying my commitment to become an emergency physician. Having the opportunity and privilege to work at that fabulous conference and listen to so many impressive speakers. I thought this rotation couldn't get any better, and then Maverick happened. My brain is still processing that one, but I haven't stopped grinning since he kissed me in that elevator.

8:43 pm: Finally, back home in my apartment. Maverick might have just texted that he's on his way over.

Obstetrics

Song: Passion Pit. "Little Secrets." *Manners*. Columbia
Records. 2009.
Drink: MadTree Happy Amber Red Ale

May 18: Sunday

1:15 pm: I slept incredibly well after being sleep
deprived all last week and working nonstop for the previous
couple of weeks. Also, because a certain EM doc kept me up
late. After a lazy morning, I made coffee while Maverick ran
downstairs and picked up breakfast sandwiches from the deli
for us. We dined on my deck, enjoying the sunshine and
chatting until he had to leave for work. I kind of can't
believe that last night and this morning happened.

7:52 pm: I'm contentedly zoning out while working
on my painting for The Boss. Originally it was just supposed
to be a 'thank you' present for everything she has done for
me professionally. Now it can also be a 'Please don't be mad
at me for sleeping with one of your residents after you
specifically told me not to' present.

Ob-gyn is a surgical specialty and the hours are
going to be brutal. Like arrive before 6 am and stay all day
brutal. A necessary evil. I can't believe I'm on my last
rotation and wrapping up third year!

May 19: Monday

6:05 am: I finally get to work with Magnus again.
Peds was nearly insufferable without him providing his
sarcastic commentary and comic relief.

11:20 am: Everyone appears equally unhappy about
starting ob.

11:36 am: I officially passed peds. I missed earning
honors by one point but considering how little I studied for
the final exam I can't really complain.

1:05 pm: Finally received my schedule. I'm starting
off ob-gyn with two straight weeks of nights, including a 29

hour call this weekend. At least I don't work tonight; they were kind enough to have me start tomorrow.

10:58 pm: The best thing about transitioning to working nights is that I can stay up as late as I want tonight and sleep all day tomorrow. I don't really mind nights all that much. They're disorienting and painfully tiring, but so are days waking up at 4 am.

May 20: Tuesday

6:58 am: Even though I am starting nights, turns out I still have to attend morning orientation at 7:30 am today. Why?

7:45 am: Well that was a quick and useless orientation. The course director introduced himself, told us he is divorced, and then we were dismissed. I'm so glad I woke up at 6:30 for this. Well, on my way home and back to bed.

3:44 pm: Maverick came over and took me out for lunch. Such a quick request to hang out again initially brought excitement but then immediate suspicion. I braced myself for a quick explanation that the other night shouldn't have happened or some other polite excuse as to why we shouldn't be hanging out. But no. He simply kissed me hello and during lunch he chatted casually about this and that, as if going to lunch together was a routine occurrence. Alright then.

It's convenient that he is also spending the next two weeks working nights. It's strange to be kind of involved with someone and not want to tell anyone for fear of gossip and rumors and the potential career ramifications. If this turns into something, which who knows at this point, and then something goes wrong, I'm the one who won't match here for residency. I'm the one who's screwed.

4:59 pm: I'm reasonably well rested, well fed, and well caffeinated. I guess it's time to head to work.

6:01 pm: Start of the first shift. Let the baby catching commence.

6:05 pm: Most of the ob-gyn residents are pretty, skinny, and blonde. And all of them are named Brittany.

294

There are two areas on ob: triage, and labor and delivery (L&D). The other med student and I will switch off each night between triage and L&D. L&D is (obviously) where babies are delivered. I'm starting in triage tonight. Triage is for evaluating any medical complaint or concern that a pregnant woman, typically past 20 weeks gestation, may have.

10:54 pm: Patients are trickling in. Some alone, some with partners, some with children who couldn't be left home alone. Mostly there seems to be a lot of evaluations for first-time pregnant patients in their third trimester, presenting with abdominal cramping. All of them think they are in labor. None so far have actually been in labor, and all have been sent home with a diagnosis of Braxton Hicks (false labor) contractions.

11:11 pm: Ob isn't for me. I couldn't look at vaginas all day and night.

May 21: Wednesday

1:02 am: A woman in her third trimester came in with a headache and high blood pressure. A Brittany whisked the patient off to the operating room for an emergency C-section before I could even talk to her.

3:43 am: Unfortunately, pregnant women are at a frighteningly high risk of physical, sexual, and emotional abuse, so triage evaluates a lot of those pregnant women as well.

5:52 am: Heading home soon.

3:45 pm: Maverick came over again this afternoon to hang out. Damn he's cute. And smart. And sweet. Ok I'll stop now. I'm really trying to focus on medicine over here.

5:59 pm: Assigned to L&D tonight. Let's catch some babies.

May 22: Thursday

1:12 am: So, turns out that the role of the third-year medical student is not to deliver the baby, but to deliver the placenta (afterbirth). The resident gets to deliver the baby. Well, let's be honest, the resident isn't delivering the baby. The mother is doing all the work. The resident gets to catch the baby. After the baby stretches its way out of the vaginal canal and comes out screaming, the poor woman is not done. Oh no. Now covered in sweat, blood, and poo, she next has to deliver the bloody mass of placenta. Ick. That is where I come in. As the medical student, I have the job of delivering the placenta and placing it in a little bucket. Hooray for me.

4:01 am: Delivering placentas is decidedly unpleasant. I have now delivered three healthy placentas. The rest of my night consists of running around and doing pelvic exams to see how far a woman's labor has progressed. How many nights do I have left on this service?

6:00 am: No more babies.

7:59 am: Heading home for the day. My feet hurt so much I'm having trouble walking, but there's some kind of twisted satisfaction about being on a service where you never sit and never stop moving. I felt this way on surgery and in the ED, too. The constant pressure to get shit done is almost invigorating and somehow addicting.

3:49 pm: I finally got a solid day of sleep. My brain feels rested but my feet are still aching.

5:35 pm: While walking into the hospital I passed an unmarried and childless male classmate, who spent his first day on L&D. Wide eyed, he shook his head and with a dazed look he murmured, "I'm not gay, but I'm not entirely sure I'm straight anymore."

8:00 pm: Brittany, the resident at triage, stood up and stated, "I'm gonna go eat dinner, you stay here and hold down the fort." Um... she knows I've been on ob for like two days, right?

9:49 pm: A patient and her baby are dying. I'm watching their charts from my post in triage. She has a history of abuse, which may or may not be related to her current condition. She came across as sweet when I spoke with her on my first night in triage. I wonder which team has the code pager tonight. Not that this patient is going to code... but... let's just say that if I see a medicine team appear on the floor and go running down the hall I'm going to follow.

11:30 pm: My PSA for the evening:

Dear teenagers,

For fuck's sake, please use condoms. Every single fucking time. Seriously. How many times do we have to go over this?

Thanks.

The attitude of the resident I'm working with tonight, Lisa, is fluctuating between indifferent and formally polite. My initial impression is that she's probably awesome, and I have a feeling that we'll become friends. As an aside, this resident is good friends with Maverick. Medicine is a small world.

May 23: Friday

12:03 am: The docs and nurses are discussing the frustration of performing excessive, unnecessary tests 'just in case' something bad is lurking. Per their talk, practicing defensive medicine in response to our overly litigious society and the risk of being sued results in huge wastes of time, money, and resources.

1:30 am: In addition to the horrific hours on ob, the reputation of ob residents being cliquey, bitchy sorority girls has been disseminated throughout the med students, making me really nervous to start the rotation. I know it's only been a few days, but I think these women are great. They are super-efficient, smart, and decisive, in addition to having manicured nails and perfect hair. I wonder if the rumors were started by a group of male med students and residents who were intimidated by these powerful women.

2:44 am: I seriously thought today was Thursday, not Friday. Until just now. That's a happy surprise. I still have to work tonight (Friday) but whatever. I'm quite content and entertained by my increasingly frequent text exchanges with Maverick.

3:06 am: A woman around 20 weeks pregnant came in crying, with vaginal bleeding and painful lower belly cramps. After quickly being diagnosed with a spontaneous abortion (miscarriage), all we could do was provide emotional support and some pain medication for her. She was the image of physical and emotional agony as she lay in bed, passing clumps of bloody tissue.

3:57 am: A woman came in and needed an emergency cesarean section. The baby is probably not going to live. Why so many dead babies tonight? This is terrible. Can I go back to the ED?

4:20 am: Psychotic patients are interesting. Psychotic pregnant patients even more so.

7:12 pm: Another night shift. I'm hiding in triage, trying to avoid getting pulled into the OR. The Brittany I'm working with tonight started walking purposefully somewhere a moment ago and I've decided not to follow. We'll see how long I can hide.

10:15 pm: A patient came in with severe belly pain but after she took a giant shit, she felt better and left. The residents told me this is a fairly common occurrence.

11:30 pm: It's sad to routinely see patients barely tolerating the fact that they are pregnant, instead of enjoying this stage in their life.

May 24: Saturday

1:06 am: I've been doing nothing since 10:30 pm. Can I go home now? I would never ask, but I'm focusing all of my psychic efforts on mentally willing the Brittany to send me home.

3:22 am: You know what's really boring? Sitting around doing nothing in the middle of the night.

3:32 am: Brittany left me sitting at the triage desk so she could go take a nap. Seriously I can't express my frustration about having to be here tonight.

3:56 am: Blehh.

4:40 am: Brittany got called back to triage to see a patient. She is now complaining to me that she is nauseous because, "You know, sometimes it's worse when you get a nap in." Umm… no, I don't, because I didn't get a nap in. I've been sitting here at the triage station while you went and napped in the physician lounge. Serves you right. Longest night ever.

8:55 am: Sweet sleep.

7:36 pm: I spent most of my afternoon between a coffee shop downtown and Maverick's apartment. As we hang out more, I'm slowly learning more about him and his endearing quirkiness. He told me that he's started telling his friends about me, which is awesome, but I thought we were keeping this quiet? None of my friends know anything about him yet.

Off for drinks with Piper.

May 25: Sunday

Food, shopping, sleep.

It turns out that Piper – tiny blonde, future pediatrician, and sweetest person ever – loves general surgery. Maggie and I were thrilled at this; I could totally see Piper becoming a powerhouse surgeon. Out of my friends, she seems to have changed the most. She's developed a harder shell, yes, but also more confidence, and a stronger voice. It's awesome to watch. She once told me she liked the idea of being a pediatrician because children didn't intimidate her. I'm not sure that anyone intimidates her anymore.

When I told Maggie and Piper about Maverick they immediately stated that he's a great fit for me and my personality. It's weird to want to be with someone and equally want no one to know. Being a woman in medicine is posing some interesting challenges.

5:55 pm: Off to work.

6:43 pm: There's a new senior resident working tonight. I'm not sure why, but I immediately disliked her.

8:23 pm: A pregnant woman came in for evaluation after allegedly being abused. She eventually admitted that her partner is to blame for her injuries and the cops got involved. Unfortunately, she does not want him to get arrested and if she doesn't want to press charges, there is little we can do to help her. It's the most frustrating feeling. None of her injuries are severe enough to have her admitted to the hospital, so she'll be discharged home to him shortly. Hopefully the guy doesn't murder her.

10:00 pm: Slow night at triage so I've been catching up on *Daily Beast* articles. I recommend a thoughtful article entitled "The mask your doctor hides behind, by Daniela Drake.[10] It's regarding the dangers of patient satisfaction scores and physician autonomy. In the midst of this heroin and opioid epidemic, it's a provocative read. She sheds light on some of the issues related to over-prescribing narcotics and antibiotics. Having seen so many addicts this year, it's unbelievable to me that physicians are still under so much pressure to keep prescribing these drugs. I've witnessed horrific consequences of drug abuse on every rotation, from injury and illness to depression and suicide.

3:20 am: A woman came in to triage tonight because she wants an abortion, but is stating that she cannot afford the procedure. Umm… Might be a better idea to dig up the cash now, as kids are waaaaay more expensive.

4:53 am: I don't like ob, but I'm enjoying working with these poised, badass women.

7:50 am: Done with my shift, off to bed.

May 26: Monday

12:17 pm: I've never been a good sleeper. I used to love watching Dave Attell's show *Insomniac*.

1:15 pm: Four more nights to go. I'm bringing headphones with me tonight so that I can watch videos on my iPad if things are slow.

5:57 pm: My cheeks may still be flushed and my breathing may be uneven but I made it from Maverick's apartment to work on time. With three minutes to spare even. Lisa, Maverick's close friend, suspiciously, and not subtly, eyed me up and down when I walked into work tonight. I might be imagining it but I'm usually pretty good at picking up on these things.

7:12 pm: Lisa and I have worked together for a few nights now. We initially chatted about medical stuff, then segued into gossiping about other medical students and residents, and eventually, we started opening up about ourselves.

300

At one point tonight she asked me if I was dating anyone, to which I replied, "I've just recently gotten involved with someone, but it's too early to say where it might be going." I'm incapable of lying but didn't feel like offering up any other information. As far as I know, she is unaware that Maverick and I have spent nearly every afternoon together this week before heading to our respective nightshift locales.

Sigh. He's such a bad idea, but how do you turn down the guy you've secretly had a crush on for years? Ok, really, not secretly, as many (all?) of my friends have heard me talk about him.

7:49 pm: An ED consult came in for a possible ectopic pregnancy, which is a dangerous condition where a fetus implants outside of the uterus. It's seems unlikely because her story doesn't sound quite like an ectopic, but it's always, always, always better to be safe than sorry as ectopic pregnancies can rupture, killing young women. A Brittany joked that if I go down to the ED for the consult I still must return to the ob-gyn floor for the rest of my shift.

8:21 pm: Yikes. This poor woman probably does have an ectopic pregnancy, so she's going to be taken for surgery shortly.

10:01 pm: I went to the pre-op area to pick up the patient's surgery consent form. The patient sat alone, wide-eyed, and visibly terrified. I asked if she wanted me to stay with her until she left for the OR and before even finishing the question she blurted, "Yes!"

I invited her to tell me about her family to help pass the time. She told me about her other children, who were home with her significant other. We segued into conversation about how one of her children had set her up with her now fiancé, and the family is thrilled that she is pregnant. She appeared to be relaxing, and she told me I helped her be less anxious. The OR took a while to prep and we ended up speaking for nearly 40 minutes. At one point she told me I'll be a great doctor one day. I hope she's right.

Off to the OR.

May 27: Tuesday

12:56 am: The patient awoke from surgery mouthing, "What happened to my baby?" I wasn't the one to break the news that she did indeed have an ectopic, that she was no longer pregnant, and that we had to remove one of her Fallopian tubes. Her baby never stood a chance of making it. Her belly was filled with blood and had we not gone ahead with surgery, she likely would have died.

An emergency cesarean section is going to the operating room, but the patient is seen by a private ob, not one that works with residents, so med students aren't allowed to scrub in. Oh well. Darn. So sad. Off to hang out in triage.

3:28 am: Reading a *NY Times* article by Paula Span called "Do not resuscitate: What young doctors would choose."[11] Yet another article about how physicians typically choose to die at home, peacefully and with family, instead of at the hospital, being pounded with chest compressions.

3:45 am: The new senior Brittany on service passive-aggressively commented while walking by triage, "Neither of you [the med students] made it to the C-section."

I (semi) politely replied, "It was a private patient, I thought the med students aren't allowed in."

She had a nearly imperceptible misstep in her stride before shrugging and hesitantly agreeing with me. I dislike this new resident. She is condescending to all the junior residents and has been power tripping all night.

4:03 am: Tonight is going so much faster than Friday because the other medical student is here and

4:10 am: I stopped writing mid-sentence and haven't the faintest idea where I was going with that thought.

4:54 am: One hour until the morning team arrives. Hopefully it passes quickly.

5:34 am: In case you were wondering, this shift has not ended yet. I'm so over working nights.

11:03 pm: I'm back in triage. There are several reasons I prefer triage to L&D: 1) vaginal births are gross, 2) I don't like cesarean deliveries because I don't like being in

302

the OR, 3) triage gets to see the ED consults, and 4) Maverick is working nights in the ED.

11:48 pm: I was right. Maverick told Lisa about me a couple of days ago and she absolutely was eyeing me last night. I knew it. Our discussion about Maverick segued into how ridiculous it is that I'm in my 30s and can't freely date whoever is interesting to me. Lisa agreed that dating him has the potential to rock my ability to match here for residency but that it's ridiculous to not be with someone for that reason. My private life seems unfairly intruded upon. I thought all the stupid gossip about my life ended after I finished my surgery rotation. Or high school.

May 28: Wednesday

1:13 pm: The long-term effects of chlamydia can be devastating. My guy friends have joked that it's not a big deal because it is treated so easily, but it really rots a woman's insides. Women can develop chronic abdominal pain and it can even cause infertility by scarring the fallopian tubes. I have seen each of these complications multiple times since starting on ob.

2:15 am: Lisa shared with me how she developed her relationships with the nurses. She gets along with them and is friendly with them, yet still is respected by them so that shit gets done.

5:15 am: Success! Lisa and I have exchanged numbers and plan on going for drinks sometime.

6:05 am: Magnus showed up for pre-rounding today and upon seeing me informed me that I looked like a legit Brittany because my hair has an immaculate braid in it and my makeup is still done after being here for 14 hours.

6:58 pm: Second-to-last night shift. At least I have breakfast with Maverick in the morning to look forward to.

8:28 pm: I'm in triage again. The condescending senior Brittany is sitting back here for some reason and has basically taken over. Ostensibly she is here to help the intern but she is doing EVERYTHING herself. She is obsessively micromanaging all tasks, including seeing all the patients herself, putting in every order, and writing all the notes. The intern and I shrugged and are just hanging out. The senior Brittany also has yet to acknowledge my presence and is actively avoiding looking me in the eye, as if I don't exist.

One way to ensure that no one gives a shit about your opinion, or rank, is to treat those below you poorly, have a condescending attitude, and micromanage. The junior residents have been sniping about her all week. If I knew this shitty senior would be taking over the intern's job and running triage tonight, I would have opted for L&D. So not worth it just to be able to go down to see the ED consults. This night is going to suck. It's only 8:43 pm.

Oh this is fun: the senior does not like how the intern is presenting a patient to her, so the senior is now re-presenting the patient back to the intern. It's like watching reality TV, ob edition.

9:55 pm: I paged surgery to place a consult and when they called back the senior practically ripped the phone out of my hand to do the consult herself. Whatever. I'm going to take a long dinner tonight.

11:14 pm: While walking to get a snack I got a whiff of a peculiar yet familiar scent. It took me a moment to place it, but I'm fairly certain my white coat now smells faintly of vagina.

May 29: Thursday

3:54 am: Maverick surprise visited the ob floor to say hi (ostensibly to Lisa) before heading home from his shift. His smile slays me. This is why I'm in triage again tonight instead of over in L&D. I'm jealous he gets to go home and sleep but I'm happy, happy, happy all the same and looking forward to joining him for breakfast in a few hours.

5:20 am: A patient arrived by ambulance in active labor and with zero prenatal care. She thinks she's past her due date by a couple of days, and she's "pretty sure" that the pregnancy is a singleton. She's by herself. I wish she had someone here with her.

5:58 am: After the patient delivered the baby, Brittany asked if the patient wanted to know if she had a boy or girl. The patient reportedly replied something to the extent of, "I don't care. I don't want it. It's not like I'm keeping it."

7:16 pm: On my last night shift, which will be spent over in L&D. My day flew by, though not much sleep was had. Maverick took me for breakfast at a new place that opened near his apartment. We spent most of the afternoon kind of resting, and then he cooked me dinner before I had to head back in for work tonight.

It's so strange. I still can't get over the fact that we're going out. I try to play it down when I write about him but seriously, I still can't believe we've started dating. Or, as he puts it, he's 'courting' me.

7:41 pm: The patient with no prenatal care put her baby up for adoption. As far as we can tell, the newborn is healthy and has no obvious health issues.

10:00 pm: My most recent ED consult is for abdominal pain in a pregnant woman who happens to be a homeless prostitute. She came across as embarrassed and shy, and I didn't want her to feel judged. Instead of jumping in and straight up asking, "Hey, are you a hooker?" I started my questions with, "Have you ever traded sex for a place to spend the night?" Then I asked, "Have you traded sex for drugs?" And finally, "Have you ever exchanged sex for money?" I succeeded in obtaining the medical history I needed while hopefully minimizing any discomfort she felt.

May 30: Friday

12:00 am: Starting my countdown to the morning.

1:26 am: Dinner and coffee time with a couple of Brittanys.

2:05 am: I tend to fluctuate between feeling as if I'm really progressing with my medical training and learning how to be a physician, with feelings of complete inadequacy and creeping doubts that I will never really know or understand what I'm doing. Lisa and a junior Brittany assured me that this is normal.

5:09 am: This night is dragging on painfully slowly.

8:08 am: Done and freed! I really hate ob. Sleep.

2:15 pm: Good morning. Off to get my hair done, then out to dinner with Maverick. His lighthearted personality and love of adventure is becoming more apparent and drawing me in closer.

May 31: Saturday

11:45 am: I'm having a much more difficult time transitioning back to days than I thought I would. I'm exhausted and my head is foggy. Maverick and I went for happy hour last night then out for dinner. Afterwards, we met up with some of our mutual friends. So much for keeping things quiet – he's already told several of his friends about "us." It's not that I don't trust him, but I didn't really know him before and I had no idea what he wanted from me. As for not telling people, he instead believes we should tell everyone. His reasoning is that us dating will only become a big deal if we try to hide it. If we tell people, then perhaps we can head off some of the inevitable gossip. I just want him to tell The Boss, and ideally, get her approval.

June 1: Sunday

Noon: I just woke up. Maverick left for work hours ago. I should probably head back to my own apartment.

1:36 pm: Is it really June already? Damn May went fast. This whole year went fast.

Before going over to Maverick's apartment I had dinner with Daria, Jane, and Piper. I broke the news to them about getting involved with Maverick, a tiny bit about him, and how excited I am about the whole thing starting up. They're thrilled and also commented, "Finally!"

4:46 pm: I spent my afternoon crafting my personal statement for my residency application. Unexpectedly, I started tearing up while writing the last line. This year has ripped me up emotionally, mentally, and physically. The end is in sight. I've never wanted anything more in my life than to be a physician.

June 2: Monday

6:03 am: It's no fun to be at work when I've left Maverick sleeping in my warm, cozy bed back at my apartment. We've spent nearly every day together since the

306

night we returned from the EM conference. Hanging out, listening to music, cooking together, getting to know each other. Nothing earth shattering but it's been wonderful.

9:27 am: I'm at work. During day time hours. This is exciting. Not really. Daytime ob is just as un-fun as nighttime ob.

10:02 am: Being late to your own scheduled cesarean section is poor form. I feel badly for the baby. If the parents care so little regarding the birth of their child, is there any chance that they will behave differently towards the baby after its arrival?

3:30 pm: Sitting through ob lectures. My classmates look positively pained and nearly bored to death. Magnus is making faces at me whenever the professor isn't looking, and we're all texting back and forth. We're burnt out. Done.

4:15 pm: Maverick routinely makes fun of me for always having my bed made, even when the rest of my apartment is in total chaos. Much to my surprise and amusement, on returning home from work I found that he'd made my bed before leaving my apartment.

June 3: Tuesday

5:50 am: Four more days of ob. Two days on L&D, two days at triage. The only redeeming part of being back on days is that Magnus and I can hang out and commiserate with each other during the day.

7:25 am: A patient is refusing to let us examine her. She wants to be sedated before we place an IV or draw labs. She won't let us ultrasound her. Kind of hard to get anything accomplished. I wonder how long this standoff will last.

7:49 am: Off to the OR.

10:49 am: I went to the OR and met up with the ob resident. I introduced myself to the nurses, the anesthesiology resident, and the anesthesiology attending. They were all kind and helpful, and walked me through placing an epidural (spinal anesthesia).

Once the epidural took effect, the ob attending arrived. I introduced myself to the new attending and asked if she would mind if I scrubbed in for the C-section. The attending, known as Dr. Fuckface (Dr. Ff for short), rolled her eyes and scoffed, "Yeah, that's what you're supposed to do on this rotation." She then spat some equally rude comment to the ob resident.

Med students are taught to ask permission to scrub in, especially when working with a new attending. If I had scrubbed into her case without asking and instead just showed up at her operating table I envision she would have been like, "Who the fuck do you think you are to just assume you could scrub into MY case?" There's no winning.

Oddly, during the case Dr. Ff acted absurdly sweet and polite to Brittany and me. The dramatic change puzzled me, until I heard the voice of the person being operated on chatting with her husband. Then it dawned on me: cesarean patients are numb from the nipples down, but they can hear everything. Dr. Ff has to be polite because the patient is wide awake.

At the end of the surgery, Dr. Ff scrubbed out and left the resident and me to close. The resident is really sweet and told me how this particular attending makes her so nervous. She added in a conspiratorial tone, "Of course you were right in introducing yourself and asking permission to scrub in."

12:00 pm: I'm kind of over the whole ob thing. I am sneaking off the ob-gyn floor to have lunch outside with Piper. I need to breathe fresh air and see blue skies.

1:03 pm: Yet another placenta delivery. Yay! This one ruined my sneakers with the gush of amniotic fluid, blood, pee, and poo. Note to self – wear shoe covers to deliveries. Rooky mistake.

1:35 pm: Dr. Ff is nearby and is being all deferential and ass-kissy towards a more senior attending. Way to exemplify taking advantage of the hierarchical status quo by only being a total bitch to the lowly med student. Strong work.

2:01 pm: A patient's mother asked me if I was a midwife. I'm not sure how to take that.

2:19 pm: I repeatedly remind myself that there are thousands of premeds all over the country, who did not get accepted to med school, who would kill me to take my place, be finishing third year, and about to apply for residency.

3:56 pm: My mood has significantly brightened by the solid combination of a cup of hot java, an oatmeal cookie, and Maverick offering to cook me dinner tonight.

5:45 pm: I caught a baby! Standing between the legs of a patient who had just started pushing, the senior resident leaned in close to my ear and nearly imperceptibly whispered:

Brittany: "We should have talked about this earlier."
Me: "What?"
Brittany: "You're delivering this baby."
Me: "Oh. Ok."
Brittany: "Do you know what to do?"
Me: "In theory. Pull down then up?"
Brittany: "That's pretty much it. Pull down until the first shoulder is out, then pull up and grab the feet. I'll guide your hands."

She failed to mention how freaking fast those suckers shoot out once the first shoulder is out, as well as how slippery the little buggers are. I quickly placed the newborn onto the new momma's belly and into the safe care of the baby nurses. My hands shook as I collected the cord blood and delivered the placenta.

Brittany leaned over and whispered, "Good job. And don't worry, my hands still shake sometimes at stressful deliveries."

I hadn't even realized how visibly my hands were trembling. Mother and baby (and me) are all happy and healthy. Delivering a healthy baby to a happy couple brought a wonderfully satisfying close to this shithole of a day.

10:28 pm: I nestled on Maverick's couch and edited my personal statement for residency while he prepped a lecture for an EM conference. After getting some work done, he cooked me dinner and we strolled to the local ice cream parlor down the street. I reluctantly made my way home, as he had to leave for work.

June 4: Wednesday

8:03 am: Immediately after being told to report directly to ob conference, Magnus and I skipped out and instead went for breakfast.

10:49 am: Dr. Ff is a nonstop faucet of berating and condescending comments during rounds. If she hates medical students and residents so much, why does she work at a teaching hospital? Fortunately, I'm assigned to a different attending today.

1:19 pm: I correctly identified the antibiotics to treat a particular ob condition and earned praise from my attending.

4:51 pm: Patients come to triage with all sorts of minor complaints. The second we reassure them that they are ok, they're ready to run out the door. Sometimes they get downright rude with us. It's not my fault you came in for three mosquito bites and now you have to wait to be discharged while we see other patients that have more pressing issues.

5:31 pm: So many teenagers having babies. So many.

8:50 pm: Back from dinner with Callie, during which I broke the news about Maverick. Her response? "Finally. You've been talking about him forever." True.

June 5: Thursday

5:55 am: I was in bed and sound asleep by 9:30 last night. I feel like a new person.

9:00 am: Dr. Ff ripped apart a resident during rounds today for cracking a joke about the pull out method being a form of birth control. According to Dr. Ff, by making a joke, the resident appears uneducated about valid methods of birth control. Obviously, everyone knows this, that's why it is called a joke. Note to all: do not make jokes in front of Dr. Ff.

9:15 am: Things you don't want to hear in the OR: "Is this the right end?"

10:23 am: I've been emailing back and forth with Maverick. He told me to come over and play when I'm done working.

11:14 am: Residents frequently ignore medical students. Like right now, two senior residents are openly discussing whether or not they like a resident who is rotating on ob from another specialty.

11:41 am: I'm eating lunch on the front steps outside of my medical school. I've chosen this particular lunch spot since it's as far away from the ob floor as I can possibly get without actually leaving the hospital grounds.

1:03 pm: If you are pushing a bowling-ball-sized screaming mass of baby out of your vagina you really don't have to apologize to us for cursing.

2:31 pm: Back from another C-section. While in the OR, the kind attending made a point of saying that she remembered me from yesterday and confirmed that she knew my name.

4:28 pm: It's weird to see someone in labor who still has braces on their teeth. And not like, oh, I'm an adult and just got my braces, but a legit teenage girl with braces and a baby on the way. Oh, and an STI. Nearly every teenager I have seen in the past couple of weeks has multiple STIs.

5:20 pm: Almost done working for the evening, then I'm off to a concert in a nearby park with Maverick and some friends.

June 6: Friday

6:55 am: Instead of pre-rounding for the usual hour from 6-7 am, Magnus and I pre-rounded for a solid 15 minutes and then spent the rest of our allotted time having breakfast. We're both miserable, burnt out, and don't give a shit about this rotation.

7:50 am: Last day of obstetrics. Fortunately, Dr. Ff is not here today. Turns out she ripped Magnus apart yesterday. He asked her a question and instead of answering, she replied, "Well, what do you think?" He stated he didn't know, which is why he had asked. She than yelled at him,

"You shouldn't ask questions unless you know the answer!" Head tilt. Umm… Ok. Right. Sure.

2:09 pm: Quiet day so far. I hope I didn't just curse myself for typing those words…

3:25 pm: Not a single patient came into triage. Oh darn. Time to go home.

June 7: Saturday

9:03 am: I fell asleep on my black hole of a couch and never made it out last night. I woke up to an email from Maverick inviting me rock climbing this afternoon. I've never tried it but I'm game. It looks like something I would enjoy. What should I wear?

June 8: Sunday

10:53 am: My entire body is sore today from climbing yesterday.

Even after packing on some muscle the past few months, I still struggled immensely. I'm pretty sure I had a death grip on the rocks while slowly inching my way up the wall. I didn't feel so much that I was rock climbing, but rather, I was awkwardly clinging to rocks. Fun all the same and I'm looking forward to trying it again. In between routes I hung out on the ground, probably not subtly watching Maverick's shoulders and back muscles while he climbed. After getting all sweaty and dirty climbing, we had a lazy dinner at his place before he reluctantly headed to work.

1:20 pm: I'm thrilled to say farewell to ob! You can take nearly every single problem I've encountered this year – high blood pressure, diabetes, sepsis, amputations, wound infections, suicide attempts, STIs, abuse, drug addiction, psychosis, HIV/AIDS, trauma, blood clots, on and on – and on top of that add a teeny, tiny helpless baby. It's insanity. At least I learned the basics about helping women deliver their babies. Ob, by far, is the most stressful rotation I've been on this year, and I'm thrilled to put it behind me.

5:27 pm: Maverick is heading over for dinner before his shift starts. He's increasingly affectionate and attentive, yet not overwhelming. His brains and looks are equally appealing and most importantly, he makes me laugh. Other than the fact that he eats ice cream with a fork, I'm seeing no red flags.

9:38 pm: Ok he left. Time to study vaginas a bit before starting gynecology tomorrow. I can't believe this is it, my last three weeks of third year.

Gynecology

Song: The Naked and Famous. "Young Blood." *Passive Me, Aggressive You*. Somewhat Damaged Records. 2010.
Drink: Woodford Reserve Double Oaked Bourbon

June 9: Monday

6:02 am: This is it. The final stretch. I'm at The Private Hospital, where I completed general (and vascular) surgery a lifetime ago, back in September. No more catching babies. Now it's time to learn about all the gynecology-related health issues that plague women, ranging from uterine cancer to heavy menses to overactive bladders. I have two weeks of gyn surgery, followed by one week of outpatient gyn at various clinics.

9:35 am: The operating rooms are sparkling and bright here. Unlike the windowless general surgery ORs, the gyn ORs are located on the top floor of the hospital, with large windows allowing sunlight to pour in. The nurses are still as cheerful and welcoming as when I did general surgery here.

2:11 pm: As I placed a Foley catheter in a woman's urethra and watched the tubing and little bagging fill with urine, I thought about how my worst day this year is still an improvement over any day during the first two years of medical school.

6:14 pm: Gyn is, on first impression, a reasonably enjoyable rotation. There are no babies, no children, and no men. On the flip side, I have to look at vaginas all day long.

June 10: Tuesday

10:42 am: Scrubbing into hysterectomies makes my vagina hurt.

11:10 am: Again, the nurses here at The Private Hospital are so awesome.

1:05 pm: Off to afternoon clinic.

1:15 pm: My first patient is a hungover pregnant woman.

2:20 pm: The highlight of my day featured a discussion of sex toys with a hilarious geriatric patient.

4:10 pm: Rumors are floating around about how many of the fourth-year medical students are either breaking up or getting engaged, based on how The Match went for them. I'm getting uneasy thinking about next year.

9:56 pm: The Boss is currently in New York City and at the moment she is out drinking with my mother. Yep. The Boss and my mom are at a trendy mid-town Manhattan wine bar while I'm getting ready for bed. Lame.

June 11: Wednesday

5:15 am: Good morning city. This is not a civilized time to be leaving for work. Blehh. No fun being on a surgical rotation, though I enjoy that nearly all of the residents are female. According to our society, being an ob-gyn is an acceptable residency choice for women, so no one, yet, has assumed I'm a nurse.

7:09 am: A surgeon invited me into a robotic surgery case. I still get frightened before going into the OR with a new surgeon. You never know if they'll pimp you the whole time, ignore you, yell at you, or teach.

10:52 am: Happily, today contained mostly teaching, with a light sprinkling of pimping mixed in. The surgeon liked me enough to invite me to his afternoon case. I'd never seen a robotic surgery before. It's kind of like watching someone else play video games for a couple of hours.

2:13 pm: More light pimping in the afternoon case. I answered his string of questions correctly so then he shrugged, "Well, you know the answers to my questions, so I'm going to push you a bit." He then proceeded to start pimping me about male anatomy. Well that's just not fair. I didn't study male pelvic anatomy. I've spent the last three weeks learning about female anatomy. Oh well. The pimping continues.

I successfully removed a uterus through a patient's vagina.

3:14 pm: Let out early! Got my nails done.

Maverick has been out of town since Monday. I've gotten quite accustomed to seeing him on a near-daily basis. I'm hoping to see him tomorrow night before I skip town for the weekend. Some female surgery resident friends and I rented a lake house a few hours away, complete with a private dock and boat. I've barely started packing. So far I've only placed bathing suits, sunscreen, a beach ball, and alcohol in my bag. Hmm... actually, I think I'm done packing.

June 12: Thursday

9:40 am: During my mid-rotation evaluation I received excellent feedback and perfect clinical grades. I imagine this will be yet another rotation where I do fabulously well clinically, yet my final exam grade will ruin my opportunity to get honors or high pass for the rotation.

10:40 am: Back to the OR today with another new attending. Apparently this one fluctuates wildly between really kind and really cruel, depending on his mood. Ok...

12:42 pm: I got lucky. The surgeon arrived in a pleasant mood and joked with the nurses throughout the case.

12:55 pm: Done for the day. My OR cases are over and there are only a few clinic patients so the intern and a senior resident let me go. Sweet.

1:10 pm: Oh, that hurts. I ran into a different senior on my way out of the hospital and she remarked, "Oh good, we can walk over to clinic together." Freedom snatched away at the last moment. Sigh.

1:42 pm: As horrible as ob turned out, gyn is pretty entertaining. While doing a pelvic exam to assess a woman's vaginal bleeding, the resident discussed safety tips for rough sex to help prevent the patient's issue from recurring.

2:23 pm: There are no patients at clinic right now. I'm just chilling.

2:30 pm: Sent home. Thank you, residents.

Maverick is back in town and on his way over.

June 13: Friday

7:30 am: Waiting for morning lectures to start. My mind is wandering to Maverick playing with my hair whenever he kisses me.

12:26 pm: Busted. Turns out all the EM and ob people already know about Maverick. After this weekend, the female surgery residents at the lake house will know. On Monday night, I'm going to have to tell The Boss to ensure she doesn't hear it through the grapevine. She's gonna yell at me. Epic fail on my part, but I couldn't help myself.

4:02 pm: All packed and ready for the lake. One bag has clothes and lake gear, another contains homemade mini-muffins and cupcakes, and the last bag is full of alcohol and games.

9:59 pm: A rowdy game of Cards Against Humanity kicked off our lake weekend. Bedtime now.

June 14: Saturday

10:15 am: On the boat!

7:03 pm: A beautiful cloudless sky created the perfect backdrop for sailing around all day. When back on dry land, we grilled dinner on the huge back porch overlooking the water. We drank beers and cocktails, traded stories from work, and enjoyed the peace and quiet of being far, far away from any hospitals.

10:05 pm: I'm lying in bed and I feel as if I'm still at sea.

June 15: Sunday

2:40 pm: Home from my girl's weekend at the lake. I'm exhausted but we had such a blast.

4:53 pm: Maverick is on his way over.

June 16: Monday

6:14 am: Terrible night's sleep. I found myself alone in the dark with an unknown terror creeping in the shadows. I managed to find some friends and we all hid together. Another shadow approached, which turned out to be Maverick, and he hid with us. A masked, shadowy figure with a machete grabbed one of my friends and slit their throat. I couldn't yell out in my dream to stop them. I had no voice. I tried to scream, over and over, but no sound came out.

I awoke stifling a scream, sitting bolt upright in bed, sweating and panting before becoming fully conscious. Maverick didn't wake up; his breathing didn't change so I don't think he was pretending. Unfair. I drifted off to sleep last night feeling content, relaxed, and safe. Shouldn't that lead to pleasant dreams? Are there creeping fears about residency?

7:43 am: It's painful to operate with someone who's a total jackass. An encouraging surgeon really makes the whole day so much more pleasant and productive. I hope I'm assigned to a good one today.

11:43 am: Awesome day! The surgeon I worked with totally rocked. He referred to me as Dr. Silvia, taught the entire time, and he let me perform multiple steps during each case, including the initial incision and the final closure. The best part was that all of his cases were accompanied by music from the likes of REM, Counting Crows, U2, and Live.

12:30 pm: Lunchtime with Magnus, who inquired about how things were going with Maverick. I told him how Maverick and I hung out when I got back into town last night. Magnus choked on his food and proceeded to clarify the Sunday night timeframe.

Magnus: "He went to your house last night?"

Me: "Yes."

Magnus: "He skipped the season four finale of *Game of Thrones* to hang out with you?"

Me: "Yeah."

Magnus: "You know what that's called?"

Me: "What?"

Magnus: "Love."

Well, whatever it is, it's time to tell The Boss about it. I'm having dinner with her tonight and I'm guessing she's not going to be too pleased with me.

1:20 pm: Off to more ob-gyn lectures.

June 17: Tuesday

318

5:58 am: Waking up before 6 am is made even more painful when there is some playful EM resident who keeps kept pulling me back into bed.

10:08 am: I'm hiding on my favorite rooftop at The Private Hospital. I probably only have to scrub into one more case today, but I wanted to sit outside for a moment. I'm exhausted. The Boss and I went for dinner last night. The minute I sat down she crossed her hands on the table, leaned in, and started the conversation by eyeing me and stating seriously, "Let's discuss Dr. Maverick…"

So I spilled the rest of the beans. The Boss laughed while rolling her eyes at me and informing me that she suspected it all along. She revealed that he's been outright avoiding her for the past month, and he appeared skittish whenever they had to interact. Fortunately, she had only good things to say about him as a resident and as a person, so I have her approval. Phew. What a relief!

After dinner I met up with Maverick and his friends. Everyone knows and it's all out in the open but what matters most right now is that I'm absurdly happy.

11:40 am: I got to first-assist on a couple of cases this morning with the awesome gyn surgeon and same nursing team from yesterday. Gyn is turning out to not be too painful.

12:50 pm: Off to clinic for the afternoon. While walking to clinic, the residents and I passed a couple of nurses and they remarked, "Don't you guys ever go home?"

2:22 pm: A patient opened up to me today about her extensive history of sexual abuse. She shared that she has never told anyone before about her years of torment and fear. Providing support and resources for her felt important, as if I was actually making a difference in her life and helping pave the way for a better future for her. She thanked me warmly, but still, I wish I could do more for her.

Towards the end of her appointment she wanted to give me advice in return. She told me to not work too much, to get a man, to enjoy my life, and upon finding out my age, she told me to get on having kids. She also informed me, "A pretty little thing like you should have a man in your life, but keep your standards high." After all of her years of hardship and abuse, she sat there smiling and had the loveliest personality. She didn't even think her life was so bad because she was still alive. She was a survivor.

I don't know how you endure something like that and still maintain such a positive outlook on life. Some patients, like this one, I do wish I could follow up on, to see what happens, and to see how their life turns out.

3:05 pm: As much as I don't like ob-gyn overall, I truly enjoy talking to women about women's health issues. For example, this week I partook in various discussions about sex toys, heavy menses, birth control, sexual abuse, and menopause.

4:12 pm: I'm bad at ob-gyn clinic. Many of these patients have multiple medical problems and I have difficulty ignoring the issues that are not relevant to ob-gyn. For example, a patient (without a primary care doc) came in for a routine gyn exam, and I noticed that her blood pressure is high. I want to discuss her hypertension, but it's irrelevant to this visit. All the ob-gyns can do is recommend, "Go see a primary care doc about your high blood pressure." Which they probably won't. Patients often don't have the time, money, transportation, or motivation to go. I could never be a specialist. I want to be able to focus on whatever the most pressing issue is, regardless of what body part is involved.

June 18: Wednesday

9:39 am: Hoping to get done with my cases early today to go play with Maverick. At times I still don't really believe that we're dating.

10:25 am: Finally got my EM grade: honors! This is a big deal and super important for my residency application. Earning honors increases my odds of being invited for interviews at competitive residency programs. And all of my studying paid off. I earned a 98% on the department exam. I haven't scored that high on any test in all of med school. I'm wondering if I got the highest grade all year in my class. It's astonishing how well I can do when I actually enjoy the reading material and am not studying under duress (like right now on ob-gyn or when I rotated on peds).

10:52 am: I love the nurses here. They're smart and caring, and teach me all sorts of useful stuff. They seem genuinely motivated and proud of their work. Thank you nurses of The Private Hospital.

12:14 pm: While having lunch, I was informed that I can leave after my next case. Excellent. Maverick is off early today too and neither of us have to work tonight so we can actually spend a decent amount of time together today.

June 19: Thursday

7:30 am: Just saw a woman who'd suffered a miscarriage late in pregnancy –devastating. Sometimes the "products of conception" pass naturally; sometimes a procedure is necessary to remove them. In this case, the dead fetus is still intrauterine and won't pass. The gyn surgeon will go in and remove it for her so that the tissue doesn't cause an infection, which can be life threatening. I can't imagine the pain, anger, and sadness of a miscarriage. Why does it seem that couples who want children have the most difficulty conceiving, while the careless or unlucky teens are the ones who wind up pregnant?

8:45 am: So much blood. We removed the fetal tissue using a suction device while the woman was under general anesthesia. A somber day in the OR.

9:05 am: Random fun fact: did you know that the antibiotic Rifampin turns your tears and urine an orange-red color?

2:50 pm: Sitting in lecture. An irate lecturer has yelled at our class for the past 50 straight minutes. I'm not entirely sure what he is so pissy about.

Magnus attempted to answer a question and the lecturer yelled at him, "You're wrong! Don't question me. I'm the expert here." Well, yeah, but don't be a dick about it.

2:55 pm: The lecturer is now screaming at The Most Interesting Man in the World for looking around the room. Looking. He wasn't chatting, or texting, or being otherwise disruptive. He literally got yelled at for looking around.

3:01 pm: My turn. I got blasted for (correctly) answering a question. Here is what happened:

Lecturer: "How long do you wait to do a follow up ultrasound?"

Me: "Six weeks."

Lecturer: "Wrong. Why would you think that?"

Me: "Because it gives women time to cycle again and it's the timeframe given in the assigned reading for today."

Lecturer: "Your text is wrong! You should know that. I never wait six weeks. Every text teaches that way, but it makes no sense."

Me: "Oh. Ok."

I'm supposed to know that every gynecology textbook is wrong? Umm... sure, but... how? I seriously want to point out that standardized tests, such as our board exams, don't give a shit about the personal preferences of individual physicians, but instead I bit my lip and turned my attention back towards texting with Maverick.

I kept lobbing up answers, stoking the yell-lecturer's wrath, solely because it was less boring than sitting quietly, staring at my iPad.

3:25 pm: Wow. The lecturer closed his talk by imparting some advice. You know what he recommended to us? "Don't be arrogant." AYFKM? That's your pearl of wisdom? After the bullshit yelling you just put us through about not trusting the information in textbooks?

3:31 pm: Done. Finally. Ok so overall not the best day in surgery or in the classroom... and by not best I mean worst.

June 20: Friday

6:27 am: Last day of gyn surgery at The Private Hospital!

6:48 am: For reasons unknown there are almost no residents here today.

1:14 pm: Awesome. Without residents, I got to first-assist on all the morning cases! I helped make the laparoscopic incisions, drive the camera, do injections, use the laparoscopic stapler and other laparoscopic tools, fish out the parts being removed, as well as help close at the end of the case. As I will never scrub into another surgery as a med student, being first-assist all morning is definitely a high note on which to go out.

I might have snuck out during lunch when no one was looking.

2:20 pm: House party at Maverick's place tonight.

June 21: Saturday

10:11 am: Woke up to find that Maverick had left me water, coffee, ibuprofen, and breakfast next to his bed before he departed for work. So sweet and thoughtful.

The party last night totally rocked. Maverick occasionally roamed over to chat, or put his arm around me, or kiss my cheek, in front of all of his friends and co-residents, no less. He made it feel like an official thing now. Like a boyfriend-type thing.

7:23 pm: Today felt semi-productive. I have to stay in tonight so that tomorrow I can get some hardcore studying done.

June 22: Sunday

11:45 am: Brunch with Daria and Jane. They're such a cute couple. My morning has not yet been productive as my motivation to study ob-gyn is fairly nonexistent.

2:05 pm: Sitting on my balcony, surrounded by my little herbs and vegetables that are slowly growing, while prepping for my last exam of third year. What a wonderful feeling. I just need to push through this week of outpatient gyn clinic and I'm free. I hope this week doesn't drag on too terribly slowly.

2:54 pm: Ahh no. I had every intention of being productive but Magnus invited me to go watch the US World Cup game with him. Soccer or study? Soccer or study? Soccer!

9:45 pm: Ok so today turned out to be kind of not productive. At all. Oops. Oh, and Maverick is on his way over, so I'm certainly not going to start being productive at this point in time.

June 23: Monday

9:01 am: Last week of third-year clinical rotations. First day on outpatient gyn clinic.

9:30 am: I started my book exactly one year ago to the day. The rising third years start their first intersession today. Next Monday, I will be a fourth-year medical student, and the new third years will begin their descent towards Cerberus. At this very moment, The Dean of Something Educational is probably giving her welcome speech, telling them to study hard, lean on each other, not commit suicide, tattle on the attendings who throw things at them, blah, blah, blah...

As I inch up the medical totem pole, there will now and forever more be medical students below me. I hope I remember to let them participate in patient care so that they have a sense of responsibility for their patients, and a feeling of belonging on the team. I also pledge to send them home when there's nothing to do, and not to pimp them unnecessarily hard.

June 24: Tuesday

10:11 am: I'm over it. Gyn is cool and all, but I'm starting to miss seeing male patients, peds patients, and even the babies. I want to see every patient, no matter the background, no matter the injury or illness. Bring 'em all.

4:10 pm: I've been texting with some of my newfound friends from this year. I would like to keep collecting friends and drinking buddies as I continue through my medical training. Workdays are made so much more enjoyable when you're friendly with your coworkers. Cheers to Dr. Red from family medicine, Dr. NY from psych, Allie from pediatrics, and Lisa from ob-gyn!

June 25: Wednesday

9:23 am: A young patient turned to me mid-appointment and queried, "I gotta ask – why'd you choose to look at vaginas all day?"

My honest reply, "I'm actually going into emergency medicine, I'm just rotating through here." And at the same time I'm thinking to myself, "I have no idea why anyone would choose this either."

2:31 pm: As I wrapped up my last day at clinic, I thought about my experiences this past year and all the different residents, attendings, and nurses with whom I've worked. A few of my friends suffered at the hands of terrible assholes, but for the most part, I never experienced any torture by my superiors. Of course, there existed the occasional asshole (umm hello Gump and Dr. Ff), but I'm fairly certain that an ass or two can be found in any profession.

The overwhelming majority of docs with whom I worked were enthusiastic teachers and excellent physician role models. If anything, I'm hopeful that the younger generations of physicians, including my peers, will be increasingly less malignant towards med students and those junior to us. At least in my experience this year, the days of physically and mentally torturing med students are dwindling. Maybe I was just lucky and isolated from such behavior.

As for the nurses, I'd always been told that they are invaluable to medical students, but I didn't really appreciate what that meant until this year. Nurses have a great ability to really impact a med student's education and experience on rotations. There were so many instances where their guidance and helpfulness really brightened my day and made my life so much easier. Thank you for being kind to me (most of the time), teaching me about patient care, and for taking such wonderful care of our critically sick patients.

3:35 pm: My last patient has gone and my last note is done. That's it. I can't believe I'm done with third year rotations.

4:59 pm: Off to go celebrate my rotations being done!

June 26: Thursday

11:42 am: I'm finally home. Maverick and I spent last night celebrating and partying with our friends.

We spent a lazy morning together and after cooking me breakfast, he attempted to teach me to play a few chords on his guitar. My hands are tiny and I have no musical talents, but he remained patient, encouraging, and openly amused by my attempts. There's a growing feeling of warmth, comfort, and happiness throughout me when we're together. I would have loved to spend the rest of the day with him watching World Cup matches, but I am being responsible and came home to study for my ob-gyn exam tomorrow.

9:13 pm: On the eve of my final exam of third year. I'm burnt out, my brain hurts, and I'm tired. Is it over yet? This year has been too long. Fourth year is so close.

As I finish up ob-gyn tomorrow, Maverick is starting a month-long rotation in the surgical ICU. EM residents rotate all over the hospital because they have to know how to care for all patients.

On a related note, Casey is back in town after his two months rotating away and will be starting on trauma surgery, so those two will likely cross paths. I'm glad Casey was gone the past two months; it gave me time to develop my relationship with Maverick without Casey's interference. Not that Casey trying to intrude would've made any difference; as far as I'm concerned, no other guys in the world exist right now. Hopefully, it won't be a big deal when Casey and Maverick have to work together this month. My hope (and guess) is that Casey won't care about Maverick being in my life. Casey hasn't contacted me since getting back into town and I'm expecting he'll leave well enough alone. I would like for Casey to be happy with himself and his life, but to be happy in a place that is far away from me and mine.

10:54 pm: Maverick just dropped by my apartment for a kiss and to bring me a cupcake before he headed to work. The relationship scares me. He scares me. I'm scared of how much I like him and how badly he'd be able to hurt me. I'm in deep. It's the most unreal feeling.

11:10 pm: I probably should have studied more during this rotation but I don't care anymore.

June 27: Friday

6:25 am: Two standardized patients, two pages of short answer questions, and a suturing test kick off my Friday morning. Yes, this is the only rotation that requires anything beyond taking the written multiple-choice exam. The written exam will be in the afternoon.

9:20 am: Ok, the first part is done. Definitely the more difficult part, so I'm glad it's over. Now I have a few hours to kill until the written exam.

11:30 am: The ob-gyn final is at 1:00 pm. One hundred multiple-choice questions stand between me, fourth year, and one glorious week of vacation. I kind of thought about studying, but instead I'm sitting outside of the med school and gossiping with my classmates.

3:17 pm: Done. Now what?

I'm a bit dazed at the moment. What do I do with myself right now? Is it too early to start celebrating?

I usually have an immediate dissociative fugue after exams and forget every question. But on this exam I noted, and seriously had to refrain from snickering during the test, when one potential answer to a test question stated, "Inadequate coital technique." WTF does that even mean? Like he routinely puts it in the wrong hole?

4:02 pm: My classmates and I relocated to the pool after grabbing some mouth-watering chicken and waffles. We are soaking in the warm sun and enjoying our newfound freedom. Magnus is sitting next to me wearing a pair of pastel Chubbies, drinking a beer, and smoking a cigar. He seems entirely unchanged and unfazed by this past year. OMG he is leaning over my shoulder right now, reading what I'm typing, and insisting on me reporting that he gained five pounds of muscle this year. He also added, on a more serious note, that I seem unchanged as well. For a split second, I let myself believe that statement. But I know it's not true.

In the process of finding my people, I feel so much worse for the wear. Exhausted. Frustrated. Disenchanted. The image I held of being a doctor is now distorted. The stress of making life or death decisions, the sleep deprivation, the berating from superiors, and the lack of free time to unwind and decompress, often seems overwhelming. I am less disturbed by seeing people in pain. I'm immune to blood and grotesque injuries. I'm suspicious of patients who ask for pain medication. I'm no longer surprised when I hear interns and residents talk about quitting medicine. My threshold for putting up with inefficiency and with bullshit has plummeted.

On the other hand, I became stronger. Tougher. Unyielding. Confident. My understanding of what it means to be a doctor is more realistic. I have a greater appreciation of the sacrifice that is required from those who dedicate their lives to caring for other people. Naïve optimism may have helped me survive pre-med and early med school, but grit and determination is what will carry me forward. I feel ready to face whatever comes next.

I'd like to believe that I have retained my good-natured personality, sense of self, and generally optimistic outlook on life. I hope I haven't become too disheartened and jaded. Perhaps it's too soon to judge what the lasting effects of third year will be. Either way, I plan to rely on healthy methods of self-care, such as journaling, painting, and working out as I move forward.

Looking around at my classmates, it's hard to imagine all of us moving away next summer. Where to from here? I'll be applying for residency all over the country, from Fresno to Charlotte, Philly to Austin. I have no idea where in this country I will be moving to next year for my EM residency. But now is not the time for contemplating that. Now is the time for a dip in the pool.

7:22 pm: Piper, Sophia, Jane, and Daria will be arriving shortly for celebratory beer, wine, and pizza.

11:58 pm: Celebrating with my tribe of women felt wonderful. We have all committed to different specialties:

328

Sophia is heading to internal medicine, Maggie is off to ob-gyn, Piper is heading into pediatrics, and Jane will go into family medicine. Their patients will be lucky to have them as their doctors one day. We popped the champagne that my parents had gifted me on my 30th birthday. We cheered the end of third year, the start of fourth year, and being one step closer to becoming doctors. Triumphant toasts and much laughter rang throughout my apartment all evening.

June 28: Saturday

9:29 am: Where did this year go? I'm brewing chicory coffee, a present from Zooey sent from New Orleans, and about to cook breakfast. Seeing as this is my last day of digital journaling, I wonder if I'll have any difficulty transitioning back to journaling with a pen on paper. It took a while, but now I reflexively reach for my right outer white coat pocket and start tapping away at my iPad whenever I see or feel something interesting.

10:02 am: Mmm coffee. I just finished Skyping with my parents, who congratulated me on everything I accomplished this year. Couldn't have done it without their support and encouragement!

10:41 am: My only goals for today are to clean my apartment and finish my painting for The Boss. A painting for her is the least I can do. She has been such an instrumental mentor in my medical education and in my personal life as well. I don't know how to thank her enough for everything she has done for me. I imagine she will be keeping an eye on me and guiding me for years to come.

2:10 pm: I'm so content and yet so far from where I thought I'd be. Never did I imagine I'd wind up developing a relationship with the intelligent, carefree, outdoorsy Maverick. Speaking of which, Maverick is coming over for dinner tonight. For the past month or so, he has proven himself to be everything that I had imagined. Smart, charming, light-hearted, sweet, and affectionate. All the good things.

The feelings of certainty about my career path and finding my people are so much more intense, gratifying, and overwhelming than I imagined they would be. I found the place in medicine where I belong. I can't wait to jump into residency and start my official training as an emergency physician.

I'm not quite ready to type "the end" just yet. There's still too much of my story left to unfold between finishing medical school, my friends and I matching for residency, and seeing where my relationship with Maverick goes. That being said, I certainly have reached a most fortunate and satisfying interim. And at this sweet moment in time, I have it all.

Epilogue

Song: Sea Wolf. "Visions." *Song Spells, No.1: Cedarsmoke*. Self released. 2014.
Drink: Mezcal Paloma

Four and a half years later and counting

I'm halfway through my fourth and final year of my emergency medicine residency. My husband is inside playing guitar while I sit outside and watch our Rottweilers play on the lawn. I have penned five and a half hand-written journals since finishing my third year of medical school. Returning to journaling on paper was a welcomed change after spending a year glued to my iPad. The past several years have been packed with life-changing events, but only now have I had the time and energy to return to the pages of this book.

Fourth year of medical school started out great. I began interviewing at different residency programs around the country. Maverick and I continued to spend all of our free time together. We traveled abroad and he even introduced me to his family. But as I began traveling for rotations at different hospitals and the likelihood of me staying in the Midwest shrank, Maverick broke up with me.

Completely blindsided, I went through a brief period of illogical thinking where I became fairly certain I would be alone forever. He had been the first person after Casey with whom I dropped my guard. He had been the one to show me that I could once again care about another person. That also meant he turned into the first person capable of hurting me. Stunned, I slogged forward with fourth year of med school. My world shrank. I became entirely focused on two things: where I would go for residency and working out.

I continued interviewing all over the country, searching for an EM program that would be the right fit for me. I fell hard for a badass residency in California, known for its stellar reputation and long history of producing

331

outstanding emergency physicians. I went on about a dozen interviews total, but none compared to that particular program. I set my sites on moving to California and waited impatiently for Match Day to roll around.

Dates and tiramisu floated around, but no one held my interest for any period of time. Finally content being single, I spent the majority of my free time at the gym. Climbing, lifting, and running became daily habits. However, it was not until a barista at Starbucks asked me, "How on earth did you get those shoulders?" that I noticed the change in my body. During these months, *Love, Sanity, or Medical School*, sat in a hidden file on my computer. Reliving my break up with Casey, the day-to-day struggles of third year, or trying to edit scenes describing my happy moments with Maverick was too painful. Momma told me to give it time and when I felt ready, to add an epilogue.

The Boss remained a source of unwavering support for me throughout fourth year of med school. In mid-December, we traveled to the Middle East together for an international EM conference. We had a blast at a Pakistani-New Zealand Cricket game, rode camels in the sand dunes, and were inked with intricate henna tattoos by a veiled artist. The Midwest was a world away, and I felt content to be on the road. While smoking hookah one night under the desert stars, The Boss revealed to me that she had accepted a new job somewhere and would be leaving the Midwest for good come springtime. I would no longer have any ties to the Midwest, and my motivation to head to the West Coast became even more solidified.

I was in Manhattan for New Year's Eve. Sophia and Maggie road tripped to The City and we rung in the year with a dance party at my parent's apartment. I remember thinking about how much I would miss them the following year, as I suspected we would likely move away from each other for residency. Around this time, I booked a solo trip to Iceland, scheduled to take place right after I graduated med school and prior to starting residency. I had never been to

Iceland before, but I had an inexplicably intense feeling of certainty that I must travel to the country.

Match Day began full of nerves and hope. Standing with my closest friends, I opened my Match Day letter and read the best news I could possibly hope to find: I matched to my number one ranked program and would be moving to California for my EM residency. Success!

I finished an uneventful last few rotations in the spring of fourth year and graduated from The College of Medicine. Just prior to moving to California, I hopped a plane to Reykjavik, Iceland for the "Hooray, you finished medical school!" trip that I had planned several months earlier.

On the first day in Reykjavik I met a handsome blond Italian man named Ash, also a solo traveler. We connected instantly. I felt as if I had known him for years. We became inseparable, exploring Iceland together, spending entire nights talking and sharing our worlds, all under the glow of the magical Northern Lights. After two weeks traveling together, he booked a ticket to America. Ash arrived in the Midwest about ten days later and helped me finish packing up my apartment. Happily bidding farewell to my old life, we hopped into my car and drove Route 66 together. We made it to California but were not yet ready to part ways. He was accepted to grad school in the same city as my residency. Our relationship grew and about a year later, while visiting his family in Italy, we got engaged at his family's vineyard. Not too long ago, we were married on our favorite beach in California.

There were fleeting thoughts about finishing these pages and pursuing publication, but my busy resident schedule ate up all my free time. I would occasionally remember these chapters hidden away on my laptop, and think "One day I'll finish my book." Every so often I would flip through the entries and wonder what happened to my patients. The pages are full of encounters with kind, warm, encouraging individuals who let me bumble through caring for them. In my inexperienced hands they always greeted me with a smile and never let on that they minded that a med student was caring for them. I am grateful for everything they taught me about patient care and medicine. In my mind, they are all living happy, healthy, productive lives, free from their many afflictions, though I know that is not likely to be the case.

During residency I dealt with both personal and professional struggles and suffering. One day I awoke to the news that a close friend of mine, another emergency physician, had committed suicide by shooting himself in the head. We had recently spoken and he never let on about his suffering. Years earlier, he had been the very first person I confided in about my plan to apply to medical school. Why couldn't he turn to me or to someone else for help? I cried and cried, still hysterical as I pulled into the parking lot at work to start my shift.

My worst moments are when I have to tell a family member that their loved one is dead. I broke down crying at work one night after telling a young woman, who also happened to be a newlywed, that her husband had died. I did everything I could, but I could not save him. After not even five minutes of hiding in the bathroom crying, I returned to seeing patients.

Living patients can be a challenge, too. I routinely care for patients who have harmed others in horrific ways. I've cared for a drunk driver who crashed his car, killing nearly an entire family in the process. Convicted murderers and pedophiles get sick and need medical care, too. The victims from prison riots and gang fights have filled up our trauma bay multiple times. I have learned more about bullet wounds, firearm injuries, and ballistics than I ever wanted to know.

I repeatedly treat a woman who comes in every night with the same complaint but is really there because she is lonely at home by herself. I have found tumors and diagnosed cancers. I've seen all manner of abuse and neglect of children, pregnant women, the disabled, and frail senior citizens. Difficult patients routinely demand everything from

334

narcotics and sedatives to unnecessary and invasive tests. Seeing the complications related to obesity – such as diabetes, heart disease, and joint problems – are a daily occurrence. Many of my patients can't afford to take their medications, don't know how to take them, or are too stubborn to do so.

In the midst of the never-ending barrage of illnesses and injuries that rolls through the doors of the ED, I also witness many beautiful encounters. Loved ones come together to support each other, providing words of comfort and strength. Families pray together and hold each other up through trying times. Being privy to witnessing a person's last breath on earth is always a humbling experience.

Many of my days are fulfilling and adrenaline-fueled. I still enjoy meeting and working with patients from every background. Diagnosing a rare or unusual condition brings satisfaction. Juggling multiple tasks is a rush. Providing comfort to those who are scared or in pain is a daily goal I try to meet. The breadth of EM still surprises me, and I continue to learn more every day.

My co-residents have become my extended family. My attendings provid needed support and guidance throughout the growing pains of residency. I continue to rely on journaling, painting, working out, and other healthy methods of self-care. During third year of residency I started fencing again. Returning to a sport I loved so much provides me with a demanding mental and physical outlet. I also published several essays, articles, and book chapters. Writing continues to offer me a way to mentally debrief, unwind, and process my thoughts. I haven't been able to paint as much as I would like to, but I am slowly working through a replica of Van Gogh's *Starry Night*. Nightmares rarely occur now, faded due to a combination of working at my dream job and finally being wedded to the right person.

About halfway through third year of residency, Ash and I were discussing what our dream jobs had been when we were little kids. My goal had always been to become a doctor, an artist, and a writer. He knew about the book I had stashed away and he gently encouraged me to return to these pages and finish what I had started. With the enthusiastic support of my residency program and several physician mentors, I unearthed this file from the depths of my computer.

A strange sense of unease existed about reliving third year. I wasn't sure how I would react to rereading my thoughts. When I started editing my book, I often became angry when seeing how long I put up with Casey's indecisiveness. The amount of time and energy spent on him and on blaming myself was exhausting. The unending hours at work, being ignored or dismissed, was also frustrating to relive. Visiting those dark places and times was difficult, but I found that each rotation contained pearls of wisdom and insights that I carried with me to residency.

As an example of this, internal medicine taught me to question everything and to make no assumptions. According to our medical textbooks, a patient with an illness will present with specific symptoms. The patient will then have lab values and findings on imaging which match their medical condition, all in a neat little bundle. In reality, this is rarely the case. Patients often roll into the ED with multiple complaints, contradictory symptoms, and years of chronic ailments, all of which muddy the picture of what is actually going on. When I find myself unsure of how to proceed, I return to my patient's bedside and start gathering more information. Internal medicine taught me to dig for answers, as asking the right questions and getting to the crux of what is really going on is the heart of medicine.

While working with residents from other programs, I find that I enjoy working with surgeons the most. I think this is mainly because I appreciate their efficiency, a skill I first envied and tried to emulate back in med school. My days in the operating room triggered my love of procedures, and I continue to enjoy working with my hands. When I teach medical students new procedures, it is often obvious which students love the challenge and which ones are uncomfortable. For the students who are interested and competent, I try to give them as much hands-on experience as possible. I see the gleam in their eye that I must have had on days where I successfully placed sutures, lines, or tubes.

Many aspects of medicine remain a challenge. Seeing the often-irreversible problems caused by brain injuries and non-accidental trauma is still disturbing. Nearly all patients arriving to the ED, even the ones with no psychiatric complaints, appear to be stressed and anxious. In that sense, psychiatry is unequivocally useful. Every sick or injured patient I evaluate has had their daily life suddenly disrupted, sometimes in quite dramatic fashion. People typically do not plan their day knowing that it involves a trip to the emergency department. Knowing how to work with a person who is tense and hassled is a valuable skill, both in helping to build rapport with patients and to help make their time in the ED easier.

I enjoyed my time working in family medicine, but I didn't truly appreciate the value of a primary care doctor until I worked with patients who did not have one. Patients without a family doctor often come to the ED for basic healthcare needs, including checkups, medication refills, and evaluations for chronic conditions. This leads to the ED being routinely overcrowded with patients without emergencies, but who have no other access to medical care. Patients needing follow up after ED visits also end up returning to the ED, when instead they could have seen their own family doctor. While this topic is a landmine fraught with complicating issues, I'll just note that my admiration for primary care doctors has increased greatly and that I believe all people would benefit from having access to primary care.

I still prefer treating adults to children and babies, though as an emergency physician I am trained to work with all age groups. No day is worse for me than a day where I have to tell a parent that their child has died from their injury or illness. Fortunately, this is a rare occurrence. As much as I dislike pediatrics, I still love working with pediatricians. Their stereotype of being friendly and bright is as true here

337

in California as it was back in the Midwest. One skill I have certainly improved is my ability to deliver babies. Since my third year ob rotation I have safely delivered 15 babies and helped with several cesarean sections. I still find the process stressful, but not as terrifying as that first delivery several years back.

Third year of medical school created the foundation on which the rest of my medical education rests. The events of my personal life created a foundation of independence and fearlessness, which I also carry with me to this day. Forcing myself to break up with Casey was one of the most difficult things I have ever done. Choosing to upend my life, unsure of how it would play out, terrified me. But it became the best thing I ever did. While there were multiple moments of doubt, questions, AND questionable behavior throughout third year, I pushed through. I emerged stronger, more independent, and with a greater appreciation for my own resilience. I finished third year with a low tolerance for putting up with bullshit and uncertainty from subsequent relationships.

From the day I met Ash, his affection towards me always came across as open and unreserved. A line in his wedding vows sweetly declared that meeting me was the best thing that ever happened to him. Hearing those words, and truly believing them, created a magical moment. A couple of years into our marriage, the amount of energy I put towards building a life with Ash is still met with equal effort and enthusiasm from him. It is hard to believe I ever put up with less!

I've grown from a bumbling intern, terrified that I'd kill someone, into a confident senior resident, on the verge of becoming an attending emergency physician. As fourth year of residency draws to a close, my husband and I are now looking ahead to the next steps. We'll be moving to southern California next summer so that I can start an Emergency Medical Services (EMS) and Disaster Medicine fellowship. During my fellowship, I will devote my energy to better preparing the country to withstand any future terrorist attacks, pandemics, and natural disasters. My goal is to decrease the impact and suffering that is caused by such terrible events.

The path to becoming a physician is grueling. Third year of med school is our first exposure to the realities of medicine. Seeing patients for the first time is an eye opening and sometimes shocking experience. To those out there plodding away through their own medical training, I promise that is does get better. To those who are already senior residents and attendings, try to remember occasionally how challenging the path is to get to where we are now. Cut the med student some slack. If you're one of our patients, try to remember that med students and doctors are people too. We have triumphs and tragedies the same as you, except that we're expected to hide it at work. We are going through breakups, dealing with deaths, missing the weddings and other celebrations of our loved ones – all in a high stress environment, and often while sleep deprived, just so that we can take care of you and your family.

There are days, particularly the ones where I feel overworked and burnt out, when I go home and question my chosen career path. I often dwell on medical decisions I've made, and the burden of potential mistakes weighs on me. But I couldn't imagine doing anything else. Being a physician is a privilege that I take seriously. I help save people's lives on a daily basis. The adrenaline rush of pulling a patient back from the brink of death is unparalleled. My medical knowledge is broad, and I am ready for anything that rolls through the doors. I don't want you to get ill or injured, but I promise to be there for you if you do. If I ever care for you or your family member, I'll do everything I can to treat your illness or injury with care and compassion.

Time to put on my scrubs and head to work. My next shift is about to start.

The End

Acknowledgements

First and foremost, thank you to my parents, Sandra and Howard Benjamin. Their steadfast support of me throughout my whole life provided an unbreakable backbone on which I relied during my struggle to become a doctor. They never doubted me and have always been my biggest cheerleaders. Failure was never an option.

I am deeply indebted to my fabulous physician mentor Dr. Andra Blomkalns. I can't thank her enough for everything she has done for me. Over the past decade she has guided me from being a clueless pre-med into an emergency physician, ready to take on fellowship. I would not be the physician I am today without her guidance and support.

I'm fairly convinced that my husband is the best person in the entire world. Alex Angeli's unwavering support allowed me to survive my job as an EM resident while simultaneously reliving the horrors of med school as a writer. His encouragement and enthusiasm are remarkable. My big sister Felissa Benjamin Allard warrants hugs and thanks as well. She ensured that as many people as possible knew about my book. At one point, she even went so far as to threaten her friend's lives if they did not visit my website and buy a copy.

There are two emergency physicians, Dr. Michael Burg and Dr. Jessica Mason, who mean the world to me. It is not an exaggeration to claim that this book would not exist without them. As a physician author, Dr. Burg enthusiastically supported this project. He provided guidance on everything from the book's title, to marketing advice, to helping me network with other writers in healthcare, to editing every single word. Dr. Mason also deserves special mention. For when I struggled through a dark patch in residency, she was the person who helped me zero in on what mattered most in my life. In doing so, she rekindled my motivation to write and to finish my book.

341

As I'd never before written a book, I assembled a team of incredible professionals to help me out. Warm thanks to my expert editor Gary Smailes, my witty copywriter Noa Gavin, and my fabulous illustrator James. If I ever go down this road again, I will be sure to seek your help once more. Also thank you to Kati Beshore, for taking a professional and lovely headshot of me, so that I wouldn't have to use my lame med school graduation photo on the back of the book.

My residency, UCSF Fresno, is truly the most badass EM program out there. For all its emphasis on clinical training and education, the program equally values the personal growth of the individual residents. Thank you to Dr. James Comes and Dr. Stacy Sawtelle for allowing me the time and space to bring my book to life.

My sincerest thanks to my team of beta readers, specifically: Tamara Eklund, Leyla Farshidpour, Nathan Garvin, Lily Hitchner, Anne Fritz Linval, Jason O'Brien, Carrie Pergram, Brenda Seaver, and Allie Thompson. Your input and help in getting this book ready for release is greatly appreciated!

Most importantly, thank you to my friends and classmates who helped me survive third year. As is probably obvious from the book, I would not have survived the year without them. You guys are the absolute best people ever. Thank you for everything. Your patients are lucky to have you as their doctors!

About the Author

Dr. Stephanie Benjamin is an award winning writer and emergency physician. Her writing has been published in *Annals of Emergency Medicine, Journal of the American Heart Association*, as well as on multiple medical and non-medical websites.

After Dr. Benjamin graduated from medical school, she moved to California for her emergency medicine residency at University of California San Francisco Fresno. She is a rising expert within the disaster medicine community, frequently publishing and lecturing about disaster preparedness and emergency response. After residency, she will move to southern California for an Emergency Medical Services and Disaster Medicine Fellowship at the University of California San Diego.

When not at work or writing, Dr. Benjamin can be found rock climbing, epee fencing, flipping around on aerial silks, or at the beach with her husband Alex and their two Rottweilers.

Endnotes

[1] Hojat, Mohammadreza PhD; Vergare, Michael J. MD; Maxwell, Kaye; Brainard, George PhD; Herrine, Steven K. MD; Isenberg, Gerald A. MD; Veloski, Jon MS; Gonnella, Joseph S. MD. The Devil is in the Third Year: A Longitudinal Study of Erosion of Empathy in Medical School. Academic Medicine: Sept 2009 - Vol 84 - Issue 9 - p 1182-1191. doi: 10.1097/ACM.0b013e3181b17e55

[2] Ofri, Danielle. "The Darkest Year of Medical School: Students come in altruistic and empathetic. They leave jaded and bitter." *Medical Examiner, Slate.* 4 June 2013. *The Slate Group.* Web. 24 June 2013.

[3] Murray, Ken. "How doctors choose to die." *The Guardian.* 8 Feb 2012. *Society, The Guardian.* Web. 10 July 2013.

[4] Hoffman, Jan. "Nightmares After the I.C.U." *The New York Times.* 22 Jul 2013. *Well Blogs, The New York Times.* Web. 25 Jul 2013.

[5] Epstein, Mark. "The Trauma of Being Alive." *The New York Times.* 3 Aug 2013. *Sunday Review, Opinion, The New York Times.* Web. 4 Aug 2013.

[6] Chen, Pauline. "Reinventing the Third-Year Medical Student." *The New York Times.* 19 Apr 2012. *Well Blogs, The New York Times.* Web. 29 Jan 2014.

[7] Silverstein, Shel. "Whatif." A Light in the Attic. New York: Harper and Row, 1981. Page 169.

[8] Eggenberger, Nicole & Peros, Jennifer. "Jamie Anderson, Olympic Snowboarder: "Tinder in the Olympic Village Is Next Level"." *Us Weekly.* 12 Feb 2014. *Celebrity News, Us Magazine.* Web. 12 Feb 2014.

[9] Drake, Daniela. "How being a doctor became the most miserable profession." *The Daily Beast.* 14 Apr 2014. *The Daily Beast.* Web. 16 Apr 2014.

[10] Daniela Drake. "The mask your doctor hides behind." *The Daily Beast.* 21 May 2014. *The Daily Beast.* Web. 25 May 2014.

[11] Span, Paula. "Do Not resuscitate: what young doctors would choose." *The New York Times.* 20 May 2014. *The New Old Age, Caring and Coping, The New York Times.* Web. 27 May 2014.